MICROBIOLOGY

WITH HEALTH CARE APPLICATIONS

MICROBIOLOGY

WITH HEALTH CARE APPLICATIONS

Second Edition

Isaiah Amiel Benathen

Kingsborough Community College

of

The City University of New York

Brooklyn, New York

Star

PUBLISHING COMPANY, INC.

Belmont, CA 94002

Star Publishing Company, Inc.
Redwood City, CA 94063

Managing Editor: Stuart Hoffman

Revised Printing 2015

Printed in the United States of America

ISBN: 978-0-89863-305-4   20 19 18 17 16 15

This manual is dedicated with love to my wife, Jane, and my sons, Marc and Steven.

Contents

Preface   ix

Unit I:
Microscopy, Survey of Microorganisms and Asepsis   1

1   Microscopy   3
2   The Fungi: Molds and Yeasts   9
3   Protozoa   15
4   Microbes Are Everywhere   21
5   Aseptic Transfer Techniques   25
    Case Study 1   30

Unit II:
Staining Microorganisms and Studying Motility   31

6   Smear Preparation and the Simple Stain   33
7   The Negative Stain   37
8   The Gram Stain   39
9   The Acid-Fast Stain   43
10   The Endospore Stain
     (The Schaeffer-Fulton Procedure)   47
11   The Capsule Stain (A Negative Stain Procedure)   51
12   Bacterial Motility Studies   53
13   Morphological Unknown Characterization   59
    Case Study 2   62

Unit III:
Culturing of Microorganisms   63

14   Pure Culture Isolation Skills   65
15   The Quantitative Plate Count   71
16   Growth Curve Determination   75
17   Quantitative T-2 Virus Count   81
18   Determination of Oxygen Requirements   87
19   Cultural Conditions   93
20   Temperature and Bacterial Growth   99
21   Lethal Effects of Temperature   103
22   Steam Sterilization: The Autoclave   107
23   Osmotic Pressure and Bacterial Growth   109
24   pH and Microbial Growth   113
25   The Importance of Handwashing   117
    Case Study 3   121

Unit IV:
Microbial Relationships and Disease   123

26   Commensalism   125
27   Synergism   129
28   Antagonism   133
    Case Study 4   137

Unit V:

Water, Food and Diary Microbiology   139

29   Microbiology of Water   141
30   Food Microbiology   151
31   Microbiology of Milk   159
32   Reductase Activity in Milk   163
     Case Study 5   166

Unit VI:

Clinical Unknown   167

33   Clinical Unknown   169
34   Fermentation of Carbohydrates   173
35   The Oxidation Fermentation (O-F) Test   181
36   Differences in Respiratory Behavior   184
37   Differential Identification I: Amino Acid and
     Specialty Tests   195
38   Differential Identification II: Macromolecule and
     Specialty Tests   205
39   Rapid Multimedia Test: Enterotube II®   215
     Case Study 6   223

Unit VII:

Control of Microorganisms   225

40   Chemical Control of Microorganisms   227
41   Antibiotic Sensitivity Testing: A Differential Decision   231
42   Effects of Antiseptic Agents on Transmission of Oral Flora
     or Nasal Flora   237
43   Beta-Lactamase Activity in Gram-Positive Cocci   241
44   Oligodynamic Action Against Bacteria   245
45   Ultraviolet Lethality and Photoreactivation   249
     Case Study 7   253

Unit VIII:

Medical Microbiology   255

46   A Model for Soft Tissue Infection   257
47   A Lethal Action of Lysozyme on Bacteria   263
48   Staphylococci on Skin   267
49   Upper Respiratory Tract Culture   271
50   Gastrointestinal Infections   281
51   Urinary Tract Infections   289
51   Optional: Uricult System for Urinary Tract Infection   297
52   Snyder Test for Dental Caries Susceptibility   299
53   Salmonella Serology: Slide Agglutination Test   303
54   Mutagens and Carcinogens: The Ames Test   307
     Case Study 8   311

Results and Observations   313

Media Directory   481

Descriptive Directory of Commonly Used Microorganisms   491

Index   497

Acknowledgments

I gratefully acknowledge the contributions of the following individuals who provided valuable suggestions and information:

Eugene V. DeFelice, General Attorney, and Ray Lug, Marketing Manager, Roche Diagnostics, a subsidiary of Hoffmann-LaRoche; James E. Fitts, Dairy Products Specialist, N.Y. State Department of Agriculture and Markets; Paul S. Berger, Ph.D., and Robert H. Bordner, Ph.D., U.S. Environmental Protection Agency; Mark Kaufman, President, and Nancy Stoehr, Marketing Services Representative, Access Analytical Systems; Maryalice Francisco, Product Manager, Yvonne McCombs, Technical Represenative, and John Putko, V.P., Unipath Co./Oxoid Division; and Patricia J. McWethy, Executive Director, National Association of Biology Teachers, publishers of *The American Biology Teacher*, for permission to quote from my article: *Isolation of Pure Cultures from Mixed Cultures: A Modern Approach*, Vol. 52, No. 1, January 1990.

The author thanks Marion Saccardi, the microbiology technician for providing cultures and media for testing of the exercises in this manual.

The upbringing, rich in education and love of learning, given to me by my parents has been the inspiration for writing this book. I appreciate the patience, sacrifices, good humor and sensitivity of my wife, Jane, and my sons, Marc and Steven, during the writing of this laboratory manual. And I am grateful to my wife for the extra hours of caring for our sons, which allowed me to write and complete this project.

Additionally, the author and publisher thank the numerous faculty members that contributed comments regarding my manuscript and critiques of other laboratory manuals. In particular, we thank William Boyko of Sinclair Community College and Lois Lindberg of San Jose University, who patiently interpreted reviewer's comments, answered technical questions, carefully checked details, and helped select photographs.

Preface

During the past twenty years that I have taught microbiology, I continue to be asked the following questions by many students:

1. Why am I taking microbiology?
2. What relevance does this laboratory course have to my professional career?
3. What practical information will I learn from the exercises in the microbiology laboratory that would benefit me in my career?

This revised printing continues the theme of synthesizing theoretical and practical information in medical microbiology by using simple laboratory culture experiments designed to illustrate asepsis, virulence factors, models for the development of infection together with the differential diagnosis of the causes of microbial infection. Traditional experiments on staining of microorganisms, culturing of microorganisms and microbial physiology along with applied microbiology are presented and woven into this theme. Many of the experiments were developed during my years of teaching this course. The experiments in this manual have been taught in the classroom with many students and work well. This revised edition contains new additional exercises that expand and enrich this medical theme.

They are:

1. Growth Curve Determination which permits the students to see first hand the rapidity with which microorganisms can multiply in a new environment such as a container of broth or conceivably the human body.

2. A Quantitative Virus Count which gives students the experience of working with the obligate parasite T-2 virus and determining a plaque count for a sample of this virus.

3. Steam Sterilization: The Autoclave which teaches the absoluteness of sterilization and how it can be verified by culture experiments.

4. Effects of Antiseptic Agents on Transmission of Oral Flora or Nasal Flora which demonstrates how antiseptic agents can prevent the transmission of infectious bacteria and stresses the need for the practice of medical and surgical asepsis to prevent the spread of infection.

5. Beta-Lactamase Activity in Gram-Positive Cocci emphasizes the serious problem of the antibiotic resistance of gram-positive cocci to penicillin and cephalosporin antibiotics and shows how it can be detected.

6. Staphylococci on Skin demonstrates that staphylococci are common inhabitants of the skin and can be transferred to others to cause serious skin or systemic infections.

7. A Lethal Action of Lysozyme demonstrates the protective action of the innate protective enzyme called lysozyme that can kill some microorganisms.

8. A Model for Soft Tissue Infection uses bacterial inoculated apples to demonstrate infection and the tissue damage produced.

In addition Exercise 14—Pure Culture Techniques has been expanded to include a larger variety of selective and differential media used in medical laboratories to identify microorganisms. By completing this exercise the student will have a clearer appreciation of the role of specific metabolic reactions used in the differential identification of bacteria that can cause infection. Exercise 18—

Determination of Oxygen Requirements now contains a helpful summary chart that describes the oxygen requirements of specific microorganisms. Exercise 21—Lethal Effects of Temperature now includes the addition of a sporulated culture of the obligate thermophile *Bacillus stereothermophilus* which is used to measure heat resistance. This gives the student the opportunity to work with a thermophilic sporeformer that has high heat resistance. Exercise 36—Differences in Respiratory Behavior has a new central figure that clearly focuses on aerobic respiration by showing how the Krebs Cycle can act as a bridge between glycolysis and the stages of electron transport phosphorylation. The catalase, oxidase and nitrate reduction reactions are woven into the information in this figure to help the student understand the importance of respiration in microbial survival and identification. Exercise 49—Upper Respiratory Tract Culture has been extensively rewritten. In this revised format, the student can readily identify Group A streptococci and can simply culture and more readily identify the kind(s) of staphylococci present in the oral cavity or nasal cavity. The Taxo A (bacitracin) sensitivity test for Group A streptococci has been included in this exercise. Exercise 51—Urinary Tract Infections now includes as an option the Uricult CLED/EMB Dipslide procedures for the enumeration of and identification of urinary pathogens.

MICROBIOLOGY WITH HEALTH CARE APPLICATIONS is designed for the student preparing for a career in health sciences, including careers in nursing, dental hygiene, food sciences and pre-medical sciences. This manual contains exercises covering topics usually present in general microbiology courses that emphasize health related subjects.

The exercises in this manual are organized into eight distinct units. They are:

Unit I—Microscopy, Survey of Microorganisms and Asepsis which focuses on the uses of the microscope to identify microorganisms and asepsis techniques needed in any microbiology laboratory.

Unit II—Staining Microorganisms and Studying Motility focuses on simple staining and differential staining as tools to characterize bacteria and help in their identification. Motility is introduced and presented as a model for a puncture infection.

Unit III—Culturing of Microorganisms studies a diversity of factors that affect microbial growth with appropriate applications to medical models. Pure culture isolations by use of selective and differential media are covered along with physical factors that affect growth of microbes. Bacteria and virus enumeration are covered in this unit. The universal precaution of handwashing is covered in this unit.

Unit IV—Microbial Relationships and Disease develops models for infection in the human body through commensalism and synergism as well as studying microbial antibiosis through antagonism.

Unit V—Water, Food and Dairy Microbiology incorporates the latest techniques for microbial analysis for coliforms in drinking water approved by the Federal Environmental Protection Agency and demonstrates the importance of water, food and dairy as vehicles for the transmission of disease organisms.

Unit VI—Clinical Unknown uses common nosocomial and community acquired infectious bacteria to present a diagnostic problem that requires the process of ruling out of unwanted organisms to make a final differential decision for the identity of the microorganism causing the infection. The Enterotube II, a rapid miniaturized multitest kit is introduced in this unit to emphasize the need for accurate and fast decisions regarding the causes of infections.

Unit VII—Control of Microorganisms contains exercises on chemical control of microorganisms and differential sensitivity of microorganisms to antibiotics as well as exercises on the sensitivity of bacteria to the oligodynamic action of metals and sensitivity to ultraviolet light and photoreactivation. In addition, this unit contains two new exercises. The first, Exercise 42—Effects of Antiseptic Agents on Transmission of Oral Flora or Nasal Flora demonstrates the effects of bactericidal and bacteriostatic chemical agents on the transmission of oral or nasal flora and the second, Exercise 43—Beta-Lactamase Activity in Gram-Positive Cocci, demonstrates the presence of the antibiotic resistance activity known as beta-lactamase in selected gram-positive cocci.

Unit VIII—Medical Microbiology contains simulations of respiratory, gastrointestinal and urinary tract infections presented as problem solving experiences that require accurate diagnostic decisions. Exercise 49—Upper Respiratory Tract Culture has been extensively expanded to include bacitracin sensitivity testing of isolates and new approaches to characterize the types of staphylococci present in the upper respiratory tract. The revised Exercise 51—Urinary Tract Infections now includes *Pseudomonas aeruginosa* as a potential urinary pathogen and a new optional exercise using the Uricult® CLED/EMB dipslide paddle for differential identification and enumeration of urinary pathogens in a simulated urine sample. Three new exercises are also added to this unit. They are: Exercise 46—A Model for Soft Tissue Infection which uses apples as hosts to simulate a model for infection of tissue, Exercise 47—A Lethal Action of Lysozyme on Bacteria which measures the effectiveness of this innate immune system enzyme on selected gram-positive and gram-negative bacteria and Exercise 48—Staphylococci on Skin which differentiates staphylococci present on human skin. This latter exercise also has an optional demonstration to emphasize importance of degerming skin prior to any puncture for the purpose of drawing blood, inserting an intravenous line or injection of medication.

MICROBIOLOGY WITH HEALTH CARE APPLICATIONS incorporates new approaches and technologies, not commonly found in microbiology laboratory manuals, that are readily adapted to the classroom. These approaches include using both traditional exercises to demonstrate problems in medical microbiology and the use of procedures commonly used in medical and clinical laboratories. For example, the use of Colilert® in drinking water analysis to simply and rapidly identify and confirm the presence of coliforms, the use of the Oxoid® oxidase stick for identifying oxidase positive bacteria (a more rapid and safer alternative to the traditional methods of performing this test), the use of calibrated loops to directly streak "urine" samples to CLED agar for determining the presence and enumeration of urinary pathogens and the Uricult® dipslide option for the enumeration and identification of urinary pathogens. However, for those who prefer them, in each of these exercises, the traditional approaches are presented in complete and up to date formats.

Each exercise in this manual contains objectives, background information, an overview section of the exercise, materials, procedures, results and extensive questions. The objectives emphasize major ideas that each student should master. The background sections contain major biological and medical concepts and relationships necessary for a meaningful understanding of the exercise.

The overview section summarizes the procedures used for the exercise, clearly explains what the results should be so that the actual results may be checked against a standard reference, and covers pertinent medical applications of the exercise. This novel approach blends the theoretical, practical and medical aspects of the exercise into a concise package.

The materials and procedures sections list all the required cultures and equipment as well as simple, step-by-step, illustrated procedures. These procedures have been carefully evaluated to assure predictable results. Results pages for all the exercises are located at the end of the manual in a separate section. This section provides an organized format for students to summarize their findings and for instructors to evaluate these results. Many of the exercises require that a statement of conclusions be completed regarding the significance of the exercise. Furthermore, each exercise includes questions that require written answers in sentences, completion questions and a novel form of true and false question that require false statements to be corrected. Answering these questions guides students to re-focus on the goals, significance and results of the exercise.

The following advisories are offered regarding pipetting and incubation: (1) Pipetting. In accordance with the recommendations of the American Society for Microbiology, no mouth pipetting should be allowed. Pipettes should be attached to a pipette pump or similar device which permits accurate pipetting and dispensing of culture fluids and other liquids. Implementing this policy eliminates the risk of ingestion of culture fluids and the risk of infection associated with mouth pipetting. (2) Incubation. Incubation of inoculated microbiological media at 35°C for 24 to 48 hours followed by refrigeration may be impractical for those classes that meet only once a week. In those cases, an instructor may have the students incubate the plates in inverted fashion and the tubes in stable racks or cups at room temperature for a week in a secure, undisturbed area. Their results can then be evaluated at the next laboratory class meeting. If the laboratory class meets twice a week, the instructor should allow at least 72 hours incubation time at room temperature for adequate growth of the microorganisms.

MICROBIOLOGY WITH HEALTH CARE APPLICATIONS may be used successfully with a wide variety of textbooks. There is not a specific text that is a companion to this manual. However, it is assumed that a microbiology textbook is used in this course along with the manual. This is a very adaptable manual, offering a wide variety of exercises to choose from and flexibility in assigning the sequence of many of the exercises.

For your assistance, a comprehensive *Instructor's Manual* is available to accompany this book. It has a complete listing of necessary cultures, materials used, sources, suggestions and time requirements. The suggestions section of the Instructor's Manual includes hints regarding presentation of the exercises, problems to avoid, major concepts to emphasize, and cautionary statements. A copy of the Instructor's Manual is available from the publisher.

I welcome any suggestions and comments on the use of these exercises.

Isaiah A. Benathen

To the Student

This manual is designed for students preparing for a career in health science, such as: nursing, dental hygiene, food sciences, kinesiology, physical therapy, and those in preparation for postgraduate schools such as medical, dental and pharmaceutical schools. I've written this manual to present the subject in a style that will maximize your success in both lab and lecture.

To realize that goal, you must read the exercise *before* coming to the laboratory class. When you read the exercise, carefully read the objectives for each exercise to determine the goals of the exercise. Reading the background will give you the necessary biological and medical insights to understand and appreciate the purposes, goals and applications of the exercise. The overview section concisely explains the procedures to be followed in the exercise.

In conducting each exercise, perform each step. The illustrations were prepared to help you understand the steps and sequence of the steps in each procedure.

Be sure to fully record your observations in the Results section. Do not rely on your memory or scraps of paper. There is no substitute for a thorough written recording of the findings in the Results section. The questions at the end of the exercise are based on materials in the exercise. Answer all the questions; re-read the exercise and your results if necessary to find the answers. The goal of this laboratory manual is to provide you with up-to-date laboratory skills, useful practical and theoretical information, and to expose you to solving problems in medical microbiology.

Pay careful attention to any caution statements regarding the use of pathogens. These "cautions" are for your protection and that of your classmates. For your safety and health, wear a laboratory coat while engaged in any laboratory work and be sure to obey the laboratory safety rules described in this manual and those of your school.

Laboratory Safety

General Safety Guidelines

The laboratory experiments included in the text may be hazardous if the materials or equipment are handled improperly or if procedures are conducted incorrectly. Before performing any experiment in this text, you must be trained and instructed in the proper techniques for the procedures, equipment, and materials involved. If you have not been so trained and instructed, do not perform the experiment until you have been trained and instructed.

Safety precautions are necessary when you are working with chemicals, microbiological cultures, glassware, hot water baths, sharp instruments, and other equipment, materials or procedures in this course. Your school has set regulations regarding safety procedures that your instructor will explain to you. Should you have any problems with or questions about equipment, chemicals, materials, microbiological cultures or media, or procedures, ask your instructor for help. If you have any questions at all about what to do or not to do, stop and do not proceed until you are fully aware and knowledgeable about the procedure you are doing. The experiments and procedures in this text are only to be carried out under the supervision of a trained instructor. Do not perform any laboratory experiment or procedure in the absence of such supervision.

1. A laboratory coat must be worn in the laboratory. Dyes and many other materials CANNOT be removed from clothing.

2. Smoking, eating, or drinking any beverage is absolutely forbidden in the microbiology laboratory.

3. All materials and clothing other than the laboratory manual and notebook are to be kept off and away from the lab bench.

4. Prepare for the laboratory session before coming to the laboratory by reading each exercise carefully so that you know what is to be done and the principles involved.

5. At the beginning and at the conclusion of each laboratory session, scrub and/or sponge the bench top work area with disinfectant solution. Be sure your work area is clean and properly organized while you work and before leaving the laboratory.

6. Scrub your hands with antiseptic soap anytime you spill a culture, or when you leave the laboratory, and at the conclusion of the laboratory session.

7. Students with long hair must tie their hair back securely and be especially cautious around Bunsen burners.

8. All cultures for the laboratory are in labeled containers. All cultures must be returned to these containers unless your instructor gives other directions.

9. All media for the laboratory are located on the supply table; media removed from the supply table should NOT be returned to the supply table under any circumstances.

10. All culture discards must be placed in metal leakproof discard bins. These discards must be autoclaved. Plastic disposable loops, pipettes and cotton swabs must be placed in containers of disinfectant. If appropriate discard bins and disinfectant containers are not available, see your instructor. DO NOT leave tubes or plates laying around the lab. DO NOT pour any cultures into a sink.

11. Microscopes require special care: Clean the ocular and all objectives with clean lens paper only. If the microscope is not in proper condition when you take it out, let your instructor know before you use it. Microscopes must be replaced in the microscope cabinet with the low power objective locked into position and no oil on the lens.

12. Report all accidents such as cuts, burns, or spilled cultures to your instructor immediately. All spills must be covered with disinfectant and contained.

13. Mouth pipetting is not permitted. In accordance with guidelines of the American Society for Microbiology, students are to use a pipette pump or other device that can be attached to a pipette. These devices permit accurate pipetting and dispensing of culture fluid or other liquid and avoid the danger of ingestion and infection associated with mouth pipetting.

14. Do not put any pens, pencils, erasers, or gummed labels for labelling tubes in your mouth.

15. Keep your hands away from the face or mucous membranes while in the microbiology laboratory.

16. It is advisable that all students wear long pants, socks and closed shoes while working in the microbiology laboratory.

17. Perform only specifically assigned exercises. Performance of unauthorized experiments is strictly forbidden.

18. Each and every student should receive two copies of the safety instructions. One copy must be signed and returned to the instructor signifying that the student has read, understands, and will abide by these safety regulations.

Laboratory Safety

General Safety Guidelines

The laboratory experiments included in the text may be hazardous if the materials or equipment are handled improperly or if procedures are conducted incorrectly. Before performing any experiment in this text, you must be trained and instructed in the proper techniques for the procedures, equipment, and materials involved. If you have not been so trained and instructed, do not perform the experiment until you have been trained and instructed.

Safety precautions are necessary when you are working with chemicals, microbiological cultures, glassware, hot water baths, sharp instruments, and other equipment, materials or procedures in this course. Your school has set regulations regarding safety procedures that your instructor will explain to you. Should you have any problems with or questions about equipment, chemicals, materials, microbiological cultures or media, or procedures, ask your instructor for help. If you have any questions at all about what to do or not to do, stop and do not proceed until you are fully aware and knowledgeable about the procedure you are doing. The experiments and procedures in this text are only to be carried out under the supervision of a trained instructor. Do not perform any laboratory experiment or procedure in the absence of such supervision.

1. A laboratory coat must be worn in the laboratory. Dyes and many other materials CANNOT be removed from clothing.

2. Smoking, eating, or drinking any beverage is absolutely forbidden in the microbiology laboratory.

3. All materials and clothing other than the laboratory manual and notebook are to be kept off and away from the lab bench.

4. Prepare for the laboratory session before coming to the laboratory by reading each exercise carefully so that you know what is to be done and the principles involved.

5. At the beginning and at the conclusion of each laboratory session, scrub and/or sponge the bench top work area with disinfectant solution. Be sure your work area is clean and properly organized while you work and before leaving the laboratory.

6. Scrub your hands with antiseptic soap anytime you spill a culture, or when you leave the laboratory, and at the conclusion of the laboratory session.

7. Students with long hair must tie their hair back securely and be especially cautious around Bunsen burners.

8. All cultures for the laboratory are in labeled containers. All cultures must be returned to these containers unless your instructor gives other directions.

9. All media for the laboratory are located on the supply table; media removed from the supply table should NOT be returned to the supply table under any circumstances.

10. All culture discards must be placed in metal leakproof discard bins. These discards must be autoclaved. Plastic disposable loops, pipettes and cotton swabs must be placed in containers of disinfectant. If appropriate discard bins and disinfectant containers are not available, see your instructor. DO NOT leave tubes or plates laying around the lab. DO NOT pour any cultures into a sink.

11. Microscopes require special care: Clean the ocular and all objectives with clean lens paper only. If the microscope is not in proper condition when you take it out, let your instructor know before you use it. Microscopes must be replaced in the microscope cabinet with the low power objective locked into position and no oil on the lens.

12. Report all accidents such as cuts, burns, or spilled cultures to your instructor immediately. All spills must be covered with disinfectant and contained.

13. Mouth pipetting is not permitted. In accordance with guidelines of the American Society for Microbiology, students are to use a pipette pump or other device that can be attached to a pipette. These devices permit accurate pipetting and dispensing of culture fluid or other liquid and avoid the danger of ingestion and infection associated with mouth pipetting.

14. Do not put any pens, pencils, erasers, or gummed labels for labelling tubes in your mouth.

15. Keep your hands away from the face or mucous membranes while in the microbiology laboratory.

16. It is advisable that all students wear long pants, socks and closed shoes while working in the microbiology laboratory.

17. Perform only specifically assigned exercises. Performance of unauthorized experiments is strictly forbidden.

18. Each and every student should receive two copies of the safety instructions. One copy must be signed and returned to the instructor signifying that the student has read, understands, and will abide by these safety regulations.

I agree to follow the rules of safety, laboratory regulations and proper laboratory techniques and procedures of this course and school.

_____

Signature

_____

Print your name

_____

Social Security/Student Id #

_____

Date

Unit I

Microscopy, Survey of Microorganisms and Aseptis

1 Microscopy 3

includes identification of the parts of the microscope, factors that
affect the use of the microscope and instruction in the proper
operation of the microscope.

2 The Fungi: Molds and Yeasts 9

describes four classes of fungi and their microscopic morphology and
examines medical problems posed by the molds and yeasts.

3 Protozoa 15

describes the morphology and life cycles of selected pathogenic
protozoa as well as diseases produced by these microbes in humans.

4 Microbes Are Everywhere 21

demonstrates the presence of microorganisms on living and non-living
surfaces and introduces the problem of disease transmission.

5 Aseptic Transfer Techniques 25

introduces aseptic transfer techniques by control transfers of sterile
broth and by transfers of pure broth cultures of bacteria to fresh media.

Case Study 1 30

Microscopy

Objectives

1. Identify the parts of the microscope.
2. Define **total magnification, resolving power** and **numerical aperture.**
3. Define **working distance.**
4. List two procedures for the safe and proper handling of a microscope.

Background

Microbiology is the study of tiny living organisms that are not visible to the unaided eye: a microscope is necessary to see them. Although the microscope had been invented earlier, Anton von Leeuwenhoek, in the late 1600s, made the first observations and descriptions of microbes. These "animalcules," as he called them, were observed in samples from various sources such as pond water, rainwater, and tooth scrapings. The microscope remains an essential tool in modern microbiology.

The compound light microscope used in microbiology classes today has a number of parts. It is shown in Figure 1-1. Starting from the base of the microscope, the parts are as follows:

Base   This is the bottom of the microscope, which supports all the working parts above.

Source of Illumination   This is a bulb that provides light to illuminate the specimen on the slide.

Condenser   This unit is located below a square stage. It collects the light and directs it through the stage opening above. It also contains an iris diaphragm lever, which regulates the amount of light sent upward to the stage opening.

Stage and Stage Opening   The stage is a horizontal platform that has stage clips or a device called a mechanical stage to hold and position the slide specimen over the stage opening.

Objectives   These are located on a nosepiece or turret that can rotate and lock a particular lens in position. The important lens for microbiological work is the oil immersion lens.

Coarse Adjustment   This is a large wheel on the microscope that moves the stage or the objective up or down. The purpose is to focus the slide on the microscope. It is only used for the low-power objectives.

Fine Adjustment   This is a smaller wheel located near the coarse adjustment. It is used to fine tune the focus under low power and is used exclusively to focus the high power and oil immersion lens.

Ocular   The ocular may be a single lens, in which case the microscope is **monocular**. If two oculars are present, one on the right and one on the left, then the microscope is a **binocular** microscope.

Factors That Affect the Microscope

There are a number of factors that affect microscope function: **resolving power, numerical aperture, magnification** and **working distance.**

Resolving power is the ability of a microscope to differentiate two closely spaced objects as being distinct from one another. The light microscope uses white light and can distinguish two points that are at least 0.2 µm apart as distinct objects. The resolving power becomes greater as the magnification of an objective lens increases. Use of light of shorter wavelength than white light also increases the resolving power of a microscope. The resolving power also depends on a second factor, the numerical aperture.

Numercial aperture is the ability of a lens in a light microscope to gather light. The formula for numerical aperture is N.A. = $i \sin \theta$ where i is the refractive index of the air around the lens and $\sin \theta$ is half of the angle of light entering the microscope lens. Generally light rays move in straight lines. When light rays move from a dense medium such as glass to a less dense medium such as air, the light rays are bent so that some of the light does not enter the objective lens. This phenomenon of bending of light is called **refraction.** The amount of bending of light rays is indicated by a refractive index. The refractive index of air is 1.00. When the oil immersion lens is used, a drop of cedarwood oil is placed between the slide and the lens to condense or prevent the scattering of the light. The cedarwood oil has a refractive index of 1.56, which is almost the same as that of glass, so most of the light enters the objective. In the absence of oil the image seen in an oil immersion lens appears fuzzy. When used with oil, this lens gives the viewer a clearer image and more detail. The numerical aperture is highest for the oil immersion lens. Therefore, the resolving power is also highest. In summary, the resolving power of the microscope depends on the numerical aperture of the objective lens, the condenser lens and the wavelength of light.

Magnification is a third factor. The magnification measures how many diameters the specimen is increased in size when viewed in the microscope. The total magnification is the product of the magnification of the ocular and the objective lens. The ocular magnification of the compound lens microscope is 10×. The low-power objective is 10×. The high-power objective is 40×, and the oil immersion objective is 100×. The total magnification is 10×10 or 100 under low power, 10×40 or 400 under high power and 10×100 under oil immersion, which is 1000 times the original size of the specimen on the slide.

Working distance is the fourth factor that affects the operation of the microscope. The working distance is the distance between the objective lens and the slide specimen when the lens is in focus. As the magnification of a lens increases, the working distance decreases and the need for illumination increases. In addition, increasing the illumination tends to decrease the contrast and increase the resolving power of a lens, while decreasing the illumination tends to increase the contrast and reduce the resolving power of a lens. In summary, the numerical

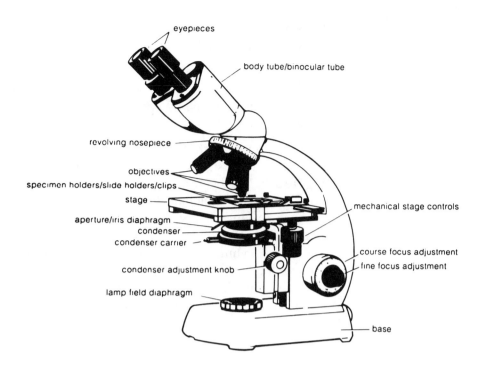

eyepieces

body tube/binocular tube

revolving nosepiece

objectives

specimen holders/slide holders/clips

stage

aperture/iris diaphragm

condenser

condenser carrier

condenser adjustment knob

lamp field diaphragm

mechanical stage controls

course focus adjustment

fine focus adjustment

base

Figure 1-1
Compound Light Microscope

Correct Way to Carry a Microscope

Figure 1-2
Carrying the Microscope

aperture is highest for the oil immersion lens, which has the greatest resolving power, shortest working distance and greatest need for light.

Microscopy: An Overview

The microscope is a valuable and necessary tool for any student of microbiology. The study should learn the parts of the microscope and should understand the four factors that influence its operation. A few basic rules for the use of the microscope must be followed. (See Figure 1-2.)

1. The microscope should never be subjected to any rough treatment.

2. The lenses should be cleaned before and after each use. Any immersion oil on the lens must be wiped dry with clean lens paper at the end of each class. This will prevent damage to the lenses by accumulated oil.

3. Any oil on the stage or other parts of the microscope must be removed with clean lens paper.

4. At the conclusion of a laboratory class, wrap the electric cord around the body of the microscope. Rotate the low-power objective lens into position and replace the microscope in the proper position in the microscope storage cabinet.

In this exercise the student will examine prepared slides of three representative bacteria that illustrate the different shapes commonly found in bacteria (see Figure 1-3. The bacteria to be viewed are a *bacillus*, a *coccus* and a *spirillum*. Some suggestions include *Bacillus anthracis* in tissue or *Bacillus subtilis*, the coccus or round-shaped *Streptococcus pyogenes* and the spirillum or spiral-shaped *Borrelia recurrentis* or other spirillum species. *Bacillus subtilus* causes pneumonia in immunocompromised individuals; *Bacillus anthracis* causes a systemic infection called anthrax. *Streptococcus pyogenes* causes cellulitis, pneumonia, rheumatic fever, strep throat and impetigo. Some strains produce fasciitis and myositis. *Borrelia recurrentis* causes relapsing fever.

Close attention should be paid to the appearance of the bacteria and to any unusual arrangements that may be present.

Materials

microscopes with oil immersion lens

lens paper

prepared slides of: *Bacillus anthracis* in tissue or *Bacillus subtilis*, *Streptococcus pyogenes* and *Borrelia recurrentis* or other spirillum species.

Procedures

Use of the Oil Immersion Lens

1. Select a representative slide of each organism.

2. Plug in the cord and turn on the light. Be sure light is visible in the top lens of the condenser. If not, open the iris diaphragm by moving the lever. Place a single slide on the stage under the stage clips or in position in the mechanical stage as directed by the instructor.

3. Center the stained specimen over the stage opening.

4. Rotate the low-power lens into position until a click is heard.

5. Lower the coarse adjustment until a stop is reached. Most microscopes have a built-in stop that prevents the low-power objective from touching the slide.

6. Slowly turn the coarse adjustment toward you, while you look through the ocular. The slide should come into focus. Fine tune the focus with the fine adjustment.

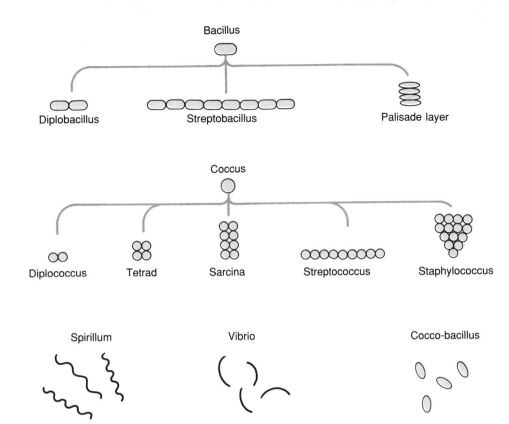

Figure 1-3
Arrangements of Cells
Seen in Microscope

7. Notice that under low power the specimen appears as stained particles. Center the specimen perfectly in the illuminated field. If you have difficulty focusing under low power, focus initially on the coverslip or the edge of the slide. Then move the slide until the specimen is centered over the top lens of the condenser, and use the fine adjustment to focus on the area of the specimen.

8. Rotate the low-power lens out of position. Increase the illumination by moving the iris diaphragm lever to admit more light through the condenser. Place a small drop of immersion oil on the slide specimen that is over the brightest part of the condenser lens. Rotate the immersion oil lens into position so that the lens is in the oil. Focus the immersion oil lens by turning the fine adjustment slightly very slowly either toward you or away from you until it is in focus. Only a slight turn is necessary since most microscopes are **parfocal**. (This means that what is in focus under low power should be nearly in focus under the immersion oil lens also.)

9. Describe the shape of this organism under the oil immersion lens. Repeat this procedure for the other two organisms. Observe their shapes.

10. Wipe off any oil from the slides and from the immersion oil lens after all work is completed. Rotate the low-power objective into position. Turn off the light, unplug the cord and wrap it around the body of the microscope and replace the microscope in the proper position in the cabinet.

11. Draw representative cells of each of these organisms in the Results section.

12. Answer the questions for the exercise.

The Fungi: Molds and Yeasts

Objectives

1. Identify specific molds from prepared slides.

2. Define the terms **hyphae, rhizoid, sporangium, spore, mycelium, sporangiophore, conidia, septate** and **nonseptate.**

3. List two molds that are opportunistic pathogens and the medical problems they produce.

4. Name a pathogenic yeast and the medical problems produced in humans.

Background

The division of microbiology that studies the fungi (that is, molds and yeasts) is mycology. Fungi are eukaryotes that are nonphotosynthetic. Molds are multicellular fungi and yeasts are unicellular fungi. Molds are composed of individual strands, of hyphae. These hyphae may have cross walls in them. In this case they are septate hyphae. If they lack cross walls, they are nonseptate. The collection of hyphae that forms a meshwork of furry growth in the mold colony is called a **mycelium**. Molds show saphrophytic nutrition and absorb preformed organic compounds from the surfaces on which they are growing. These surfaces include the human body, grains, fruits and vegetables. Some molds show asexual and sexual types of reproduction, while others only show asexual reproduction. Some molds produce opportunistic infections in humans, while others are pathogenic in humans.

The fungi commonly studied in microbiology are found in four classes. These classes are the *Zygomycetes*, the *Ascomycetes*, the *Basidiomycetes* and the *Deuteromycetes (Fungi Imperfecti)*. Except for the *Deuteromycetes*, all these classes show a sexual and asexual type of reproduction. *Deuteromycete* molds only reproduce asexually. The *Deuteromycete Division* is a holding area for those fungi for which the sexual phase has not yet been found. Once the sexual form has been recognized, the fungus is transferred to the appropriate division and given a new name. As examples, *Aspergillus*, *Penicillium* and *Blastomyces* are three molds that have been reclassified from the *Deuteromycetes* into the *Ascomycete Division* because a sexual phase has been recently recognized for each of them. The characteristics of these mold classes are briefly described below.

Zygomycetes   These molds show nonseptate hyphae and bear spore sacs or sporangia on the tips of ascending hyphae called **sporangiophores**. The sporangia contain asexual reproductive cells called **sporangiospores**. In sexual reproduction, hyphae from different + and − mating type strains of this mold contact each other, fuse and form a diploid zygospore. This zygospore under-

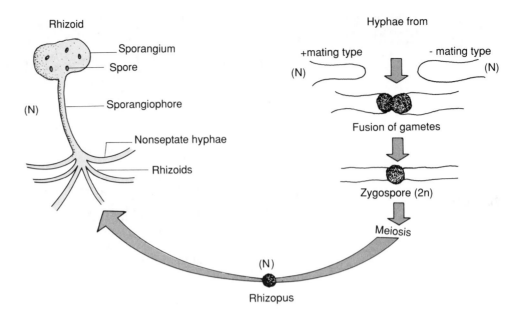

Figure 2-1
Rhizopus

goes meiosis to form four haploid sexual spores, each of which can form a haploid mold plant. These molds have descending hyphae called rhizoids that attach the molds to a surface and serve to absorb nutrients from the surface. Examples include *Rhizopus* and *Mucor* (see Figure 2-1). These molds are involved in opportunistic lung infections in immunocompromised patients, in diabetics and in chronically ill patients with depressed immune response.

Ascomycetes   These molds have septate hyphae and show aerial hyphae with chains of naked spores called conidia. They reproduce sexually by forming spores contained in a sac called an ascus. The typical example is the yeast *Saccharomyces cerevisiae* (see Figure 2-2). This yeast reproduces mitotically by forming extensions from the parent cell called buds. These buds enlarge and drop off the parent cell so that two cells are formed. This cycle repeats itself. There are two mating types of this yeast. They are called A and alpha. These haploid mating type cells fuse to form a diploid cell. The diploid cell can also undergo an asexual mitotic cycle. On meiosis the cells that are formed are contained in an ascus. Each of these ascopores can form a haploid cell. Other examples of *Ascomycetes* include *Claviceps, Blastomyces, Histoplasma, Aspergillus* and *Penicillium* (see Figure 2-3). For convenience, the imperfect name that refers to the asexually reproducing phase is chosen for *Blastomyces* and *Histoplasma*. These are the names that are generally familiar and are used in the medical community. *Claviceps* produces ergot alkaloids that have caused poisoning and death. In low concentrations they are used to induce uterine contractions after childbirth. *Blastomyces* produces lung infections, skin infections, and systemic infections. Pulmonary infections can spread to the bone, skin, nervous system and urogenital system. *Histoplasma* invades the lungs and the reticuloendothelial system. This system is distributed in the blood vessels, liver and spleen. This system removes microorganisms from the body. Ninety-five percent of *Histoplasma* infections are benign. The remaining 5% can produce severe lung infections, chronic skin infections or fatal systemic infections. Liver, spleen and lymph node enlargement are common in progressive infections. AIDS patients are frequently infected with *Histoplasma* where the organism is endemic. *Aspergillus* produces aspergillosis. This disease can appear as a pulmonary infection or a middle ear

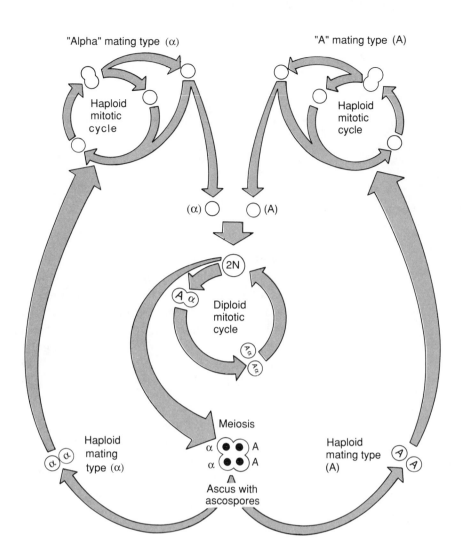

"Alpha" mating type (α)

"A" mating type (A)

Haploid
mitotic
cycle

Haploid
mitotic
cycle

(α)   (A)

2N

A α

Diploid
mitotic
cycle

A α

A α

Meiosis

Haploid
mating
type (α)

α   A
α   A

Haploid
mating type
(A)

A A

Ascus with
ascospores

Figure 2-2
Yeast Reproduction

infection. This particular mold also produces aflatoxins, which can cause liver damage and cancer. The mold *Penicillium*, which produces the antibiotic penicillin, is also in this grouping. This mold may cause pulmonary infections in immunocompromised people.

Basiodiomycetes   These include the mushrooms, rusts, smuts and toadstools. A common example is the mushroom. This mold forms a fruiting body or basidiocarp composed of three parts. They are the cap, the stipe (stem) and gills. In the life cycle of this mold, hyphae of opposite mating type fuse and form a double nucleated structure called a dikaryon. This double nucleated structure develops into the typical structure of the mushroom. On the underside of the cap are the gills. These gills bear microscopic stalklike structures called basidia. The nuclei in the tips of the basidia fuse to form a diploid nucleus. This nucleus undergoes meiosis to form four sexual haploid basidiospores. These spores are released to form the haploid structure, which starts the life cycle again. Mushrooms in the genus *Amanita* are poisonous. Symptoms of mushroom poisoning include gastrointestinal symptoms such as nausea and vomiting and other symptoms such as disorientation, problems with vision, delirium and even death. Many of these mushrooms and other nonpoisonous mushrooms grow in the woods on rotting vegetation.

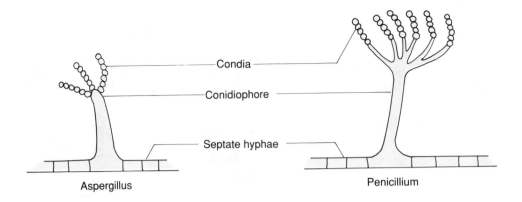

Figure 2-3
Examples of *Ascomycetes*.

Condia

Conidiophore

Septate hyphae

Aspergillus

Penicillium

Deuteromycetes   These fungi appear like yeasts or molds. They reproduce asexually and lack a known sexual stage. Many of the pathogenic fungi are in this class. One example is the yeast *Candida*. This yeast is responsible for an infection in the mouth of newborns called thrush. This problem can also appear in children and adults as a consequence of taking antibiotics for an extended period of time. *Candida* also produces vulvovaginitis, which is treated with nystatin or ketoconzaole. Another example is *Coccidioides*, which produces coccidioidomycosis. This disease appears as a lung infection and a fungal meningitis that can be fatal.

Dimorphism in Fungi: Some fungi can exist in two different forms depending on the conditions of growth. For example, the fungi *Histoplasma capsulatum* and *Blastomyces dermatitidis* shows mold mycelia when grown at room temperature. However, in the human body, which is at 37°C, these organisms appear as a yeast. *Candida albicans* appears as a yeast when grown at room temperature, but at 37°C in the human body it can show collections of oval cells attached to each other, which are called pseudomycelia.

The Fungi: Molds and Yeasts: An Overview

In this exercise the microscopic anatomies of representative fungi are examined by studying prepared slides of the organisms. These include *Rhizopus, Aspergillus, Penicillium* and *Candida*. Agar plate cultures of *Rhizopus, Aspergillus, Penicillium* and the yeast *Saccharomyces cerevisiae* are also examined to determine the gross differences between these molds and the yeast. This yeast is cultured, instead of *Candida*, for safety reasons. These dishes should be sealed around the rims to prevent opening and to prevent any spreading of the fungal spores into the laboratory. This also minimizes any chance of inhalation of mold spores and fungal infection.

Materials

Prepared slides of whole mounts of *Rhizopus, Aspergillus, Penicillium* and *Candida*.

Prepared slides of *Rhizopus* zygospores.

Cultures of the molds *Rhizopus, Aspergillus, Penicillium* and the yeast *Saccharomyces cerevisiae* grown on Sabouraud dextrose agar.

Procedures

1. Select a slide of *Rhizopus*. Identify the presence of sporangiophores, sporangia and rhizoids. Determine if the hyphae are septate or nonseptate. Observe also the slide showing *Rhizopus* zygospores. Sketch the appearance of the haploid asexual structures of this mold and the diploid sexual zygospore.

2. Construct a diagram of the asexual and sexual life cycle of this mold using the diagrams made in step 1.

3. Select a slide of *Aspergillus*. Identify the vegetative (nonreproductive) hyphae, the conidiophores and the conidia. Notice the septate hyphae. Sketch the appearance of this mold.

4. Select a slide of the mold *Penicillium*. Identify the vegetative hyphae, the conidiophore and the conidia. Notice the septate hyphae. How does this mold differ from *Aspergillus*? Sketch the appearance of this mold.

5. Select a slide of *Candida albicans*. Sketch the appearance of this yeast. Notice that this yeast is single celled and may show a pseudomycelium.

6. Examine the culture plates of the three molds and the yeast *Saccharomyces cerevisiae*. Notice the erect growth of the sporangiophores on the plate of *Rhizopus*. Notice the fuzzy or furry growth in the mold culture plates. This is the mold mycelium. Notice the color of each mold. Notice that the yeast culture does not look furry but rather is smooth and circular like bacterial colonies. *Candida* also produces a similar type of colony. The *Saccharomyces* culture is used for safety.

7. Answer the questions for the exercise.

Reference

Beneke, E. S. and Rogers, A. L. (1996). *Medical Mycology and Human Mycoses,* Belmont, California, USA: Star Publishing Company.

Protozoa

Objectives

1. Name three phyla of protozoa covered in this exercise.

2. Identify important features of each of these groups of protozoa.

3. Distinguish between schizogony and sporogony cycles in the malarial life cycle.

4. Distinguish between cyst and trophozoite.

5. Identify *Leishmania, Trypanosoma, Giardia, Trichomonas, Entamoeba,* and *Balantidium.*

Background

Protozoa are single-celled eukaryotic organisms. They are heterotrophs and either engulf their food or absorb pre-formed organic compounds through their cell membranes. The three phyla discussed in this exercise are *Apicomplexa, Sarcomastigophora* and *Ciliophora*, which include protozoa that cause medical problems in humans. Many of these protozoa produce active infective stages called trophozoites as well as cysts that are more resistant to heat, cold and disinfectants. These cysts are found in contaminated food or water and frequently are shed in urine or feces. Examples from the three phyla are shown in Figure 3-1.

Apicomplexa includes sporozoan organisms parasitic to humans. They usually have complex life cycles involving more than one host. Most of the stages in the life cycle are non-motile. This grouping includes the protozoa that cause malaria and toxoplasmosis in humans. Malaria is caused by *Plasmodium vivax, Plasmodium malariae, Plasmodium falciparum* and *Plasmodium ovale.* These plasmodia have a complex life cycle involving two hosts. The intermediate host is the human being and the final host is the female *Anopheles* mosquito. The mosquito bites a person, ingests blood and injects infective forms of the protozoa called sporozoites into the human. These protozoa migrate to the liver, where they undergo an exoerythrocytic multiplication cycle to make merozoites. Periodically these merozoites are shed into the bloodstream, where they invade red blood cells. In the red blood cells they undergo a cycle of multiplication followed by lysis of the red blood cells. This is the erythrocytic schizogony cycle. Early evidence of the protozoa in the red blood cells is the appearance of a band-shaped trophozoite called a ring stage. This trophozoite enlarges and then divides to form a distinct number of cells. This is called the mature schizont stage. The red blood cells then break open to release these protozoa, and a new cycle of red blood cell invasion occurs. In human beings, chills appear as the red blood cells break open. This is followed by fever and sweating as a new cycle of red blood cell invasion occurs. These cycles of chills, fever and sweating are closely

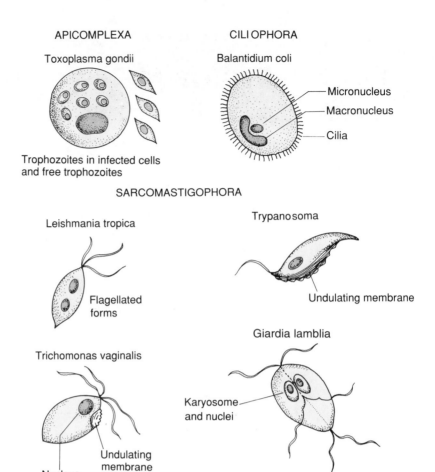

APICOMPLEXA

Toxoplasma gondii

Trophozoites in infected cells
and free trophozoites

CILIOPHORA

Balantidium coli

Micronucleus
Macronucleus
Cilia

SARCOMASTIGOPHORA

Leishmania tropica

Flagellated
forms

Trypanosoma

Undulating membrane

Trichomonas vaginalis

Undulating
membrane
Nucleus

Giardia lamblia

Karyosome
and nuclei

Figure 3-1
Examples of Protozoa

correlated to the events occurring in the red blood cells. Depending on the species of malaria, these cycles repeat themselves every 48 or 72 hours. Sometimes, during repeat erythrocyte cycle, the protozoa form male gametes (microgametocytes) and female gametes (macrogametocytes) in the red blood cells. The mosquito biting a person ingests these gametocytes. The cycle in the mosquito is called sporogony. It involves fertilization of the gametes, oocyst formation, followed by meiosis and formation of the infective sporozoites. The stages in this cycle are as follows: The male and female gametes wriggle out of the red blood cells in the mosquito stomach and fuse to form a diploid zygote. The zygote changes to an ookinete, which attaches to the mosquito stomach wall. It then forms an oocyst. Inside the oocyst, multiple meiotic divisions occur and form sporozoites. These sporozoites migrate to the salivary glands, where they are ready to infect another human being. (The cycles of malaria infection are shown in Figure 3-2.) Treatment involves the use of chloroquine for the erythrocyte stages and primaquine for the exoerythrocyte stages.

Toxoplasmosis is another example of *Apicomplexan* sporozoan disease caused by *Toxoplasma gondii*. The human is the intermediate host and the cat is the final host. In the cat, oocyst forms of the protozoa are present in the intestines. These are shed in the feces and can be present in the cat's litter box. Humans may inhale or ingest these oocysts during cleaning of the litter box. These oocysts liberate active trophozoites in the human intestines. *Toxoplasma gondii* is also found in a variety of vertebrates. Infection of humans can also occur by eating

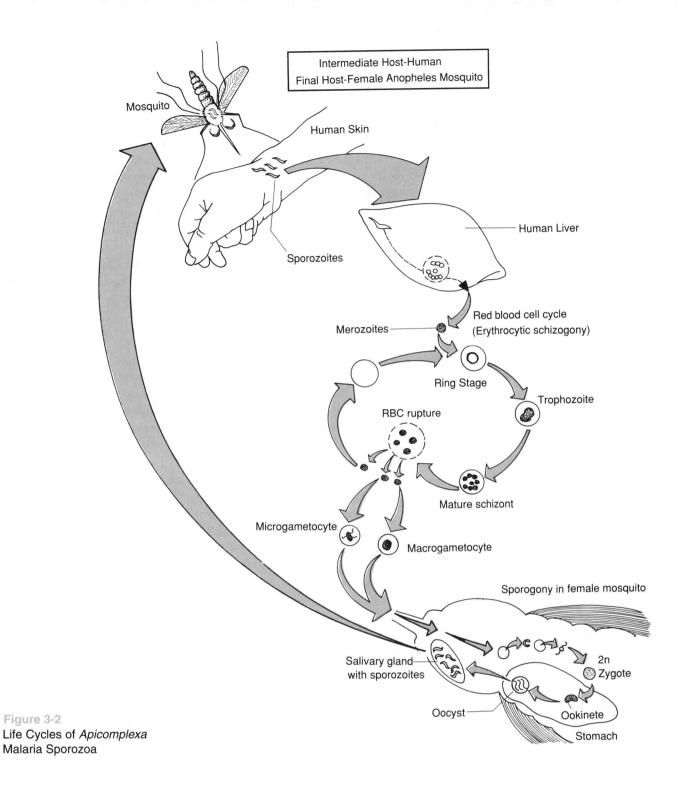

Figure 3-2
Life Cycles of *Apicomplexa*
Malaria Sporozoa

undercooked meat or raw steak (steak tartare). The trophozoites migrate to a variety of tissues to cause infection. In adults they typically produce swollen lymph nodes and nononucleosis-like symptoms. A congenital infection of toxo-plasmosis acquired during fetal development is far more life-threatening. Hydrocephaly, microcephaly, heart defects, blindness, convulsions and death in utero are possible. These birth defects are more severe if the infection occurs earlier in the pregnancy.

The phylum *Sarcomastigophora* includes the subphylum *Mastigophora* and the subphylum *Sarcodina*. *Mastigophora* are flagellated protozoa and include *Trichomonas vaginalis, Giardia,* the trypanosomes and leishmanias. *Sarcodina* includes the parasitic *Entamoeba. Trichomonas vaginalis* produces vulvovaginitis. A cream-colored or frothy white discharge is sometimes found in females. In males this protozoan can invade the urethra and the prostate gland. Males can also produce a whitish discharge. This is an example of a sexually transmitted disease. This disease is treated by having both partners take metronidazole. *Giardia lamblia* is responsible for cases of protozoan gastroenteritis. The cyst form of this organism has been found in wilderness waters. Sewage contamination of drinking water frequently involves *Giardia* in addition to coliforms. Outbreaks of giardiasis have occurred in ski resorts, day care centers and in wilderness areas. Humans usually ingest the cyst form of the protozoa, which liberates the active motile trophozoite in the intestines. The gastroenteritis produced is characterized by diarrhea, foul-smelling stools and weight loss. These infections may last for a long time. They are treated by metronidazole.

Trypanosoma brucei gambiense and *Trypanosoma brucei rhodesiense* cause sleeping sickness (African Trypanosomiasis). This protozoan is transmitted by the bite of the tsetse fly. In the blood, hemoflagellated forms that contain ribbonlike, undulating membranes are visible. In the tissues, rounded leishmanial or amastigote forms are present. These two trypanosomes invade the lymphatic and nervous systems. The symptoms include weakness, lack of eating, weight loss, encephalitis, coma and death. Drugs used include suramin sodium and pentamidine isethionate. *Trypanosoma cruzi* causes Chagas Disease (American Trypanosomiasis). This disease is found in the southern United States, in Central America and South America. It is transmitted by feces of the reduviid bug deposited on the skin and rubbed into a break in the skin. This trypanosome invades primarily the heart. Other organs invaded include the spleen, liver and bone marrow. Persons with this infection frequently die from heart failure. There is no effective treatment for this disease. *Leishmania* produces three diseases that are transmitted by the bite of the sandfly. They are visceral leishmaniasis caused by *Leishmania donovani,* cutaneous leishmaniasis caused by *Leishmania tropica* and mucocutaneous leishmaniasis (espundia) caused by *Leishmania braziliensis.* The first two diseases are found in the Near East, Far East, Africa, Russia and the Mediterranean area. The third variety is commonly found in Brazil. The symptoms of visceral leishmaniasis include liver and spleen enlargement. The protozoa multiply in the macrophages in the reticuloendothelial system. Weakness, weight loss and eventually death are commonplace. In cutaneous leishmaniasis the protozoa produce a dermal sore that ulcerates and heals with scarring of the skin. In mucocutaneous leishmaniasis the disease starts with a skin sore. This heals, but the organisms migrate to the mucous membranes of the nose and throat. They destroy the nasal septum and the hard palate. Death frequently occurs from bacterial infections in the airway. Pentavelent antimony, sodium gluconate and pentamidine isethionate are used to treat all these leishmania infections. *Sarcodina* contains the parasitic ameba *Entamoeba histolytica.* This organism is ingested in cyst form in contaminated food and water. The trophozoites are liberated in the caecum and invade the intestinal lining, producing necrotic lesions and sometimes intestinal perforation. Diarrhea, cramps, weakness and dehydration are common. The organisms may be carried through the hepatic portal vein to the liver, where they produce liver abscesses. Metronidazole is used for treatment.

The phylum *Ciliophora* contains the ciliate protozoan *Balantidium coli*. This protozoan is ingested in cyst form in contaminated food and water. The trophozoites are liberated in the colon. Diarrhea and bloody stools as well as diarrhea alternating with constipation are common. Humans have a high resistance to this organism, which is found worldwide.

Protozoa: An Overview

In this exercise prepared slides from protozoa in three phyla are examined. These include the ring stage for the erythrocyte cycle of the malarial plasmodium in humans, *Toxoplasma gondii* trophozoites, *Trichomonas vaginalis*, *Giardia lamblia* trophozoites and cysts, *Trypanosoma*, and *Balantidium coli* trophozoites. The ring stage of the malarial plasmodium is an important diagnostic feature of malaria in a blood smear. The presence of the different trophozoites, flagellates or ciliates in a smear would also indicate distinct medical conditions. Collectively these slides should be viewed as the equivalent of smears obtained from patients who have protozoan diseases. Each of these slides presents distinctive organisms that can be used to make a differential diagnosis of a protozoan disease. The student should view each of these slides as a clinical unknown obtained from patients and should use the information in the exercise as a guideline for their differential identification. The characteristics of these organisms as seen in microscope slides are noted in this exercise.

Materials

Prepared slides of the ring stage of *Plasmodium falciparum*.

Prepared slides of *Toxoplasma gondii*.

Prepared slides of *Trichomonas vaginalis*.

Prepared slides of *Giardia lamblia* (smear of trophozoites and cysts).

Prepared slides of *Trypanosoma* species.

Prepared slides of *Balantidium coli* (smear of trophozoites).

Procedures

Ring stage of *Plasmodium falciparum*

1. Select a slide of the ring stage of *Plasmodium falciparum*.

2. Observe the large number of red blood cells in the smear. Look for those red blood cells with a stained band-shaped region in the red blood cell. This is the ring stage.

Trophozoites of *Toxoplasma gondii*

1. Select a slide of the trophozoite of *Toxoplasma gondii*.

2. Observe the human cells with large nuclei. These are mononuclear cells. Look for collections of nucleated protozoan cells in the cytoplasm of these infected cells. These are the trophozoites. Some trophozoites can be seen outside of these infected cells.

Trichomonas vaginalis

1. Select a slide of *Trichomonas vaginalis*.

2. Observe the pear-shaped protozoan. Notice the large nucleus and the short ribbonlike, undulating membrane. The anterior rounded end of this protozoan shows a group of flagella.

Trophozoites and cysts of *Giardia lamblia*

1. Select a slide of *Giardia lamblia*.

2. Observe the oval-shaped t rophozoite, which has two nuclei and large karyosomes that look like eyeglasses. The trophozoites also have four pairs of flagella that may be difficult to see. The smear usually shows fewer trophozoites than cysts. The cysts are more deeply stained and contain two or four nuclei.

Trypanosoma

1. Select a slide of *Trypanosoma* (blood smear).

2. Observe the ribbonlike, undulating membrane and the long flagella emerging from the end of the undulating membrane. These are long protozoa and are found between the blood cells.

Trophozoites of *Balantidium coli*

1. Select a slide of *Balantidium coli*.

2. Observe the oval-shaped protozoan. Notice the large macronucleus and the smaller micronucleus. Notice the cilia around the edge of this organism. If cysts are present, look for the thick outer wall. The two nuclei may also be visible in the cyst.

The protozoan phyla

1. Draw representative organisms for each of these protozoa in the Results section.

2. Answer the questions in the Results section.

3. Answer the questions for the exercise.

Microbes Are Everywhere

Objectives

1. Identify three locations in which bacteria are found.

2. Describe a procedure to demonstrate the presence of bacteria in the environment.

3. Name two major categories of human infections spread by fomites to humans.

Background

Microorganisms are everywhere. They are on nonliving surfaces, or *fomites*, such as drinking glasses, silverware, tissues and towels, doorknobs and countertops. They are also on living surfaces, such as the skin and mucous membranes and other hospitable areas where they compose part of the normal flora of microorganisms found in the human body. Microorganisms are also found associated with the dust particles in the air. A portion of this broad variety of microorganisms is responsible for airborne and food- and water-borne infections in humans. Airborne infections are spread in a variety of ways. One is by aerosols, or droplet infections. This is found in the transmission of tuberculosis and the common cold. Airborne infections can be further spread by contact with doorknobs and by handshaking followed by subsequent contact with the mucous membranes of the eyes, nose or mouth. Food- and water-borne infections can be spread to humans by foods contaminated by the hands of infected food handlers or by the use of contaminated utensils in the preparation of foods.

Microbes Are Everywhere: An Overview

This exercise demonstrates the wide distribution of microorganisms in nature. These include environmental areas, the human body and air. Environmental areas such as doorknobs, table tops, drawers or shoe heels are swabbed with moistened sterile swabs. These swabs are then swabbed onto the surface of nutrient agar plates to isolate and grow colonies of microorganisms from these areas. The students also swab the skin, nostrils and hands and then transfer the swabbings to separate petri dishes of nutrient agar. Additionally, a nutrient agar petri dish is exposed to the air by removing the cover and leaving it open for at least half an hour. The cover is then replaced. Any microorganism in dust particles that settle on the agar surface will multiply to produce colonies. (The procedures are illustrated in Figure 4-1.)

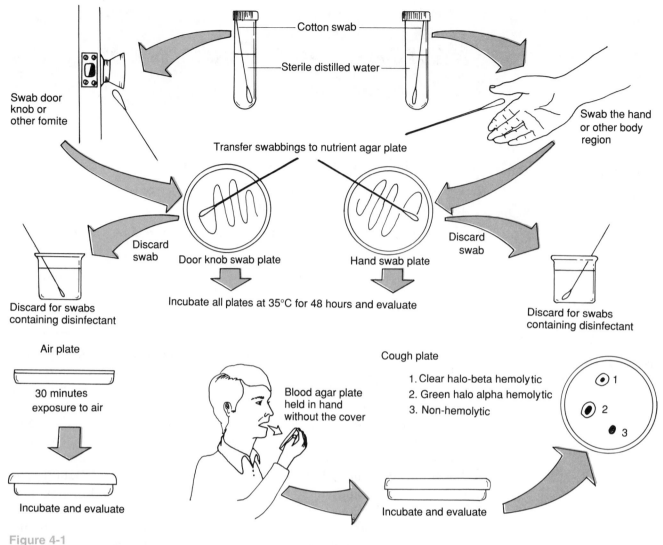

Figure 4-1
Procedures to Demonstrate
That Microbes Are Omnipresent

Within the figure:

Cotton swab
Sterile distilled water
Swab door knob or other fomite
Swab the hand or other body region
Transfer swabbings to nutrient agar plate
Discard swab
Discard swab
Door knob swab plate
Hand swab plate
Discard for swabs containing disinfectant
Discard for swabs containing disinfectant
Incubate all plates at 35°C for 48 hours and evaluate

Air plate
30 minutes exposure to air
Incubate and evaluate

Blood agar plate held in hand without the cover

Cough plate
1. Clear halo-beta hemolytic
2. Green halo alpha hemolytic
3. Non-hemolytic

Incubate and evaluate

Materials

nutrient agar plates

blood agar plates

packets of sterile swabs (6 per student)

tubes of sterile distilled water

Procedures

First Period
Environmental Survey:

1. Select three nutrient agar dishes. Label the bottom of the first dish
   Doorknob, the second Work Counter, the third Student Locker.

2. Select a sterile cotton swab. Moisten the first swab by dipping the cotton bulb in a tube of distilled water. Swab a doorknob and transfer the swabbings to the proper petri dish by swabbing the agar surface.

3. Select a second sterile swab. Moisten the swab and swab the work counter and transfer these swabbings to the agar surface of the properly labeled petri dish.

4. Select a third sterile swab and moisten it. Swab the surface of a student drawer and transfer these swabbings to the agar surface of the third petri dish. Discard the three swabs in a jar of disinfectant.

Human Body Survey:

1. Select a blood agar plate and cough strongly on the agar surface of this medium. Label this plate Cough Plate.

2. Select three nutrient agar petri dishes and label them Hair, Nostrils, and Hand. Select three more packets of swabs.

3. Moisten the first swab and swab the hair. Transfer the swabbings to the properly labeled dish. Discard this swab in a jar of disinfectant.

4. Moisten the second swab and swab the inside of the nostrils. Transfer the swabbings to the properly labeled dish. Discard this swab in a jar of disinfectant.

5. Moisten the third swab and swab the opposite hand. Transfer the swabbings to the properly labeled dish. Discard this swab in a jar of disinfectant.

Air Plate:

1. Remove the cover from a nutrient agar dish and expose the agar surface to the air for 30 minutes.

2. Replace the cover.

All Samples: Incubate all the plates in this exercise at 35°C for 48 hours.

Second Period

1. Examine all the plates for any evidence of growth.

2. Examine the blood agar plate for any evidence of clear halos or green halos around the colonies. Clear halos indicate beta-hemolysis, or complete destruction of the red blood cells in the medium. This is found for some streptococci and staphylococci. Green halos are found for some streptococci. Green halos indicate alpha-hemolysis, or partial destruction of some of the red blood cells. No halos indicates non-hemolysis and is found for some species of *Klebsiella*.

3. Record the number of colonies in the table in the Results section.

4. Answer the questions for the exercise.

Exercise 5	# Aseptic Transfer Techniques

Objectives

1. Define **aseptic technique**.
2. Describe two examples of aseptic transfer.

Background

The student of microbiology must contend with a number of problems in order to succeed in any experimental work. One problem is obtaining microbe-free or sterile media for any experimental work. Another is the ability to grow microorganisms in a pure, noncontaminated culture. A pure culture of any microorganism contains only cells of that microbe.

Routinely all media for microbiology are sterilized prior to use. One method of sterilization is the use of the autoclave or steam sterilizer. Media is sterilized at 121°C for 15 to 20 minutes. This set of conditions is sufficient to kill the most heat-resistant organism and to sterilize the media. Some liquid media that are heat-sensitive are sterilized by filtration. Glassware can be sterilized in an autoclave and dried in a hot air oven or can be sterilized in a hot air oven set at 180°C for 2 hours.

There are a variety of different nutritional environments in which bacteria are grown. One is a broth medium, which is a sterile liquid containing a variety of nutrients. A common nutrient broth contains peptone, beef extract and distilled water and provides a fairly complete assortment of the nutrients most bacteria need for growth. The medium is prepared, dispensed into tubes and capped with closures. The tubed medium is sterilized and after cooling is ready for use. Solid media, such as nutrient agar, contain the solidifying agent called agar. These media are prepared, sterilized and poured into sterile petri dishes. The agar then solidifies and the media are ready for use. In another approach the prepared liquid agar medium is poured into tubes, and the tubes are then sterilized in the steam sterilizer. This medium may then be allowed to solidify on a tilted board so that the agar surface is on a slant. Media prepared in this manner are called slants. Agar media may be allowed to solidify while the tubes are upright. The solid plug of medium in these tubes is known as an agar deep.

The ability to grow bacteria as pure cultures requires skill in aseptic transfer techniques. *Asepsis* means without any microorganisms. The common tools used for transfer of microorganisms are the inoculating needle and the inoculating loop. The inoculating needle is used to stab solid agar and transfer a small amount of microorganisms to this medium. The inoculating loop is used to transfer a loopful of a liquid suspension of microorganisms to a solid surface medium such as a petri dish of agar or an agar slant or to another liquid medium. If proper aseptic transfer techniques are used, only cells of the inoculated organism will grow in the new culture medium.

Aseptic Transfer Techniques: An Overview

The goal of these transfers is to grow only the desired microorganisms and to avoid contamination with any unwanted organisms. To achieve this goal, aseptic techniques are used to transfer microorganisms from one culture environment to another. The transfer of microorganisms from one medium to another is known as inoculation. The first step in this procedure is to sterilize the inoculating loop or needle. This is done by holding the wire portion of the inoculating tool in a flame until it glows red hot. This incinerates any microbes on the inoculating tool and sterilizes it so that it may be used to transfer bacteria to fresh media. In this exercise the student will practice sterile aseptic technique by transferring sterile broth from one tube to another and will also transfer broth to a slant medium. The student will also transfer a culture of bacteria to broth, to a slant and to an agar deep and make a pure culture. (See Figures 5-1, 5-2, 5-3, 5-4.)

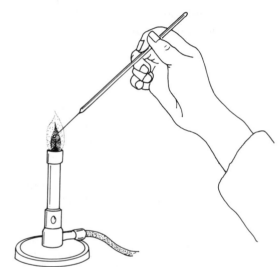

Figure 5-1
Sterilizing the Wire of An Inoculating Loop in the Flame of a Bunsen Burner

Flaming an open culture tube

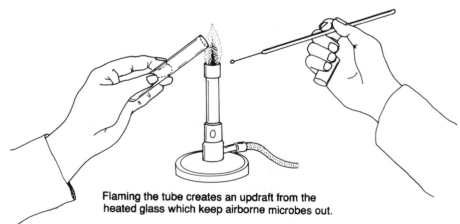

Flaming the tube creates an updraft from the heated glass which keep airborne microbes out.

Figure 5-1
Flaming An Open Culture Tube.

Note how the cap is held by the 3rd and 4th fingers of the hand holding the loop. Hold the inoculating needle the same way.

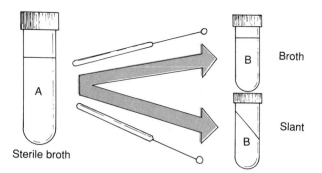

Figure 5-3
Sterile Media Transfers

Sterile broth

B   Broth

B   Slant

Materials

inoculating loop

inoculating needle

rack for holding tubes

Bunsen burner

matches

tubes of sterile nutrient broth

tubes of sterile nutrient agar deeps

slants of sterile nutrient agar

20-hour nutrient broth culture of *Staphylococcus aureus*

Procedures

First Period

1. Obtain two tubes of nutrient broth. Label them A and B. Obtain a nutrient agar slant. Label it B. Place all the tubes in a rack in an upright position.

2. Light the Bunsen burner as instructed by the instructor.

3. Hold the handle end of the inoculating loop between the thumb and fore-finger, so that the wire and loop portion are placed near the inner cone of the Bunsen burner flame. Observe that the wire glows red hot. Be sure to flame sterilize (hereafter called flame) the entire wire and loop. Then quickly pass the handle portion through the flame to incinerate any dust-containing particles. (See Figure 5-1.)

4. Grasp tube A of nutrient broth with the opposite hand. Using the third and fourth fingers of the hand holding the loop, remove the cap from the broth tube and hold it. Pass the opening of the tube through the flame. (See Figure 5-2.)

5. Pass the loop into the broth and obtain a loopful of broth. Remove the loop and quickly flame the tube opening. Replace the cap on this tube and place the tube in a rack.

6. Pick up nutrient broth tube B from the rack. Remove the cap and flame the opening and transfer the loopful of sterile broth into this tube.

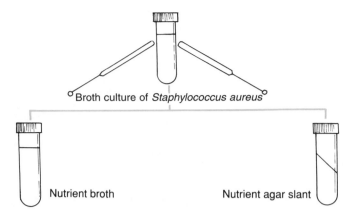

Figure 5-4
Sterile Broth Transfers

Broth culture of *Staphylococcus aureus*

Nutrient broth   Nutrient agar slant

Remove the loop and quickly flame the tube opening. Replace the cap on this tube and place it in the rack. (See Figure 5-3.)

7. Flame the loop again and remove a loopful of broth from tube A as in steps 4 and 5.

8. Grasp slant B in the opposite hand and remove the cap. Pass the tube opening through the flame and transfer the loopful of broth onto the agar surface by making a single streak up the slanted agar surface. Remove the loop, flame the tube opening, replace the cap and place the tube in the rack.

9. Flame the loop. Place the loop in a rack.

10. Obtain a tube of nutrient broth and a nutrient agar slant. Label them *Staphylococcus aureus*.

11. Flame the loop and transfer first a loopful of the bacterial culture to the labeled nutrient broth tube using the techniques you have practiced above. (See Figure 5-4.)

12. Flame the loop and transfer a second loopful of the bacterial culture to the labeled nutrient agar slant as in step 8.

13. Flame the loop again and quickly pass the handle through the flame to remove any contamination, before placing it on any counter. *This final flaming must always be done to avoid any contamination or spread of microorganisms to persons in the laboratory or to contents in the locker or laboratory facilities.*

14. Obtain a nutrient agar deep tube. Grasp the inoculating needle by the handle. Grasp the bacterial broth tube with the opposite hand. Flame the wire until it glows red hot. Using the third and fourth fingers of the same hand, remove the cap from the bacterial broth culture, flame the tube opening and dip the wire portion into the liquid culture. Remove the inoculating needle, flame the tube opening and replace the cap. Place the tube in the rack.

15. Grasp the agar deep tube with the free hand not holding the needle. Using the third and fourth fingers of the hand holding the needle, remove this cap and flame the lip of the tube; then stab the agar deep with the wire portion of the inoculating needle. (See Figure 5-5.)

Agar deep

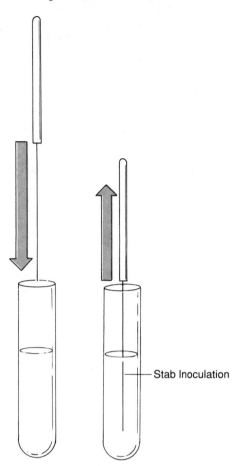

Stab Inoculation

Figure 5-5
Transfer of *Staphylococcus aureus* to a Nutrient Agar Deep Tube

16. Pass the tube opening through the flame. Replace the cap and flame the wire of the inoculating needle. Pass the handle quickly through the flame and place the inoculating needle on the counter.

17. Incubate all the tubes at 35°C for 48 hours.

Second Period

1. Examine nutrient broth tubes A and B and nutrient slant B for any evidence of growth. Growth in broth medium is detected by cloudiness in the liquid medium. Growth on a slant is seen as a film of material on the agar surface. No growth should be seen in the broth tubes or on the slant since this is a sterile, microbe-free inoculation.

2. Examine the nutrient broth and slant inoculated with *Staphylococcus aureus*. Growth is seen as cloudiness in the broth and as a yellow, smooth film on the slant surface.

3. Examine the agar deep for growth. Growth is detected by some cloudiness in the agar at the stab line.

4. Record all results in the table in the Results section.

5. Answer the questions for the exercise.

Case Study 1

An outbreak of *Acinetobacter* infections occurs in patients in an intensive care unit of a hospital. Air samples on agar petri plates, swabbings of sink traps, patient night tables and counters as well as bed linen are positive for this organism. The numbers of *Acinetobacter* are greatest near the infected patients. Telephone handsets, patient charts, and respiratory equipment also show some contamination. The decision is made that environmental surfaces and equipment can be a resevoir of infection and a source of spreading of this nosocomial pathogen.

Acinetobacter are short, fat gram-negative rods that have fimbriae and capsules that aid in their attachment to membrane surfaces. They produce endotoxins which are responsible for septicemia. They produce nosocomial-respiratory infection, bacteremia after respiratory infection, meningitis and urinary tract infection. Broad spectrum cephalosporins combined with aminoglycosides are used as treatment.

Answer the following

1. Describe procedures to demonstrate the presence of *Acinetobacter*.

_____

_____

2. Describe procedures to prevent the contamination of hospital equipment.

_____

_____

3. Describe procedures to eliminate this organism from the intensive care unit.

_____

_____

4. List procedures to prevent the spread of this organism to staff and then to other patients.

_____

_____

Reference

Bergogne-Bérézin, E. and Towner, K. J. (1996). *Acinetobacter* spp. as nosocomial pathogens: microbiological, clinical, and epidemiological features. *Clinical Microbiology Reviews,* 9,2: 148–165.

Staining Microorganisms and Studying Motility

6   **Smear Preparation and the Simple Stain**   **33**

describes smear preparation, simple staining, and microscopic
morphology of selected bacteria.

7   **The Negative Stain**   **37**

describes negative staining procedures and microscopic morphology
of selected bacteria.

8   **The Gram Stain**   **39**

describes procedures for the differential stain, the Gram stain and makes
presumptive identification of selected bacteria by their microscopic
morphology and staining reactions.

9   **The Acid-Fast Stain**   **43**

describes procedures for the Acid-Fast stain procedure and the medical
importance of this test.

10   **The Endospore Stain**
         (The Schaeffer-Fulton Procedure)   **47**

describes procedures for the endospore stain and medical problems posed
by the presence of endospores.

11   **The Capsule Stain (A Negative Stain Procedure)**   **51**

describes procedures for the capsule stain and the role of capsules in
bacterial virulence.

12   **Bacterial Motility Studies**   **53**

demonstrates motility by three different methods and considers the
medical consequences of having flagella.

13   **Morphological Unknown Characterization**   **59**

describes the morphology of bacteria after differential staining, by
motility behavior and by pigment production on growth on agar slants.

         Case Study 2   **62**

Smear Preparation and the Simple Stain

Objectives

1. Prepare a smear from cultures grown in broth and on solid agar medium.
2. Describe all the steps in heat fixation.
3. Complete a simple stain of a smear.
4. List an advantage of staining bacteria.

Background

Unstained cells are extremely difficult to see with the light microscope. For this reason a coloring agent or dye is applied to the bacterial smear to color the cells, provide contrast and make the cells visible. This process is called *staining*. The stain or dye is a salt made up of a colored portion or chromophore combined with an oppositely charged ion. For example, a basic dye consists of a positively charged color group and a negative ion, indicated as Dye^+Cl^-. An acidic dye consists of a negatively charged color group and a positive ion, indicated as Na^+ Dye^-. During staining the dye portion of the molecule combines with the oppositely charged chemical groups in the bacterial cell to color the cell. Because of the negative charge in the bacterial cell, basic dyes are used to stain the cell. Examples of basic dyes used in microbiology are crystal violet, safranin, methylene blue and carbolfuchsin.

The Simple Stain: An Overview

Bacteria are transferred from a broth or solid agar medium to a glass microscope slide to form a smear. After air drying, the smear is heat fixed to attach the bacteria to the slide. The smear is flooded with a single dye for 1 minute, rinsed with water, blotted dry and examined under the oil immersion lens. This use of a single dye for staining is called a simple stain.

Materials

18–20 hour cultures of *Bacillus mycoides, Staphylococcus aureus* and *Escherichia coli*

crystal violet and safranin

glass slides, wax marking pencil, Bunsen burner, inoculating loop and bibulous paper

Procedures

Bacterial Smear Preparation from a Broth Culture

1. Select a microscope slide and label it in the left corner with the initials of the bacteria.

2. Sterilize the loop by holding the wire portion of the loop in a Bunsen burner flame until it glows red hot. Allow the loop to cool. (See Figure 6-1.)

3. Remove the cap from the broth culture tube, flame the opening of the tube and aseptically transfer a loopful of the bacterial suspension from the tube to a glass slide. Flame the opening of the tube (see Figure 6-2) and replace the cap. Repeat steps 2 and 3 each time to transfer several more loopfuls of the bacteria to the glass slide.

4. Spread the bacteria into an oval smear that occupies about two-thirds of the length of the slide surface.

5. Allow the smear to air dry. (See Figure 6-3.)

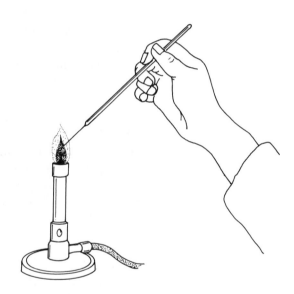

Figure 6-1
Sterilizing the Wire
Inoculating Loop in the
Flame of a Bunsen Burner

Flaming an open culture tube

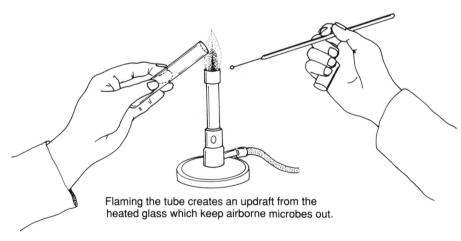

Figure 6-2
Flaming An Open Culture
Tube.

Flaming the tube creates an updraft from the
heated glass which keep airborne microbes out.

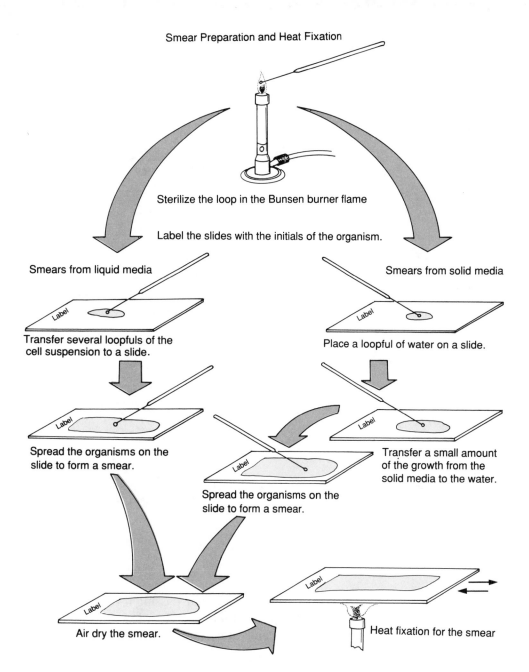

Figure 6-3
Smear Preparation and
Heat Fixation

Smear Preparation and Heat Fixation

Sterilize the loop in the Bunsen burner flame

Label the slides with the initials of the organism.

Smears from liquid media

Label

Transfer several loopfuls of the
cell suspension to a slide.

Label

Spread the organisms on the
slide to form a smear.

Smears from solid media

Label

Place a loopful of water on a slide.

Label

Transfer a small amount
of the growth from the
solid media to the water.

Label

Spread the organisms on the
slide to form a smear.

Label

Air dry the smear.

Label

Heat fixation for the smear

Bacterial Smear Preparation from Solid Agar

1. Select a glass microscope slide and label it on the left end with the initials of the bacteria.

2. Sterilize the loop by holding it in the flame until it glows red hot. Let it cool and transfer a loopful of water to the surface of a slide.

3. Flame the loop for sterility and transfer a small quantity of the bacterial growth from the agar surface to the drop of water on the slide.

4. Mix the bacteria in the water and spread the bacteria into an oval smear that occupies two-thirds of the surface of the slide.

5. Allow the smear to air dry.

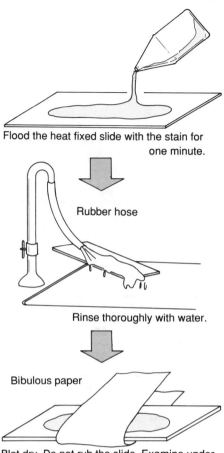

Flood the heat fixed slide with the stain for one minute.

Rubber hose

Rinse thoroughly with water.

Bibulous paper

Figure 6-4
Simple Stain Procedure

Blot dry. Do not rub the slide. Examine under the oil immersion lens of the microscope.

Heat Fixation

1. Heat fix the smear by passing it through a flame of a Bunsen burner, smear side up, several times. Heat fixation rapidly kills the cells with minimal distortion and attaches the cells to the slide. (See Figure 6-3.)

Simple Staining

1. Flood the smear with a single dye for 1 minute. Either crystal violet or safranin can be used. Use each dye for at least one slide. (See Figure 6-4.)

2. Rinse the slide with water to remove excess dye and to prevent dye crystal formation on the slide.

3. Blot the slide dry with bibulous paper.

4. Examine the slide under the oil immersion lens of the microscope. Crystal violet colors bacteria violet and safranin colors bacteria pink. Indicate the color and shape of the bacteria. Draw typical cells in the Results section. (If a thick stained smear is prepared, it will be difficult to identify single organisms; under these circumstances look near the edge of the stained smear to find individual organisms.

5. Answer the questions for the exercise.

The Negative Stain

Objectives

1. Prepare a negative stain.

2. Explain why the negative stain procedure does not stain the bacterial cell.

3. List one advantage of negative staining.

Background

One technique used to identify bacterial morphology is the negative stain. In this procedure the background is stained and the cells are unstained. The cells appear as clear areas against a dark background because this preparation uses the acidic dye nigrosine, which does not bind to the acidic cytoplasm of the cell and stains only the background of the slide. This preparation is not heat fixed, so no distortion of the typical shape of the bacterial cell occurs.

The Negative Stain: An Overview

In this procedure a live bacterial culture, suspended in a drop of nigrosine dye, is spread as a film on the surface of a glass slide. It is not heat fixed. Unstained cells appear as clear and nondistorted areas in a dark background. (See Figure 7-1.) Since the cells are alive, care must be taken not to contact the nigrosine-stained areas on the slide. Handle the slide by the edges and dispose of the slide after examination in a container of disinfectant solution or in a microbiological waste discard bin.

Materials

20-hour nutrient broth cultures of *Bacillus subtilis* and *Staphylococcus aureus*

nigrosine in dropper bottles

microscope slides

staining rack

Procedures

1. Place a small drop of nigrosine dye near the right end of a slide.

2. Aseptically, transfer two loopfuls of the first bacterial culture into the drop of nigrosine. Mix gently.

3. Select a clean glass slide. Place the left edge of this slide against the drop of bacteria and nigrosine suspension on the bottom slide. The free edge of the top slide should make a 30-degree angle with the bottom slide so that

1.

Place a drop of nigrosine on a slide.

2.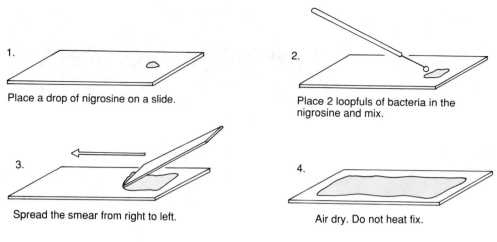

Place 2 loopfuls of bacteria in the nigrosine and mix.

3.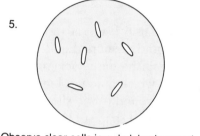

Spread the smear from right to left.

4.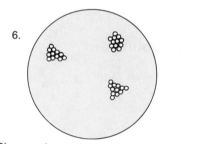

Air dry. Do not heat fix.

5.

Observe clear cells in a dark background.

6.

Observe clear cells in a dark background.

Figure 7-1
The Negative Stain
Procedure

the nigrosine suspension pools along the underside of the edge of the top slide.

4. Push the top slide from right to left to spread the nigrosine suspension to form a dark gray film on the surface of the bottom slide.

5. Allow the slide to air dry. Do not heat fix.

6. Repeat steps 1–5 for the second bacterial culture.

7. Observe the bacteria under the oil immersion lens of the microscope. Observe clear bacilli and clusters of cocci. Diagram the results in the Results section.

8. After examination, dispose of the slides in a container of disinfectant solution or in a microbiological discard bin.

(This negative stain smear procedure will be used again in the Capsule Stain Procedure in Exercise 11.)

9. Answer the questions for the exercise.

The Gram Stain

Objectives

1. Perform a Gram-stain.

2. Identify the purpose of each chemical and procedure used in the Gram stain.

3. List the results in each step of the Gram stain procedure.

4. List three characteristic differences between gram-positive and gram-negative bacteria.

5. Identify the Gram reaction, shape and microscopic arrangement for 10 different bacteria.

Background

As demonstrated earlier, the application of a single stain to a fixed smear of bacteria is a simple stain. In contrast, this exercise introduces a procedure called the Gram stain, which was developed by Christian Gram in 1884. This procedure is differential; at least two different stains are used, and, depending on the bacteria used, two distinctly different results can be seen. After staining the cells appear either violet or pink. Violet colored cells are defined as gram-positive and pink colored cells are defined as gram-negative.

The Gram stain is an important diagnostic test for the clinical identification of many pathogens. For example, a Gram stain of a sputum sample showing gram-positive diplococci and short streptococci could offer a clinician presumptive evidence for the presence of *Streptococcus pneumoniae* as the cause of the pneumonia. Thus, the Gram stain could be used to rule out a number of possible causes of the infection and help direct follow-up laboratory studies toward the identification of a specific pathogen. The clinician could then institute appropriate empiric, possibly lifesaving, therapy that could be confirmed as proper on completion of later laboratory studies. Also, one of the methods approved by the American Society for Microbiology for the microbiological examination of urine samples from patients with urinary tract infections is the Gram stain. Gram stains of a properly collected urine sample showing one or more bacteria per field together with white blood cells are strong evidence of greater than 100,000 bacteria per ml of urine and indicate a urinary tract infection. In addition, the specific organism can be presumptively identified by its appearance in a Gram stain. For example, the gram-positive *Enterococcus faecalis* and gram-negative *Escherichia coli* look different in a Gram stained smear. A clinician could use this information to select appropriate empiric antibiotic therapy for a patient.

The Gram stain has distinct advantages. This procedure is cost-effective, is rapidly performed, and offers evidence for the presence of specific organisms causing distinct medical problems. Gram stain results can give useful preliminary information in forming a decision for specific antibiotic therapy for a patient.

The chemistry of gram-positive and gram-negative bacteria shows a number of differences between these cells. Gram-positive cells are more sensitive to the antimicrobial activity of penicillins, phenols, detergents and basic dyes than are gram-negative cells. Gram-positive cells are more sensitive than gram-negative cells to the cellular destructive action of the enzyme lysozyme, which is found in human body secretions. Gram-positive cells lack the outer lipopolysaccharide layer in the cell wall that is present in gram-negative cells. Gram-positive cells lack endotoxins in the cell wall; gram-negative cells have an endotoxin layer in the cell wall. Gram-positive cells have teichoic acids in the cell wall; gram-negative cells lack these compounds.

Generally most cells are gram-negative. Gram-positive cells include some bacteria, yeasts and some fungi. Validity and reliability of the gram-reaction are highly dependent on the age of the culture. Gram stains made from gram-positive cultures older than 24 hours tend to become gram-variable. This means that some of the cells stain gram-positive while others stain gram-negative. Gram-negative cells do not undergo any change in reaction or color with age of the culture.

The Gram Stain: An Overview

The sequence of reagents used in the Gram-stain procedure is:

1. Primary stain—crystal violet

2. Mordant—Gram's iodine

3. Decolorizing agent—95% alcohol

4. Counterstain—safranin

In this procedure a heat fixed smear is flooded with the primary stain and the bacteria stain violet. After the smear is rinsed with water, the mordant is added to the smear. The mordant forms a crystal violet iodine complex, which binds tightly to the cell wall of gram-positive cells and the complex is loosely bound to the surface of gram-negative cells. The mordant is rinsed off with water and the decolorizing agent is added. The alcohol shrinks the pores of gram-positive cells so that the crystal violet iodine complex is not removed. In gram-negative cells the large lipid content is removed along with the loosely bound crystal violet iodine complex so the cells become unstained. The smear is rinsed with water to stop further decolorization, and the counterstain is added. (See Figure 8-1.) Only the gram-negative cells are stained by the counterstain. The gram-positive cells that bind the primary stain do not bind any counterstain. Gram stained smears made from gram-positive bacilli sometimes show unstained ovals in the cells when observed under the oil immersion lens of the microscope. These are not artifacts. These ovals are endospores. Endospores are resistant to heat and chemicals and do not stain in the Gram stain procedure.

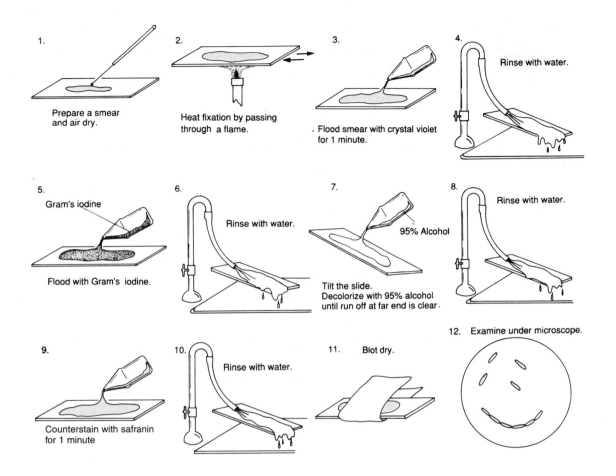

1. Prepare a smear and air dry.

2. Heat fixation by passing through a flame.

3. Flood smear with crystal violet for 1 minute.

4. Rinse with water.

5. Gram's iodine. Flood with Gram's iodine.

6. Rinse with water.

7. 95% Alcohol. Tilt the slide. Decolorize with 95% alcohol until run off at far end is clear.

8. Rinse with water.

9. Counterstain with safranin for 1 minute.

10. Rinse with water.

11. Blot dry.

12. Examine under microscope.

Figure 8-1

Materials

18–20-hour cultures of *Bacillus mycoides, Bacillus subtilis, Moraxella (Branhamella) catarrhalis, Escherichia coli, Klebsiella pneumoniae, Mycobacterium smegmatis, Proteus vulgaris, Pseudomonas aeruginosa, Staphylococcus aureus* and *Streptococcus pyogenes* (Your instructor may select from or add to this list of organisms.)

Optional: A mixed culture of *Staphyloccus aureus* and *Escherichia coli*

Gram's crystal violet

Gram's iodine

95% alcohol

Gram's safranin

glass slides

Bunsen burner

bibulous paper

staining rack

Procedures

1. Select clean slides and prepare a smear of each organism.

2. Air dry and heat fix the smear by passing the slide smear side up through the flame several times.

3. Flood the smear with crystal violet for 1 minute. Rinse briefly with water.

4. Flood the smear with Gram's iodine for 1 minute. Rinse with water.

5. Hold the slide at an angle and drip the alcohol onto the smear so that it runs over the smear. The violet color of the primary stain will wash off the smear and the free edge of the smear will appear violet. Gradually this edge will become lighter. When this edge is clear, thoroughly rinse the slide in water to stop the decolorizing action of the alcohol. Do not over-decolorize since gram-positive cells can lose the primary stain in the presence of excess alcohol and stain gram-negative.

6. Flood the smear with safranin for 1 minute. Rinse with water and blot dry (do not rub) with bibulous paper.

7. Examine the smear under the oil immersion lens of the microscope. Identify the Gram-reaction of each organism and the shape and cellular arrangements observed. Draw representative cells and arrangements in the Results section.

8. Answer the questions for the exercise.

The Acid-Fast Stain

Objectives

1. Define the term *acid-fast*.

2. Perform an acid-fast stain.

3. Identify the purpose of each chemical and procedure used in the acid-fast stain.

Background

Most bacteria can be stained by the Gram stain procedure. However, bacteria in the genus *Mycobacterium* frequently do not stain uniformly with this procedure. This genus includes the causative agents of tuberculosis and leprosy, and the acid-fast stain aids in diagnosis of these diseases. Because of the large amounts of the waxy lipid called mycolic acid found in the cell walls of these organisms, they tend to show a variable Gram-stain reaction. Mycolic acid resists entry of the crystal violet primary stain into the cell. Some cells may stain gram-positive, while others stain gram-negative or do not stain at all. Because of this problem the differential stain called the acid-fast procedure is used for these bacteria. Once stained by the carbolfuchsin primary stain of the acid-fast procedure, these bacteria are not readily decolorized by the acid-alcohol used as the decolorizing agent. The waxy lipids hold the stain tightly and prevent the entry of the acid-alcohol into the cell. Those bacteria that retain the primary stain after acid-alcohol decolorization treatment are called acid-fast, while other bacteria that lose this primary stain are non-acid-fast. Acid-fast stains can also be done routinely to monitor the effectiveness of therapy against *Mycobacterium tuberculosis*. Decreases in sputum sample numbers of acid-fast mycobacteria can be seen as drug treatment continues.

The Acid-Fast Stain: An Overview

The sequence of reagents used in the acid-fast procedure is:

1. Primary stain—carbolfuchsin

2. Decolorizing agent—acid-alcohol

3. Counterstain—methylene blue

In this procedure a fixed smear is flooded with carbolfuchsin primary dye and steamed to force the dye into the cell. The smear is decolorized with acid-alcohol and rinsed with water to stop further decolorization. The smear is then counterstained with methylene blue. Acid-fast cells are pink and non–acid-fast cells are blue. (See Figure 9-1.)

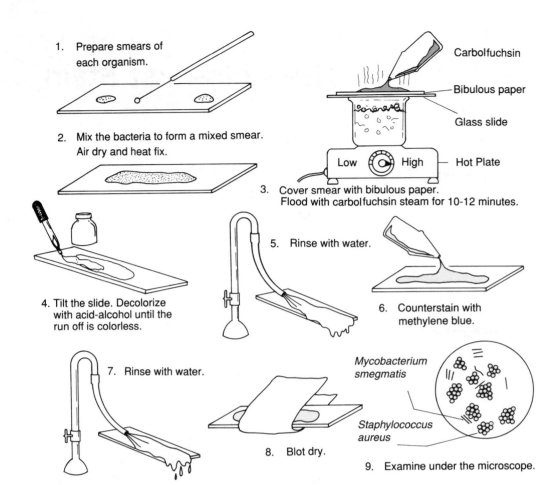

1. Prepare smears of each organism.

2. Mix the bacteria to form a mixed smear. Air dry and heat fix.

Carbolfuchsin

Bibulous paper

Glass slide

Low ⊙ High — Hot Plate

3. Cover smear with bibulous paper. Flood with carbolfuchsin steam for 10-12 minutes.

4. Tilt the slide. Decolorize with acid-alcohol until the run off is colorless.

5. Rinse with water.

6. Counterstain with methylene blue.

7. Rinse with water.

8. Blot dry.

Mycobacterium smegmatis

Staphylococcus aureus

9. Examine under the microscope.

Figure 9-1
The Acid-Fast Stain
Procedure

Materials

18–20-hour nutrient agar slant culture of *Staphylococcus aureus*

4-day-old nutrient agar slant culture of *Mycobacterium smegmatis*

hot plate and beaker

inoculating needle and loop

bibulous paper or paper towels

carbolfuchsin

acid-alcohol

methylene blue

staining rack

Procedures

1. Fill a beaker two-thirds full with water. Place it on top of a hot plate. Turn the hot plate setting to high.

2. Select a clean slide and place 2 drops of water on the left side of the slide. Transfer some of the growth from the slant of *Mycobacterium*

smegmatis into the water. Break up this growth with the tip of the inoculating needle.

3. Place 2 drops of water on the right side of the slide. Transfer some of the growth from the slant of *Staphylococcus aureus* into the drop of water.

4. Mix both cultures on the slide with an inoculating loop to make a mixed smear.

5. Air dry and heat fix this smear.

6. Cut a sheet of bibulous paper (or paper towel) to fit the dimensions of the slide and place this paper on top of the smear.

7. When the water is boiling, place the paper-covered slide on top of the beaker.

8. Add carbolfuchsin to the paper covering the smear. Steam the preparation for 10–12 minutes. Do not let the paper dry out. Add more carbolfuchsin to keep the paper wet while steaming.

9. At the end of the steaming, discard the paper in a microbiological waste discard bin. Allow the slide to cool.

10. Tilt the slide. Drip the acid-alcohol onto the smear so that it runs on the smear. The pink color of the primary stain will wash off the smear, and the free edge of the slide will appear pink. Gradually this edge will become lighter. When this edge is colorless, thoroughly rinse the slide with water to stop further decolorization. Non–acid-fast bacteria, which lack the waxy lipids, will lose the primary stain, while acid-fast bacteria, which have the waxy lipids, will retain the primary stain in the presence of acid-alcohol.

11. Counterstain the smear with methylene blue for 1 minute. Rinse with water and blot dry.

12. Examine the smear under the oil immersion lens of the microscope. Identify the reaction of these two organisms to the acid-fast procedure. Notice that scattered clumps of pink bacilli of *Mycobacterium smegmatis* appear in a background of blue cocci of *Staphylococcus aureus*. Draw representative cells and arrangements in the Results section.

13. Answer the questions about the procedure.

Alternate Procedure

An alternate procedure uses the Kinyoun acid-fast stain method. This "cold-method" does not require heating the carbolfuchsin. The detergent wetting action allows the dye to get past the cell wall.

1. Cover an air-dried and heat-fixed smear with a small rectangle of bibulous paper (or filter paper).

2. Apply enough Kinyoun's carbolfuchsin (5–7 drops) to completely moisten the paper.

3. Allow the covered slide to stand 5 minutes, adding more stain if the filter paper dries. Do not heat the smear and stain.

4. Remove filter paper.

5. Rinse with water and drain.

6. Decolorize with acid-alcohol until no more stain appears in the washing (about 2 minutes).

7. Counterstain with methylene blue (1–2 minutes).

8. Rinse, drain and air dry.

9. Examine under oil immersion lens. Mycobacteria are stained red; non–acid-fast bacteria will stain light blue, but they will be slightly darker than the background.

10. Answer the questions for the exercise.

The Endospore Stain
(Schaeffer-Fulton Procedure)

Objectives

1. Perform an endospore stain.

2. Identify the purpose of each chemical and procedure used in the spore stain procedure.

3. List two genera that form spores.

4. List three pathogenic bacteria that produce spores and the diseases produced by these microorganisms.

5. Explain the nature of the sterilization problem presented by endospores.

Background

The bacterial endospore or spore is an oval, metabolically inactive structure that is formed within the bacterial vegetative cell. The spore is highly resistant to drying, freezing, ultra-violet light, high heat, many chemicals and disinfectants and is not easily stained by dyes. The vegetative cells are metabolically active and are considerably more sensitive to these conditions and agents. Not all bacteria can produce endospores. Commonly, aerobic bacteria that form endospores are found in the genus *Bacillus*, while anaerobic bacteria that form endospores are found in the genus *Clostridium*. Both of these genera are gram-positive and contain bacillus-shaped bacteria. The location of the spore in the bacterial vegetative cell does not change for a given bacterial cell. For example, *Clostridium tetani* shows a spore located at the end of the cell, or a terminal location for an endospore. Other bacteria show the spore located more toward one end, or a subterminal location. Still others show the spore located in the center of the cell, or a central location. Sporogenesis, or spore formation, is triggered frequently but not always by a reduction in carbon or nitrogen nutrient sources. During sporogenesis a multilayered spore wall is formed inside the original vegetative bacterial cell. This original cell is called the sporangium. Only one spore is formed in a cell. As the spore forms, it loses water and accumulates calcium and dipicolinic acid. The dormancy of the spore is related to the high level of these two substances. Sometimes, when the spore is fully formed, it is released from the vegetative sporangium as the cell decays. Germination is the process concerned with the change of the spore into the metabolically active vegetative cell. This occurs when endospores are in a medium favorable for growth. Typically the vegetative cell grows out of the spore and leaves behind the empty spore wall casing. The endospore represents a resistant phase in the life cycle of a bacterial cell; endospore formation is not a method of reproduction, since one cell forms one endospore and vice versa.

Medically significant bacteria that produce endospores include *Clostridium tetani*, which is commonly found in soil and produces the toxin that causes the potentially fatal, rigid paralysis of tetanus. Also, *Clostridium botulinum*, from which the food-poisoning term botulism is derived, produces a deadly nerve toxin. Although the spores are very heat-resistant, the toxin is not. Several other species of *Clostridium* cause gas gangrene. *Bacillus anthracis* are the bacteria responsible for anthrax, a deadly farm animal disease that is also transmittable and fatal to humans. This microbe is known to have viable spores after hundreds of years of dormancy.

The Schaeffer-Fulton Method: An Overview

In this procedure a bacterial spore smear preparation is flooded with malachite green and steamed to force the dye into the spore wall. After removal of excess stain with water the counterstain safranin is applied. On completion of this procedure the spore is stained green and the sporangium is stained pink. (See Figure 10-1.)

Materials

48-hour nutrient agar slant culture of *Bacillus subtilis*

hot plates and beakers

bibulous paper or paper towels

5% aqueous malachite green in dropper bottles

0.5% aqueous safranin in dropper bottles

staining rack

Procedures

1. Fill a beaker two-thirds full with water and place it on top of a hot plate. Set the hot plate dial on high.

2. Prepare a smear of the *Bacillus subtilis*.

3. Heat fix the slide preparation.

4. Cut a piece of bibulous paper (or paper towel) to fit the dimensions of the slide and place this paper on top of the smear.

5. When the water is boiling, place the paper-covered slide on top of the beaker.

6. Add malachite green to the paper covering the smear. Do not let the paper dry out. Steam the preparation for 10 minutes. Be sure to keep the paper wet with this stain while steaming.

7. At the end of the steaming treatment, discard the paper in a microbiological discard bin. Allow the slide to cool.

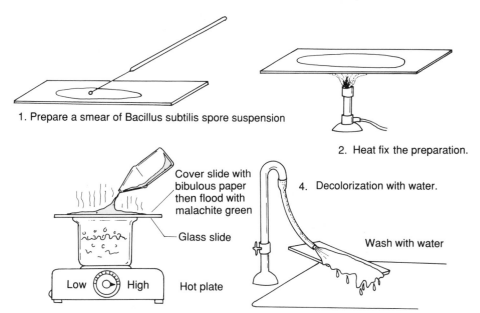

1. Prepare a smear of Bacillus subtilis spore suspension

2. Heat fix the preparation.

Cover slide with bibulous paper then flood with malachite green

Glass slide

Low ⊙ High   Hot plate

3. Steam with malachite green for 10 minutes.

4. Decolorization with water.

Wash with water

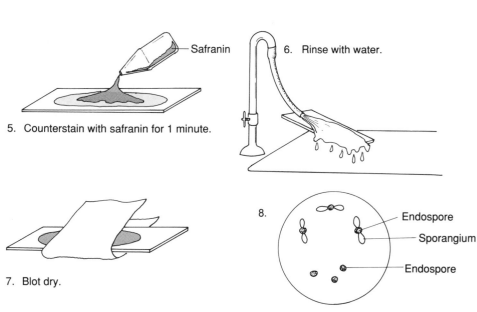

Safranin

5. Counterstain with safranin for 1 minute.

6. Rinse with water.

7. Blot dry.

8.

Endospore
Sporangium
Endospore

Figure 10-1
Endospore Stain Procedure

8. Rinse the slide with water.

9. Counterstain with safranin for 1 minute.

10. Rinse with water and blot dry with bibulous paper or a paper towel.

11. Examine the preparation under the oil immersion lens of a microscope. Identify the spore, the sporangium and the location of the spore and compare the color of the spores seen in this preparation to that of spores seen in the Gram-stain.

12. Answer the questions for the exercise.

The Capsule Stain
(A Negative Stain Procedure)

Objectives

1. Perform a capsule stain.

2. Draw a bacterial cell with a capsule and label each part.

3. List two features of capsules that enhance the disease process.

Background

A capsule is an additional covering around the outside of a cell. It is produced by the cell and released outside the cell to form an additional covering around the organism. Usually capsules are composed of polysaccharide, which is somewhat water soluble. Capsules enhance the virulence of bacteria in a number of ways. They interfere with phagocytosis. Capsules also promote the process of infection because encapsulated bacteria can attach more readily to host cells. Gram-negative encapsulated bacteria are also more resistant to the lethal action of complement and other serum factors. Encapsulated bacteria are more resistant to the lethal action of heavy metals, dehydrating, and attack by bacterial viruses than are nonencapsulated cells.

Capsular swelling in the presence of specific antibody is known as the Quellung Test and is a valuable laboratory test for the sero-identification of specific encapsulated bacteria.

The Negative Capsule Stain Method: An Overview

In this capsule stain procedure a small sample of a bacterial culture is mixed with India ink and is spread over the surface of a slide. The bacterial film is stained with crystal violet. the cells stain violet and the capsules appear as clear bright halos around the stained cells. The background is stained dark gray or black. Because the capsule is not stained, this procedure is considered a negative stain. (See Figure 11-1.)

Materials

48-hour skim milk culture of *Klebsiella pneumoniae*

India ink

crystal violet

glass slide

inoculating loop

Bunsen burner

bibulous paper

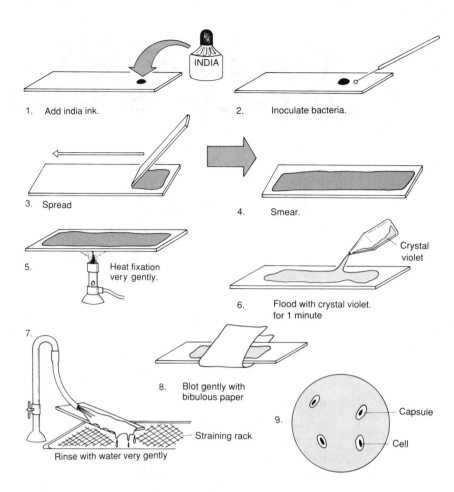

1. Add india ink.

2. Inoculate bacteria.

3. Spread

4. Smear.

5. Heat fixation very gently.

6. Flood with crystal violet. for 1 minute

Crystal violet

7.

8. Blot gently with bibulous paper

Straining rack

Rinse with water very gently

9.

Capsule

Cell

Figure 11-1
Capsule Stain Procedure

Procedures

1. Place a small drop of India ink near the right end of a clean glass slide.

2. Aseptically transfer 4 loopfuls of the *Klebsiella pneumoniae* culture into the drop of India ink.

3. Using the loop, mix the bacteria into the India ink.

4. With a clean glass slide, spread the drop of India ink and bacteria from right to left to form a dark gray film on the culture slide. This procedure is the same as is used in Exercise 7, "The Negative Stain."

5. Heat the slide **very gently** to affix the bacteria to the slide.

6. Flood the smear with crystal violet for 1 minute.

7. Wash the slide **very gently** to remove excess crystal violet.

8. Blot dry gently with bibulous paper.

9. Examine the preparation under the oil immersion lens of the microscope. Identify the bacterial cells and the capsules. In the Results section, draw a labeled diagram showing both structures. Notice that the cells are stained and the capsules are clear.

10. Answer the questions for this exercise.

<table>
<tr><td></td><td></td></tr>
</table>

Exercise 12

Bacterial Motility Studies

Objectives

1. Define motility and Brownian movement.

2. Inoculate tubes of motility agar medium and interpret the observed results for motile and nonmotile bacteria.

3. List the steps for making a hanging drop preparation to study motility.

4. List and define the types of flagellar arrangements in bacteria.

Background

Many microorganisms move with the aid of protein strands called **flagella**. These flagella are composed of a protein called **flagellin**. Flagella staining requires the use of special mordants to thicken the flagella filament and specific stains to stain it, because flagella are extremely thin and are not visible in a Gram-stained cell. They consist of a basal body located at the junction of the cell membrane and the cell wall, a hook, and a long filament that extends from the cell. Flagella move the cell by rotating the filament portion.

Flagella show different arrangements in different bacteria; bacteria are classified by the location of the flagella in the cells. Bacteria that lack flagella are **atrichous**. Bacteria that have a single flagellum are **monotrichous**, or **polar**. Bacteria with a single flagella or cluster at each end are called **amphitrichous**. Bacteria with a cluster of flagella at one end are **lophotrichous**. Bacteria with flagella distributed around the cell surface are **peritrichous**. (See Figure 12-1.)

Flagella Locations in Bacteria

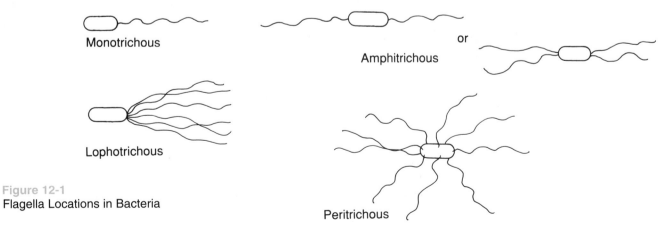

Monotrichous

Amphitrichous

or

Lophotrichous

Peritrichous

Figure 12-1
Flagella Locations in Bacteria

Bacteria can move toward useful substances in the environment or away from harmful substances. This type of movement is called **chemotaxis**. Flagellated bacteria show positive chemotaxis when they move toward a more favorable environment such as one containing more nutrient. They show negative chemotaxis when they move away from hostile or harmful environments. Bacteria have chemoreceptors located in the periplasmic space (space between the cell membrane and the cell wall). These chemoreceptors detect nutrients or harmful substances and send a signal to the flagella to trigger the counterclockwise rotation that causes forward motion of the cell toward nutrient or rotation in a clockwise direction that causes a tumbling motion away from harmful substances.

Flagella also help pathogenic bacteria to spread in the body fluids. This directed motion of bacteria is called **motility**. In contrast, in **Brownian movement**, the bacteria show a random, back-and-forth jiggling motion due to collisions of water molecules with the cells. This type of movement lacks a distinct direction and can be seen together with motility in a hanging drop preparation of motile bacteria.

Flagella play an important role in pathogenesis of *Pseudomonas aeruginosa*-produced pulmonary infections. Feldman (1998) *et al* show that flagella have multiple functions. They are immunogenic and can attach to macrophages and polymorphonuclear leucocytes which remove these organisms from mucosal surfaces as well as attaching to the mucin of respiratory epithelium. This membrane attachment permits the flagella to act as a tether to the mucosal surface which promotes pilin attachment and subsequent infection. However, clearance of these flagellated cells by the white blood cells is frequently followed by selection and attachment of nonflagellated cells to continue the infection.

Arora (1998) *et al* demonstrated that *Pseudomonas aeruginosa* has a flagellar cap protein (FliD) located on the tip of the flagella which is able to attach to the mucin covering of mucous membranes to start an infection. This protein is also found in flagellated strains of *Escherichia coli*, *proteus* strains and *salmonellae*. This protein is important for colonization of urinary tract membranes and for ascending urinary tract infections.

Bacterial Motility Studies: An Overview

Evidence of motility can be demonstrated by three procedures. They are: observation of a slide of bacteria showing stained flagella; making a hanging drop preparation of live bacteria to see motility; and a stab inoculation of bacteria into motility agar medium in tubes to see the swarming that occurs after incubation. Incubation of motility agar inoculated with motile organisms shows cloudiness spreading away from the streak line within the agar and may show spreading growth on the surface. The cloudiness and spreading growth represent motile organisms swarming through the agar. This medium can be viewed as the equivalent of the epidermis and dermis, and this type of inoculation can be viewed as a simulation of a puncture wound. In a puncture wound, organisms are injected below the skin with a sharp instrument somewhat similar to the inoculating needle piercing the agar. The cloudiness represents bacteria swarming through the dermis and releasing tissue-destructive enzymes such as hyaluronidase or spreading factor, which hydrolyses connective tissue. These same bacteria also release collagenase, which destroys collagen fibers that are abundant in the dermis. They also release streptokinase as well as streptodornase; these destroy large proteins and DNA, respectively. The end result is that an abscess is established. This could lead to massive destruction of tissue typically found in cellulitis. The restriction of nonmotile organisms to the stab line in an incubated motility agar stab inoculation simulates multiplication of organisms along the injection line into tissue. The same consequences regarding destruction of tissue could occur here as well. Microorganisms that produce these tissue-destructive effects include *Staphylococcus aureus*, *Streptococcus pyogenes*, and many gram-negative bacilli such as *Pseudomonas aeruginosa*.

Materials

prepared slide of *Proteus vulgaris* bacteria showing stained flagella

18-hour nutrient broth pure cultures of *Micrococcus luteus*, *Proteus vulgaris* and *Pseudomonas aeruginosa*.

depression slides

coverslips

lubricant gel (such as Vaseline®)

toothpicks

beaker or other container of disinfectant for disposing of hanging drop preparation. A recommended disinfectant is Lysol® or chlorhexidine-gluconate solution.

3 tubes of motility agar medium

Procedures

First Period

1. **Flagella Slide Observation:**

    a. Select a prepared slide of *Proteus vulgaris* showing stained flagella. Observe the peritrichous flagella.

    b. Observe the size of the flagella in comparison to the size of the cells.

    c. Draw representative cells.

2. **Hanging Drop Preparation (see Figure 12-2):**
    (This may be done as a demonstration by the Instructor if desired.)

    a. Obtain a depression slide, a coverslip, toothpicks and a container of lubricant gel. (See Figure 12-2.)

    b. Apply a small dot of lubricant to each corner of the coverslip with a toothpick.

    c. Transfer a loopful of *Pseudomonas aeruginosa* from the broth culture to the center of the coverslip.

    d. Invert the depression slide over the coverslip. Press it on the coverslip so the lubricant just contacts the surface of the depression slide. Do not use excessive pressure.

    e. Turn the preparation right side up.

Hanging Drop Preparation

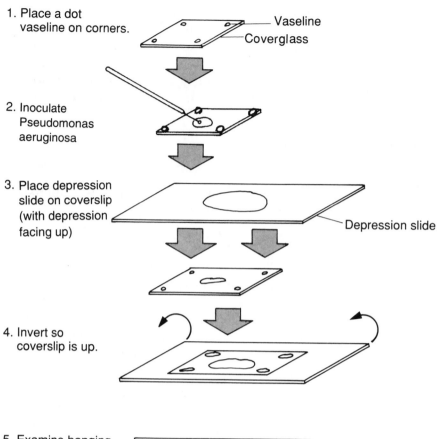

1. Place a dot vaseline on corners. — Vaseline — Coverglass

2. Inoculate Pseudomonas aeruginosa

3. Place depression slide on coverslip (with depression facing up) — Depression slide

4. Invert so coverslip is up.

Figure 12-2
Hanging Drop Preparation

5. Examine hanging drop preparation with microscope.

f. Place the preparation on the microscope stage and focus on the edge of the drop under low power. Reduce the illumination for best contrast and scan the drop for the bacteria.

g. Shift to the oil immersion lens. Adjust the illumination and focus to see the unstained bacteria. Remember that unstained cells are difficult to see because of their low contrast with the background.

h. Distinguish between cells that show true motility and those that show Brownian movement.

i. Observe some cells and draw a motion track for motile cells.

j. *Warning:* The hanging drop preparation contains a drop of culture fluid that has live bacteria. This intact preparation must be disposed of in a container of disinfectant such as Lysol®. This slide preparation can then be autoclaved to ensure sterility. The depression slide can then be reused again safely. These practices are done to eliminate the possibility of accidental contamination of students, faculty or staff in microbiology.

Bacterial Motility Studies

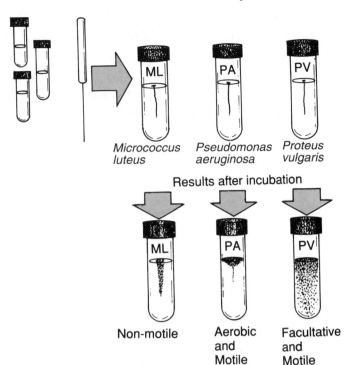

Figure 12-3
Motility Agar Stab

3. **Motility agar Stab Inoculation:**

   a. Obtain three tubes of motility agar medium and the cultures of *Micrococcus luteus*, *Proteus vulgaris* and P*seudomonas aeruginosa*. (See Figure 12-3.)

   b. Mark each tube of motility agar medium with the initials of a single different organism.

   c. Use a straight inoculating needle to stab each motility agar tube with a single organism. Be careful to withdraw the needle along the stab line.

   d. Incubate the tubes at 25°C or room temperature for 5 to 7 days for optimal results.

Second Period

1. **Motility Agar Stab Culture Evaluation:**

   a. Examine the tubes for motility. Motility is seen as cloudiness in the agar on either side of the stab line and as spreading growth at the surface of the agar. Because of the greater content of oxygen at the surface, aerobic bacteria tend to swarm at the agar surface and show less cloudiness within the agar where oxygen content is lower. Facultative bacteria show spreading growth at the surface and cloudiness within the agar. Because nonmotile bacteria lack flagella, the growth is restricted to the stab line.

2. Answer the questions for the exercise.

Exercise 12 Bacterial Motility Studies ■ 57

References

Feldman, M., Bryan, R., Rajan, S., Scheffler, L., Brunnert, S., Tang, H. and Prince, A. (1998). Role of flagella in pathogenesis of *Pseudomonas aeruginosa* in pulmonary infection. *Infection and Immunity*, 66(1): 43–51.

Arora, S., Ritchings, B., Almira, E., Lory, S. and Ramphal, R. (1998). The *Pseudomonas aeruginosa* flagellar cap protein, FliD, is responsible for mucin adhesion. *Infection and Immunity*, 66(3): 1000–1007.

Exercise 13

Morphological Unknown Characterization

Objectives

1. Characterize unknown bacteria by their responses to specific staining procedures.

2. Classify unknown bacteria by their growth response in soft agar as motile or nonmotile.

3. Determine if bacteria produce pigment during growth.

Background and Review

The Gram stain is the first step in the identification of an unknown microorganism. This procedure identifies bacteria as gram-positive or gram-negative and shows the shapes and arrangements of the cells. The bacteria may be a bacillus, coccus or spirillum.

Gram positive cells may or may not contain **endospores**, which appear as clear, unstained ovals within the violet-stained gram-positive bacilli. Endospores are commonly found in the genera *Bacillus* and *Clostridium*.

Gram-positive cocci may occur as **diplococci**, as chains of cells called **streptococci**, as cubical packets of four cells called **tetrads** (gaffkya) or as packets of 8–16 cells called **sarcinae**. Gram-positive cocci also occur as irregularly grouped bunches of cells called **staphylococci**.

Gram-negative bacteria such as *Neisseriae* and *Branhamella* are diplococci. Other gram-negative bacteria such as the coliforms *Escherichia coli*, *Enterobacter aerogenes*, and *Klebsiella pneumoniae* or the pseudomonads are bacilli. The spirilli will not be considered in this exercise.

The Gram stain is also valuable as a clinical tool. Many bacteria and fungi are gram-positive. Certain antibiotics such as erythromycin and penicillin display a differential effectiveness against gram-positive cells, while others such as the aminoglycosides are particularly effective against gram-negative cells.

Weakly stained gram-positive nonsporulating bacilli may belong in the category of the acid-fast *Mycobacterium*. These cells frequently show a branching arrangement of thin bacilli in which the cells line up parallel to each other. The cell walls of these cells contain waxy lipids that cause the cells to clump together. These lipids interfere with the entry of the Gram stain reagents. These bacteria are stained by the acid-fast procedure by steaming with hot carbolfuchsin followed by decolorization with acid-alcohol. In mixed cultures those cells not decolorized by the acid-alcohol and retaining the pink primary dye are acid-fast. Those decolorized by the acid-alcohol are non–acid fast.

Many gram-positive and gram-negative bacteria form an external covering called a capsule. This covering usually contains polysaccharide and helps the cells stick to mucous membrane surfaces and resist phagocytosis.

Two additional features that will be studied are bacterial movement, or **motility**, and pigment production. Many bacteria have flagella and are motile. Motility is easily studied by a stab inoculation of motility agar followed by observation of cloudiness within the agar, or spreading growth at the surface after incubation. Lastly, some bacteria produce a pigment during growth on agar. The pigment can color the medium, the colonies, or both.

Morphological Unknown Characterization: An Overview

The purpose of this exercise is to characterize the morphology of an unknown microorganism by means of staining reactions, motility agar study, and examination for pigment production after growth on a nutrient agar slant. The student must stain the unknown microorganism by the Gram-stain to determine the morphology, arrangements and Gram reaction. The presence of endospores, which may be seen as clear refractile objects inside the cell, should be noted at this time. A capsule stain and acid-fast stain must also be completed. The microscopic examination after these staining procedures defines the shape, arrangements, Gram-reaction, property of acid-fastness and presence or absence of a capsule. The culture studies using soft agar and nutrient agar slants indicate whether the organism is motile or not and whether it produces a pigment. The student should refer to the proper exercises on staining and culturing for additional information.

Materials

20-hour nutrient broth cultures of *Bacillus subtilis, Moraxella (Branhamella) catarrhalis, Escherichia coli, Klebsiella pneumoniae, Micrococcus luteus, Mycobacterium smegmatis, Pseudomonas aeruginosa* and *Staphylococcus aureus*. These cultures are identified by number only.

Gram-stain reagents

acid-fast stain reagents

capsule stain reagents

tubes of motility agar

tubes of nutrient agar slants

inoculating loop

inoculating needle

Procedures

First Period (See Figure 13-1.)

1. Complete a Gram stain, an acid-fast stain and a capsule stain of your unknown.

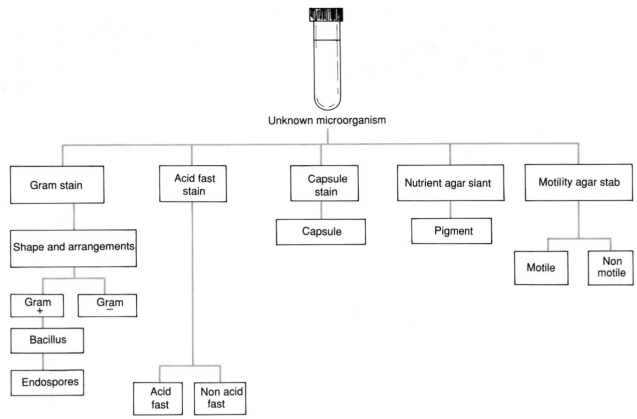

Figure 13-1
Morphological Unknown
Characterization

2. Stab a tube of motility agar medium with the unknown culture.

3. Streak a nutrient agar slant tube with a loopful of the unknown culture.

4. Examine all stained slides in the microscope. Indicate the Gram-reaction and the shape and arrangements of the cells. Indicate whether the cell is acid-fast and whether it has a capsule. Indicate your findings in the Results section.

5. Incubate the motility agar and nutrient agar slant tubes at 30°C for one week, or as directed by your instructor.

Second Period

1. Examine the tubes for motility and pigment production.

2. Indicate your observations in the Results section.

3. Write a summary statement of your findings in the Results section.

4. Answer the questions for the exercise.

Case Study 2

Early one morning, a patient is admitted to a hospital for a respiratory disease. As part of the admission procedure, a sample of urine is taken from the patient, left at the nursing station desk, and taken to the lab in the afternoon. Later, laboratory analysis shows the presence of counts of *Escherichia coli* of 300,000 bacteria per ml. The resident determines that a urinary infection exists and orders antibiotic therapy for that infection. The respiratory infection worsens and the patient is placed in intensive care. Sputum cultures show the presence of gram-positive diplococci. Antibiotic sensitivity testing shows sensitivity to ceclor and ciprofloxacin and resistance to other antibiotics. Therapy is started with ceclor and recovery occurs.

Answer the following:

1. List any error that may have occurred.

   _____

   _____

2. Indicate whether a urinary infection was present on admission and explain your answer.

   _____

   _____

3. Indicate what good medical practices should have been practiced in this case.

   _____

   _____

4. Name a presumptive pathogen indicated by the Gram stain results.

   _____

   _____

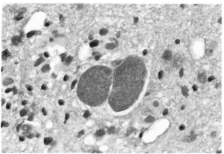

I–1 *Toxoplasma gondii* in brain of AIDS patient. Note the protozoa in the tissue.
←

I–2 *Pneumocystis carinii* in sputum specimen. This causes fatal pneumonia in immunocompromised patients.
→

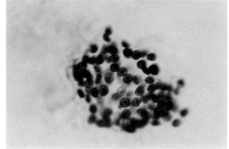

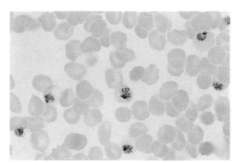

I–3 *Plasmodium falciparum*, the cause of malignant tertian malaria. The peripheral blood smear shows stages of erythrocytic cycle in humans.
←

I–4 *Cryptococcus neoformans*, a yeast-like fungus in human lung of a liver transplant.
→

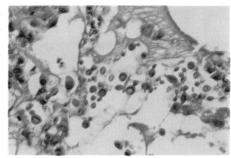

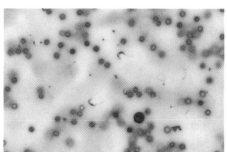

I–5 *Trypanosoma cruzi*, the cause of Chagas disease. The peripheral blood smear shows two trypanosomes.
←

I–6 *Candida albicans*. Note the cells and pseudohyphae.
→

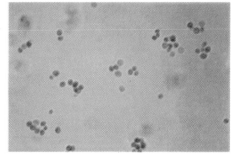

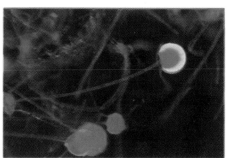

I–7 *Rhizopus* fungus presented in a dark field view.
←

I–8 *Trypanosoma brucei* in a blood smear, stained by the Giemsa stain.
→

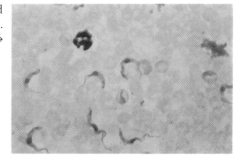

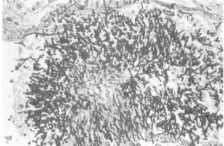

I–9 *Candida albicans* in lung of an immunocompromised patient. Note massive numbers of pseudohyphae present.
←

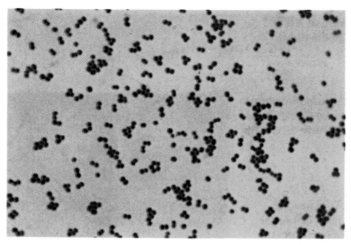

I–10 Gram stain of *Staphylococcus epidermidis*. Note the purple stained clusters of large gram-positive cocci, the diplococci, and short chains of cocci. Bacteria are classified as gram-positive or gram-negative based on their reactions with Gram stain reagents. The Gram reaction is directly related to the structure of the cell and provides a quick and easy step in the identification of specific microorganisms. Gram-positive cells are more susceptible to commonly used antibiotics such as penicillin.
←

I–11 *Bacillus subtilis* stained by the Gram procedure. Note the purple gram-positive bacilli.
←

I–12 *Treponema pallidum* in fetal tissue. This organism causes syphilis. Note the tightly coiled spirochetes.
→

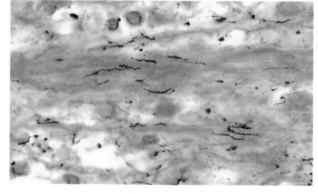

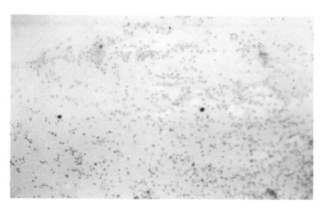

I–13 Acceptable sputum sample: contains very few epithelial cells and many white blood cells. An acceptable sputum sample is expectorated from the lower respiratory tract and is not merely saliva.
←

I–14 Unacceptable sputum sample: contains many epithelial cells and a variety of bacteria representative of the indigenous flora of the upper respiratory tract. An unacceptable specimen is unlikely to yield the etiological agent of a lower respiratory disease.
→

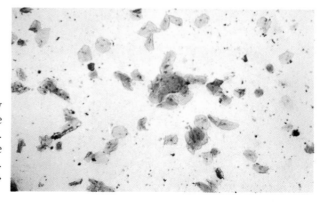

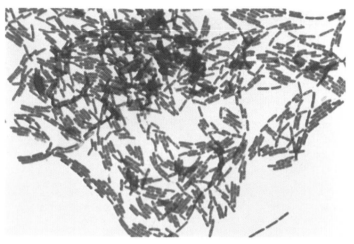

II–1 *Bacillus subtilis* spore stain. Note the oval spores in the cells.
←

II–2 *Clostridium tetani* spore stain. This organism causes tetanus and has terminal spores.
→

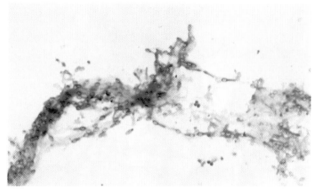

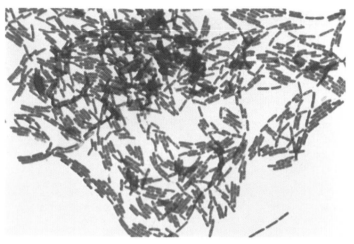

II–3 Stain preparation of *Escherichia coli*. Note the gram-negative short bacilli.
←

II–4 Gram stain from mixed culture of *Escherichia coli* and a streptococcus species. Note the gram-negative short bacilli and gram-positive cocci.
→

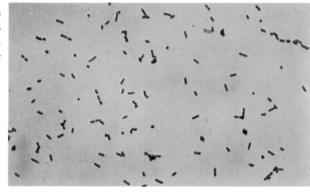

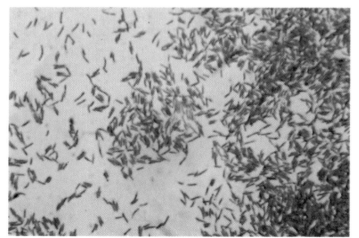

II–5 Acid-fast stain of *Mycobacterium tuberculosis*. Note the pink acid-fast cells.
←

II–6 *Neisseria gonorrhoeae* showing gram-negative diplococci.
→

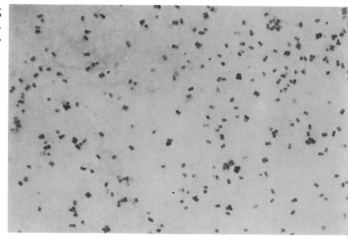

II–7 Gram stain of *Streptococcus* from a blood culture.
←

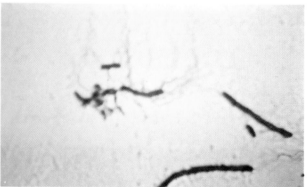

II–8 Gram stain of *Staphylococcus aureus* prepared from a pure culture. Note the clusters of purple gram-positive cocci.
→

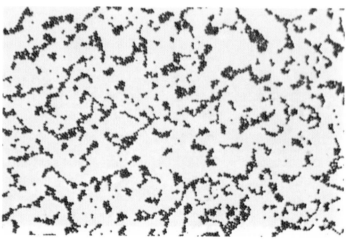

II–9 Flagella stain of *Proteus vulgaris* showing a peritrichous arrangement.
←

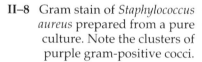

II–10 A negative stain of a capsule. Note the clear capsule and the stained cell and background.
→

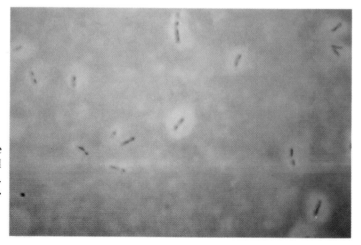

UNIT III - Culturing Microorganisms

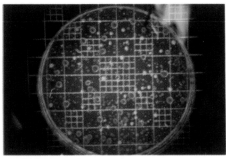

III–1 Petri dish culture containing bacterial colonies. The dish is placed on the grid plate of an illuminated colony counter.
←

III–2 Serial ten fold dilution platings of *Escherichia coli* on agar. Note the decrease in number of colonies with increasing dilution.
→

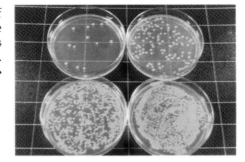

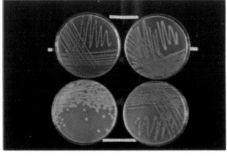

III–3 A quadrant streak plate of 3 organisms showing separate distinct pure culture colonies. Yellow is *Micrococcus luteus*, red is *Serratia marcescens*, white is *Escherichia coli*.
←

III–4 Growth of *Staphylococcus aureus* in 6.5% NaCl. The left tube is positive and the right tube is positive (indicating osmotolerance).
→

III–5 Pigment produced by *Serratia marcescens* (top plates) and *Pseudomonas aeruginosa* (bottom plates). Left plates incubated at room temperature and right plates incubated at 37°C. Note influence of temperature on pigment production.
←

UNIT IV - Microbial Relationships and Disease

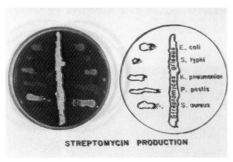

IV–1 Inhibition of selected gram-positive and gram-negative bacteria by streptomycin produced by *Streptomyces griseus*.
←

IV–2 This nutritionally variant streptococcus growing as satelliting colonies around streaks of *Staphylococcus aureus* is an example of commensalism. This can be the etiological agent of endocarditis, yet might not have grown on standard media due to a lack of vitimin B_6.
→

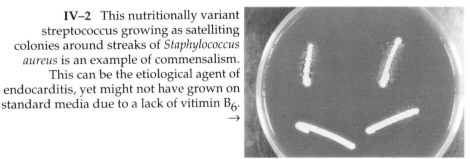

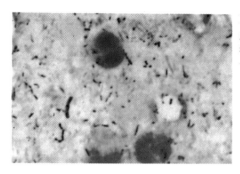

IV–3 Peritoneal fluid showing PMNs, gram-negative bacilli, and cocci. This specimen resembles mixed fecal flora.
←

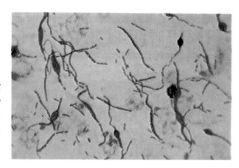

IV–4 Gram stain of anaerobic culture of peritoneal exudate containing *Bacteroides* species.
→

UNIT V - Water, Food and Dairy Microbiology

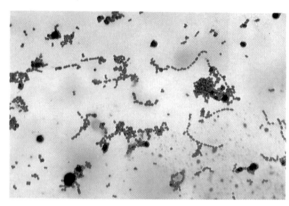

V–1 Stain of *Streptococcus lactis*, a thermoduric organism commonly found in dairy products. Note the cocci in chains.
←

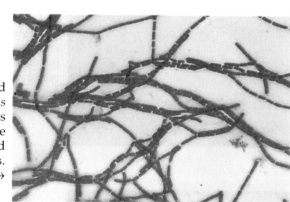

V–2 A stained smear of *Bacillus cereus*. This organism is a source of enterotoxins and food intoxications.
→

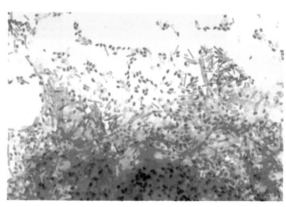

V–3 A stained smear of *Clostridium botulinum*. This is the cause of a fatal food intoxication called botulism. Note the presence of spores.
←

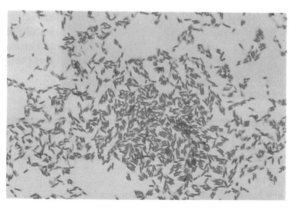

V–4 Gram stain smear of *Escherichia coli* showing gram-negative bacteria. This coliform is a bacterial indicator of fecal pollution of drinking water.
→

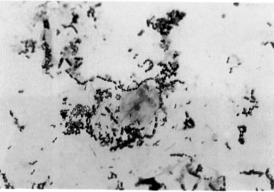

V–5 *Giardia lamblia* trophozoite surrounded by bacteria.
←

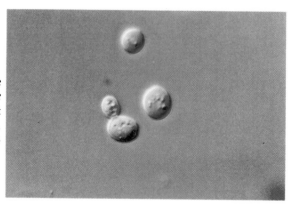

V–6 The Ascomycete *Saccharomyces cerevisiae* shows yeast cells that are budding.
→

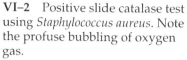

VI–1 Enterotube prior to incubation. Note the colors of the chambers containing the different media.
→

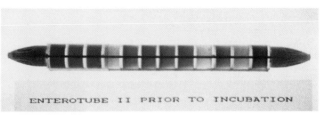

VI–2 Positive slide catalase test using *Staphylococcus aureus*. Note the profuse bubbling of oxygen gas.
←

VI–3 Results observed after inoculation and incubation of 4 separate Enterotubes. Note the different sequence of colors and reactions in the chambers of each tube.
→

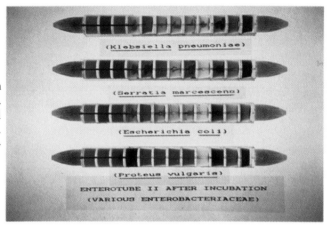

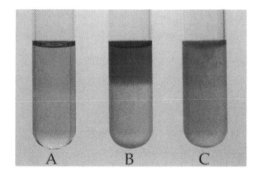

VI–4 Methyl-Red test for mixed acid production and a pH of 4.4 or less. A is uninoculated control, B is a positive test, C is a negative test. All tubes indicate color reactions after addition of Methyl-Red indicator solution. Red color is a positive reaction, Yellow color is a negative reaction. This test is important for distinguishing members of *Enterobacteriaceae*.
←

VI–5 Positive and negative test results for hydrolysis of bile esculin medium to esculetin and glucose. The observed blackening of this medium is a positive diagnostic test result for identification of *Enterococcus faecalis*.
→

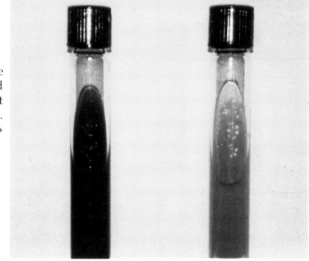

VI–6 Uninoculated, positive and negative results for citrate utilization. This test is important for distinguishing members of *Enterobacteriaceae*.
←

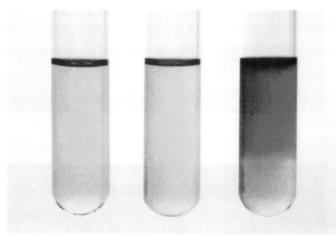

VI-7 Voges-Proskauer test for fermentation of dextrose to the neutral product acetoin. Barritt's A and Barritt's B reagents added to a sample of each culture tube. A red color indicates a positive reaction. A-uninoculated control, B-negative test and C-positive test.

←

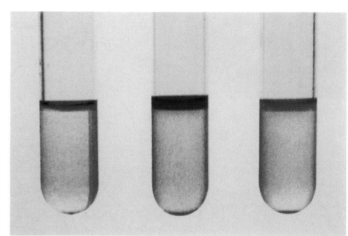

VI–8 Control, positive and negative test results for hydrolysis of trytophan to indole, pyruvic acid, and ammonia. Production of indole with the observed red ring on addition of Kovac's reagent is an important test result to distinguish *Escherichia coli* from *Enterobacter aerogenes*.

→

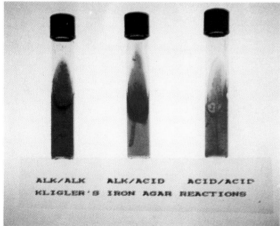

VI–9 Hydrogen sulfide production after growth in Kligler's iron agar. This is an important test for the identification of *Proteus* and *Salmonella*. Left tube is a positive result, right tube is a negative result.

←

VI–10 Positive and negative results for the hydrolysis and liquefaction of the protein gelatin. Positive result in the left tube and negative result in the right tube.

→

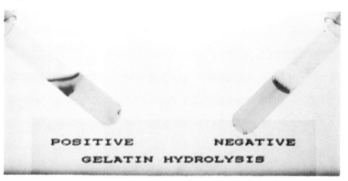

POSITIVE   NEGATIVE

GELATIN HYDROLYSIS

VI–11 Fermentation or its absence on Kligler's iron agar. Alk/alk (all red) indicates no fermetion or reversion to an alkaline state after fermentation, alk/acid (red slant/yellow deep) indicates dextrose fermentation, and acid/acid (all yellow) indicates dextrose and lactose fermentation.

←

ALK/ALK   ALK/ACID   ACID/ACID

KLIGLER'S IRON AGAR REACTIONS

VI-12 Uninoculated, positive and negative test results for urea hydrolysis. Production of ammonia, and carbon dioxide in a positive test is useful for the identification of *Proteus vulgaris*.

→

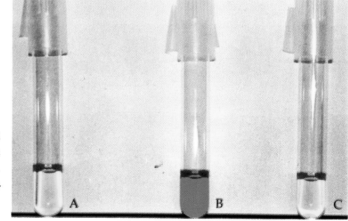

A   B   C

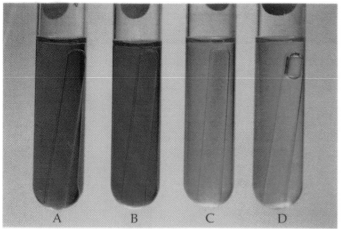

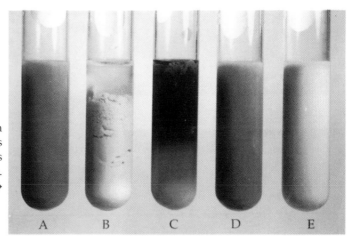

VI–13 Durham tube sugar fermentation reactions. A- is an uninoculated control, B- is an alkaline reaction or lack of fermentation (reversion after fermentation would also appear the same), C- is an acidic fermentation, D- is a fermentation producing acid and gas. Gas is seen as an empty space in the Durham tube.
←

VI–14 Litmus milk reactions. A- Control, B- acid reaction with curd and clear whey fluid at the top, C- proteolysis (peptonization), D- Alkaline reaction, E- reduction of the litmus indicator to leuco litmus.
→

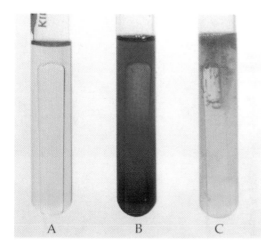

VI–15 Nitrate reduction test reactions. Nitrate test reagents added to all tubes prior to evaluation of results. A- uninoculated control, B- reduction of nitrates to nitrites, C - reduction of nitrates beyond nitrites to produce nitrogen gas. Notice the gas space in the Durham tube.
←

UNIT VII - Control of Microorganisms

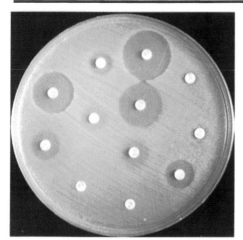

VII–1 Kirby-Bauer disc diffusion antibiotic susceptibility tests for *Staphylococcus aureus*. The antibiotic discs include the following: S-streptomycin, Te-tetracycline, P-penicillin G, E-erythromycin, AM-ampicillin, FD in center for nitrofurantoin. Note the varying degrees of inhibition found. These zones are measured and the results are compared to those found in a standard table to determine the degree of antibiotic sensitivity.
→

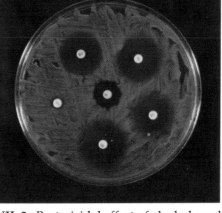

↑ **VII–3** Kirby-Bauer disc diffusion antibiotic susceptibility test. Note zones of inhibition. Diameters must be measured to classify the antibiotic susceptibility response of the organism. This method is not recommended for testing antibiotic susceptibility of anaerobes.

VII–2 Bactericidal effect of alcohol on skin flora. Thumb pressed onto surface of agar (right) shows growth of indigenous skin flora; the left side shows lack of growth when thumb has been wiped with alcohol.
←

UNIT VIII - Medical Microbiology

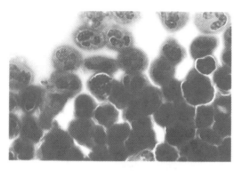

VIII–1 *Neisseria gonorrhoeae* in pus from a human penis. Note the diplococci in cytoplasm of the neutrophils.
←

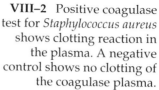

VIII–2 Positive coagulase test for *Staphylococcus aureus* shows clotting reaction in the plasma. A negative control shows no clotting of the coagulase plasma.
→

VIII–3 Strep throat. Growth on blood agar of a throat culture. Note presence of tiny colonies of beta-hemolytic *Streptococcus pyogenes*.
←

VIII–4 Gram stain of *Streptococcus pneumoniae* prepared from a colony of this organism. Note the purple gram-positive diplococci and short chains of cocci.
→

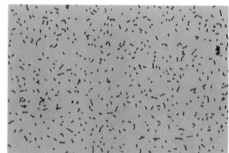

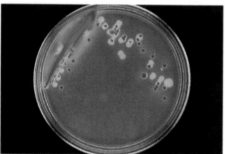

VIII–5 A mixed culture of *Salmonella typhimurium* and *Escherichia coli* streaked on MacConkey agar. *Escherichia coli* forms red colonies and *Salmonella typhimurium* forms white or clear colonies.
←

VIII–6 0.04 units Bacitracin disc sensitivity test for identification of group A beta-hemolytic *Streptococcus pyogenes*. The presence of a zone of inhibition around this disc on blood agar is evidence for the presence of this organism.
→

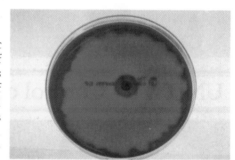

VIII–7 Alpha hemolysis reaction by *Streptococcus pneumoniae* grown on blood agar.
←

VIII–8 Positive (left) and negative (right) results for slide agglutination test. This is used for identification of *Salmonella*.
←

Unit III   Culturing of Microorganisms

14   **Pure Culture Isolation Skills**   **65**

describes procedures for obtaining pure cultures from mixed cultures
using nutrient agar, and differential and selective media.

15   **The Quantitative Plate Count**   **71**

describes procedures for the quantitative plate count of viable bacteria
in broth cultures or simulated clinical specimens.

16   **Growth Curve Determination**   **75**

describes the early and middle stages in growth of a bacterial broth
culture by spectrophotometric and viable plate count procedures.

17   **Quantitative T-2 Virus Count**   **81**

describes the procedures for the quantitative plaque count estimation
of the number of virus particles in a lysate.

18   **Determination of Oxygen Requirements**   **87**

characterizes the types of oxygen requirements in selected bacteria with the
use of the GasPak jar and thioglycollate broth and their relationships to
the disease process.

19   **Cultural Conditions**   **93**

characterizes the different types of growth responses of bacteria in
different solid and broth media and examines a virulence factor simulation
of tissue proteolysis.

20   **Temperature and Bacterial Growth**   **99**

characterizes the temperature requirements for growth of selected bacteria
and their relationships to the disease process.

21   **Lethal Effects of Temperature**   **103**

evaluates the heat resistance of selected bacteria and endospores and their
relationships to asepsis and the disease process.

22   **Steam Sterilization: The Autoclave**   **107**

describes culture procedures for the evaluation of the effectiveness of
steam sterilization by the autoclave.

23   **Osmotic Pressure and Bacterial Growth**   **109**

evaluates the differential growth responses of selected bacteria in increasing salt concentration and their relationships to the disease state.

24   **pH and Microbial Growth**   **113**

evaluates the role of pH on growth, inhibition of growth and regional infection by specific microorganisms in the body.

25   **The Importance of Handwashing**   **117**

evaluates different methods and scrubs for their effectiveness in removing and killing microorganisms and preventing the spread of disease from one person to another.

Case Study 3   **121**

Pure Culture Isolation Skills

Objectives

1. Isolate a pure culture from mixed cultures by the streak plate method and the loop dilution method.

2. Define **specialized differential** and **selective media**.

3. Use specialized media to isolate pure cultures from mixed cultures.

Background

Mixed flora of bacteria are commonly found in the healthy human body, as well as in infections, and in the environment. For example, the normal flora of the oral cavity includes staphylococci, streptococci, anaerobes such as *Bacteroides* and other gram-negative bacteria. Collectively, these organisms can cause respiratory infections. Staphylococci and streptococci are also found in infections of the skin. In the abdominal region a variety of anaerobic bacteria, such as *Peptostreptococcus* species (gram-positive) and *Bacteroides* species (gram-negative) are causes of abdominal and pelvic infections.

In the environment, studies of the microbiological content of fecal contaminated waters demonstrate the presence of coliforms, enterococci, *Campylobacter* and hepatitis virus. Dairy microbiologists have shown that pasteurized milk may contain lactobacilli, streptococci and coliforms. The U.S. Public Health Service standards for Grade A milk quality allow up to 20,000 bacteria per ml and 10 coliforms per ml.

In medicine, sputum cultures, urine cultures and blood cultures can contain a variety of microorganisms. In all the areas described above, knowledge of the techniques of pure culture isolation is essential for identification of the causes of microbial infection or contamination.

Pure Culture Isolation Skills: An Overview

The goal of this exercise is to present techniques commonly used to isolate pure cultures from mixed cultures. This unit emphasizes the streak plate and loop dilution techniques on nutrient agar and the use of specialized differential and selective media to isolate pure cultures from mixed cultures.

In the **streak plate** technique a small inoculum of bacteria is streaked and diluted over the surface of the agar in a petri dish. The cells are separated from one another on the agar surface. The descendents of each isolated cell created by division form a visible mass of cells called a colony. Each colony represents a **pure culture** since it contains only one kind of cell.

In the **loop dilution** procedure a loopful of bacteria from a mixed culture is serially diluted into three tubes of melted nutrient agar. The agar is then poured into dishes and allowed to harden. This serial dilution procedure reduces the number of cells and separates the cells from each other so that isolated colonies are observed after incubation. These colonies are located on the agar surface, or within the agar as convex-appearing lenticulate colonies or as flat colonies under the agar at the bottom of the petri dish.

In the third method a sample of the mixed culture is streaked onto specialized differential and selective media. The media used for this exercise are Mac-Conkey agar, phenylethyl alcohol agar with blood (PEAB), mannitol-salt agar, eosin-methylene blue agar, and Salmonella-Shigella agar. MacConkey agar is an example of a selective and differential agar. **Selective** media favor the growth of distinct microorganisms, while inhibiting others. **Differential** media permit one to distinguish microorganisms having a defined metabolic activity from those lacking it. MacConkey agar contains lactose, 1.5% bile salts and the indicator neutral red. The bile salts inhibit the gram-positive bacteria and allow gram-negatives to grow. Those gram-negative bacteria that ferment lactose to acids cause the indicator neutral red to change color to red so that pink to red colonies are observed. Lactose nonfermenters form colorless to white colonies. Lactose fermenters include *Escherichia coli* and *Klebsiella pneumoniae*. Lactose nonfermenters include *Proteus vulgaris* and *Shigella dysenteriae*. This medium clearly allows one to differentiate between gram-negative lactose fermenters and nonfermenters. The second medium used is phenylethyl alcohol agar with blood (PEAB). This medium is routinely selective for gram-positive cocci such as streptococci and staphylococci. Generally gram-negatives do not grow on it. This portion of the exercise also shows that PEAB supports the growth of the bacillus called *Bacillus subtilis*, a microorganism commonly studied in microbiology courses. This unusual result is used for the isolation of this microorganism from a mixed culture by streaking on this medium.

Mannitol-salt agar contains 7.5% sodium chloride which inhibits most bacteria by dehydration. *Staphylococcus aureus* is osmotolerant and can grow on this medium. This medium is, therefore, highly selective for the isolation of staphylococci from mixed cultures.

The eosin and methylene blue dyes in Levine's eosin methylene blue agar inhibit gram-positive bacteria. Lactose fermenters such as *Escherichia coli* grow on this medium and show a green metallic sheen on the surface by reflected light or black centers to the colonies. Lactose non-fermenters such as *Proteus vulgaris* and *Salmonella typhimurium* show clear colonies on this medium. This medium is both selective and differential in nature. It favors the growth of gram-negative bacteria and allows one to distinguish between lactose fermenters and nonfermenters. Salmonella-Shigella (SS) agar is strongly selective for Salmonella and certain species of Shigella. The 8.5% bile salts in this medium inhibits gram-positive bacteria as well as *Escherichia coli* and other coliforms. The lactose non-fermenting *Salmonella typhimurium* produces clear to tan colonies on this medium or produces colonies with a black center. The black color is due to the liberation of hydrogen sulfide from the thiosulfate in this medium which in turn reacts with iron salts to form the black ferric sulfide that colors the colonies.

The mixed culture used in this exercise contains *Escherichia coli*, *Staphylococcus aureus* and *Bacillus subtilis*. These three bacteria grow very well on nutrient agar. However, after short incubation periods, *Escherichia coli* and *Bacillus subtilis* may produce similarly appearing colonies. After extended incubation the colony growth of *Bacillus subtilis* tends to spread over the agar surface. On MacConkey agar only the gram-negative *Escherichia coli* grows to produce round, red colonies. On PEAB both *Staphylococcus aureus* and *Bacillus subtilis* grow. Large white round colonies and small gray round colonies with white centers are observed on this medium after incubation. This medium prevents the spreading growth reaction of *Bacillus subtilis* usually found on nutrient agar. Gram stains must be done to complete the identification of the colony morphology of each organism for all these media.

These specialized media show that one can manipulate the environment of growing bacteria to favor or inhibit specific microorganisms, thus making their identification much simpler. These media also show that there are differences in the biochemistry of microorganisms. For example, gram-positive bacteria are inhibited by bile salts, but most gram-negatives are not. Some gram-negative bacteria ferment lactose, while others do not.

Materials

nutrient broth mixed culture of *Escherichia coli, Staphylococcus aureus* and *Bacillus subtilis* (culture A)

nutrient broth mixed culture of *Escherichia coli* and *Salmonella typhimurium* (culture B). Prepare separate overnight nutrient broth cultures of *Escherichia coli* and *Salmonella typhimurium*. Pipette 0.1 ml of the culture of each organism into trypticase soy broth to prepare a mixed culture. Mix the contents and distribute to the students.

nutrient agar pour plates for streaking

MacConkey agar pour plates for streaking

phenylethyl alcohol agar with blood pour plates for streaking

mannitol-salt agar plates for streaking

Levine's eosin-methylene blue agar for streaking

Salmonella-Shigella agar for streaking

tubes containing melted nutrient agar stored in a 50°C water bath

sterile petri dishes

racks for holding tubes during laboratory work

Procedures

First Period

The Streak Plate (See Figure 14-1.)

1. Select a tube of the mixed culture A and a plate of nutrient agar, MacConkey agar, and phenylethyl alcohol agar with blood, mannitol-salt agar, Levine's eosin methylene blue agar, and Salmonella-Shigella agar.

2. Mark each petri dish with the notation "mixed culture" and the names of the bacteria.

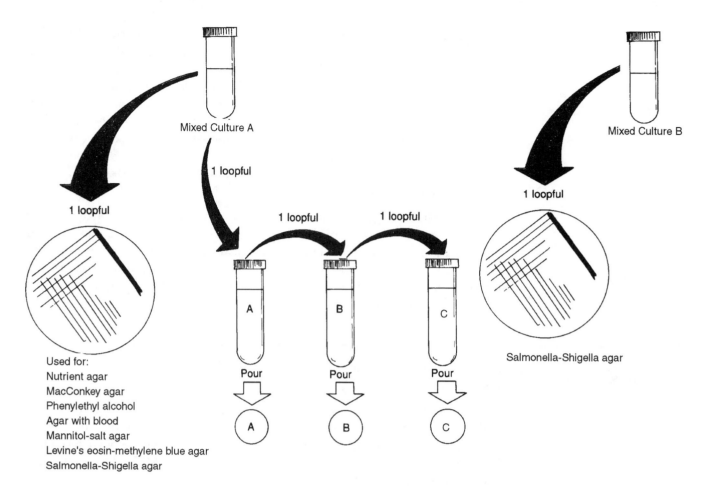

Mixed Culture A

1 loopful

1 loopful

1 loopful

1 loopful

Mixed Culture B

1 loopful

A   B   C

Pour   Pour   Pour

A   B   C

Used for:
Nutrient agar
MacConkey agar
Phenylethyl alcohol
Agar with blood
Mannitol-salt agar
Levine's eosin-methylene blue agar
Salmonella-Shigella agar

Salmonella-Shigella agar

Figure 14-1
Pure Culture Isolation Skills.
Streak Plate and Loop
Dilution.

3. Complete a "T" streak of the mixed culture on each of these media in the following manner.

4. Mix the contents of the culture tube.

5. Flame the loop and transfer a loopful of the mixed culture to one corner of the petri dish and streak several parallel short streaks on the agar.

6. Flame the loop; rotate the petri dish 90 degrees and cool the loop by touching it to a corner of the agar surface.

7. Streak several short streaks across the original streak lines; then follow with several parallel streaks that do not cross the original streak lines.

8. Flame the loop; rotate the petri dish 90 degrees and cool the loop by touching it to a corner of the agar surface.

9. Streak several short streaks across the second set of streak lines; then follow with several parallel streaks that do not cross the second streak lines. Flame the loop.

10. The purpose of this streaking procedure onto sterile agar is to separate single cells that can divide and form colonies that are pure cultures.

11. This procedure must be followed for each kind of poured plate medium.

12. Incubate the plates at 35°C for 48 hours.

13. Select a tube of the mixed culture of *Escherichia coli* and *Salmonella typhimurium* (culture B) and a plate of Salmonella-Shigella agar.

14. Mark the petri dish with the notation "mixed culture B" and the names of the bacteria.

15. Complete a streak plate of this mixed culture on SS agar to isolate single colonies as described above in steps 4–10.

16. Incubate this plate also at 35°C for 48 hours.

Loop Dilution Procedures

1. Select a tube of the mixed culture and three empty, sterile petri dishes.

2. Mark the petri dishes with the notation "mixed culture" and the letters A, B and C.

3. Obtain three tubes of melted nutrient agar and mark them A, B and C.

4. Mix the contents of the culture tube.

5. Flame the loop; transfer a loopful of the mixed culture to tube A. Flame the loop.

6. Roll tube A in the palms of your hands to uniformly distribute the bacteria in the tube.

7. Flame the loop; transfer a loopful from tube A to tube B. Flame the loop.

8. Roll tube B in the palms of your hands to uniformly distribute the bacteria in the tube.

9. Flame the loop; transfer a loopful from tube B to tube C. Flame the loop.

10. Roll tube C in the palms of your hands to uniformly distribute the bacteria in the tube.

11. Partially remove the cover from petri dish A, and pour the contents of tube A into petri dish A. Replace the cover. Gently rotate petri dish A to distribute the agar throughout the dish. Repeat the same procedures for loop dilution tubes B and C.

12. Incubate all petri dishes at 35°C for 48 hours.

Second Period

1. Examine the streak plates for isolated colonies. Note whether any of the colonies have any pigment. Gram stains must be done to complete the identification of the bacteria. Typically, *Escherichia coli* forms gray-white colonies, *Staphylococcus aureus* forms yellow colonies, and *Bacillus subtilis* forms creamy white colonies on nutrient agar. Note the presence of hemolysis in PEAB agar.

2. Examine the pour plates for isolated surface and subsurface colonies. The subsurface colonies embedded in the agar are convex in shape and are called lens-shaped or lenticulate colonies. The subsurface colonies located against the bottom of the dish are pale and flat. Note whether any of these colonies have any pigment.

3. Select representative surface colonies for Gram-staining. Note the Gram-reaction, microscopic morphology and colony appearance in the Results section.

4. Answer the questions for the exercise.

Staphylococcus aureus. *S. aureus* ferments mannitol in mannitol-salt agar to produce acids. The acids lower the pH of the medium and a yellow halo appears around the colony because the phenol-red indicator in this medium turns yellow in the presence of acid.

Escherichia coli. Colonies of *E. coli* on Levine's eosin methylene blue agar show a green metallic sheen if viewed using reflected light. The colonies themselves may be reddish purple and may have black centers. These bacteria ferment the lactose in this medium, producing acids.

Salmonella typhimurium. *S. typhimurium* produces clear to tan colonies on Salmonella-Shigella (SS) agar. These bacteria do not ferment lactose. Sometimes a black center is seen. Salmonella metabolize the thiosulfate in this agar to produce hydrogen sulfide. This, in turn, reacts with the iron salts in the medium to produce ferric sulfide which is black.

The Quantitative Plate Count

Objectives

1. Perform a standard plate count from a broth culture of bacteria.

2. Indicate two areas where a standard plate count is used.

3. Define the terms **viable count, total count, dilution** and **plate count**.

4. Compute the number of cells per ml of broth from the number of colonies counted on a given plated dilution.

Background

Bacterial population **quantitative counts** are routinely used in microbiology to determine the numbers of microorganisms in water, food and certain clinical specimens such as urine. The U.S. Public Health Service standards for bacteriological quality of milk state that Grade A pasteurized milk should not have over 20,000 bacteria per ml and should not exceed 10 coliforms per ml. The American Public Health Association has established procedures for determining the microbiological quality of water. In medicine a fresh urine sample showing greater than 100,000 bacteria per ml indicates that a urinary tract infection is present in the patient. *Escherichia coli* frequently is the cause of this infection. This exercise should reinforce the need for care in handling any microbially contaminated body fluids and cultures of microorganisms. Spills from such materials must be promptly and carefully disinfected to prevent contamination and the spread of disease.

The Quantitative Plate Count: An Overview

In this exercise a determination is made of the number of bacteria in an overnight nutrient broth culture of *Escherichia coli*. A sample of the bacteria is serially diluted in sterile distilled water, and samples are plated in petri dishes for determination of the final count. During incubation the single cells trapped in the agar reproduce to form visible masses of cells called colonies. All the cells composing a pure colony are derived ultimately from division descendents of this single cell. After incubation the plate showing between 30–300 colonies is counted. This number is multiplied by the dilution factor to yield the number of bacteria per ml of original broth sample. This plate count is an example of a **viable count** because only living cells can divide to form visible colonies. Dead cells do not form colonies. An advantage of this method is that samples of these live cells may be isolated as pure cultures and later identified. In contrast, a **total count** made with a counting chamber inserted in a microscope counts living and dead cells and thus provides only an estimate of the number of living cells present in the culture.

This exercise uses pipettes for diluting and plating. Certain precautions are necessary for the safe handling of pipettes and microbial cultures. The precautions are listed below:

1. Remove one pipette at a time when needed from the sterile container.

2. Do not touch the body or tip of the pipette. Do not wave pipettes in the air. Do not place pipettes on the countertop. All these actions will contaminate the pipette and could contaminate the user.

3. Do not under any circumstances pipette any microbial broth culture or any other fluid in a microbiology laboratory by mouth.

4. Use a pipette pump or similar device to assist pipetting. The following directions are based on the use of the 2-ml pipette pump, which can safely hold a 1-ml pipette.

5. Insert the 1-ml pipette into the pipette pump and rotate the control wheel of the pump to draw up the appropriate number of ml of fluid. Rotate the control wheel in the opposite direction to dispense the fluid into the sterile distilled water dilution bottle or other container. Remove the pipette from the pipette pump and discard the pipette in a container of disinfectant. Do not under any circumstances discard a pipette in the trash.

Materials

20-hour nutrient broth culture of *Escherichia coli*

99-ml sterile distilled water dilution bottles

sterile petri dishes

sterile 1-ml pipettes

2-ml pipette pump or other similar pipetting device

water bath set at 50°C containing tubes with sterile molten nutrient agar

Procedures

First Period

Diluting (See Figure 15-1.)

1. Select a nutrient broth culture of *Escherichia coli*.

2. Select three 99-ml sterile dilution bottles. Label the first dilution bottle "1/100," the second dilution bottle "1/10,000" and the third dilution bottle "1/1,000,000."

3. **Be sure to use a pipette pump or other pipetting device.** Select a 1-ml pipette and transfer 1 ml from the *Escherichia coli* culture to the first

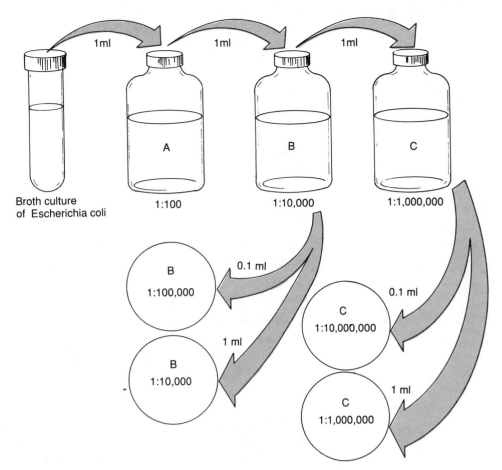

Figure 15-1
The Quantitative Plate Count

Number of cells per ml = number of colonies counted × dilution factor

dilution bottle marked "1/100." Discard this pipette in the pipette discard container.

4. Swirl the contents of the dilution bottle to distribute the bacteria evenly.

5. Select a second 1-ml pipette and transfer 1 ml from the first dilution bottle to the dilution bottle marked "1/10,000." Discard this pipette in the pipette discard container. Mix the contents of this dilution bottle.

6. Select a third 1-ml pipette and transfer 1 ml from the second dilution bottle to the dilution bottle marked "1/1,000,000." Discard this pipette in the pipette discard container. Mix the contents of this dilution bottle.

Plating

1. Mark the petri dishes "B-1/10,000–1ml," "B-1/100,000–0.1ml," "C-1/1,000,000–1ml" and C-1/10,000,000–0.1 ml."

2. Pipette 0.1 ml from the second dilution bottle to the petri dish marked B-1/100,000–0.1ml." Use the same pipette to transfer 1 ml from the second dilution bottle to the petri dish marked "B-1/10,000–1ml." Discard this pipette properly.

3. Pipette 0.1 ml from the third dilution bottle to the petri dish marked C-1/10,000,000–0.1ml." Use the same pipette to transfer 1 ml from the

third dilution bottle to the petri dish marked C-1/1,000,000–1ml." Discard this pipette properly.

4. Select four molten nutrient agar tubes from the water bath. Pour the contents of a single nutrient agar tube into each of the four petri dishes. Rotate each dish gently in a circular fashion to distribute the agar and bacteria in the dish.

5. Allow the agar to solidify in each dish. Invert and incubate all petri dishes at 35°C for 48 hours.

Second Period

Colony Counting

1. After incubation, select plates that show between 30–300 colonies on the plate. Count colonies on the surface of the agar and within the agar. Disregard plates with greater or fewer numbers of colonies because these are not statistically significant.

2. Determine the number of bacteria per ml of the original culture by multiplying the number of colonies counted by the dilution factor. The **dilution factor** is the dilution inverted. For example, 1/100 becomes 100. Use this formula:

    colonies counted × dilution factor = number of cells per ml of broth.

    For example, if 150 colonies are counted on a 1/10,000 dilution plate, then 150 × 10,000 = 1,500,000 bacteria are present in the original culture per ml. Note that the dilution factor is 1/10,000 inverted, or 10,000. Record your counts in the Results section.

3. Answer the questions for the exercise.

Exercise 16

Growth Curve Determination

Objectives

1. Describe binary fission.

2. Name the growth stages found for a bacterial culture grown in broth and describe what happens in each stage.

3. Explain the relationship between turbidity and absorbance in a spectro-photometer measurement.

Background

Growth in bacteria refers to an increase in number of cells. Bacteria multiply by a process called binary fission. In this process, the bacterial DNA replicates. The duplicate and original DNA separate from one another. The cell membrane and cell wall grow through the middle of the cell and divide the cytoplasm into two equal halves to create two new cells. The time required for an organism to divide is called the GENERATION TIME. The generation time is strongly influenced by the nutritional state of the medium, the pH, the temperature, and oxygen content of the medium. For example, an organism growing on a nutritionally poor medium or a facultative anaerobe growing under anaerobic conditions would have a longer generation time.

When cells are first inoculated into a broth medium they go through a **LAG phase**. In this phase the cell number does not increase. The cells are actively synthesizing enzymes and chemicals needed for cell division. This is followed by a **LOG phase** where the cells are dividing at a geometric rate. The cell number increases by the formula 2^n where n is the generation. If one starts with one cell, then after 2 generations $2 \times 2 = 4$ cells are present. After 10 generations $2 \times 2 \times 2 \times 2 \times 2 \times 2 \times 2 \times 2 \times 2 \times 2 = 1024$ cells. If the generation time is 30 minutes, then in 5 hours a single cell would have increased in cell number to 1024 cells. The cells in the LOG phase have very similar chemical composition and physiological abilities in biochemical tests and stain most uniformly in the Gram stain procedure. This LOG phase is followed by a **STATIONARY PHASE**. During this period, the growth slows down and the numbers of living cells tend to level off. Also during this period, toxic metabolic waste products accumulate; nutrients are present in a lesser quantity so the cells must compete for a limited amount of nutrients and some cells die. The numbers of cells that die rises to equal the numbers that survive so a leveling off in cell number occurs. The STATIONARY phase is followed by a **DECLINE** phase. During the DECLINE PHASE, excessive accumulated waste products and severe reductions in available nutrients lead to increased death of cells in the culture. The cells die in a geometric fashion.

In this exercise, the LAG, LOG and early STATIONARY phases of growth found for a nutrient broth culture of *Escherichia coli* are verified. Samples are taken at half hour intervals and the turbidity is determined by a spectrophotometric measurement. A second sample taken at each half hour interval is diluted and pour plated to determine a viable count (colony forming units/ml).

Specifically, a sample of a 24 hour nutrient broth culture of *Escherichia coli* is diluted into warm nutrient broth, contained in a 250 Ehrlenmeyer flask held at 37°C in a water bath, to give a slightly turbid suspension. Samples are immediately taken for a zero time turbidity determination and for dilution and pour plating for a viable count determination. At half hour intervals for two hours samples are taken for turbidity and viable count determinations. The turbidity determinations are recorded and graphed. After incubation, colony counts are made from the samples plated at half hourly intervals and the number of cells per ml are plotted for each time interval on graph paper.

The spectrophotometric method is based on the principle that as cell number increases, the cloudiness or turbidity of the broth increases. Monochromatic light is passed through a suspension of bacteria contained in the spectrophotometer tube. The photoelectric cell in the spectrophotometer records the amount of light transmitted through the broth tube. As the turbidity increases, less light passes through the bacterial suspension and the amount of light absorbed by the bacterial suspension increases. This absorbance value is observed on a scale on the face of the spectrophotometer. After recording the absorbance, a second sample for each time interval is diluted and plated in order to measure the actual number of cells per ml. Graphs of absorbance and cells per ml are plotted against time and compared. This exercise demonstrates the LAG, LOG and early STATIONARY phases of the growth curve.

Materials

24 hour nutrient broth culture of *Escherichia coli*

one Bausch and Lomb spectrophotometer (Spectronic 20)

spectrophotometer tubes (cuvettes)

packages of Kimwipes or non-lint producing tissues

bottles of nutrient broth

tubes containing 9 ml nutrient broth pre-warmed to 37°C

250 Ehrlenmeyer flasks containing 99 ml of nutrient broth pre-warmed to 37°C

99 ml sterile distilled water dilution bottles

sterile petri dishes

sterile 1 ml pipettes

pipette pumps

water baths set at 37°C

water bath set at 50°C containing bottles with sterile molten agar

Procedures

First Period

Use of the Spectrophotometer (See Fig. 16-1.)

1. Turn on the machine by rotating the control knob on the left clockwise. Allow the machine to warm up for 20 minutes.

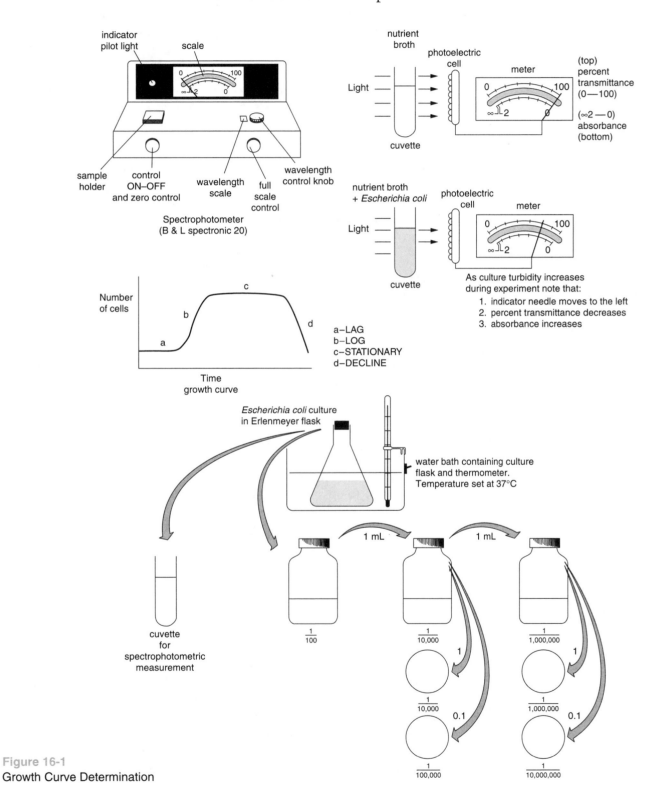

Figure 16-1
Growth Curve Determination

2. Set the wavelength to 550 nm by rotating the wavelength control located on the top right side of the machine.

3. The sample holder is empty and closed. Rotate the control knob on the left to adjust the needle to adjust the needle on the scale to 0 percent transmittance.

4. Pipette 5 ml sterile nutrient broth into a cuvette. Wipe the outside of the cuvette to remove any fingerprints. Insert the cuvette into the sample holder. Be sure to line up the mark on the cuvette with the index marker on the sample holder. Close the sample holder.

5. Rotate the light control knob on the right side of the machine so the needle reads 100 percent transmittance. The machine is now standardized for the nutrient broth. Remove the cuvette. Discard this cuvette as directed by the instructor.

Zero Time Absorbance Determination for *Escherichia coli*.

1. Select a 24 hour nutrient broth culture of *Escherichia coli*.

2. Obtain a 37°C pre-warmed Ehrlenmeyer flask containing 99 ml of nutrient broth and a sterile 1 ml pipette.

3. Transfer 1 ml of the *Escherichia coli* culture to the 99 ml of nutrient broth in the Ehrlenmeyer flask. Swirl this flask and observe for any slight turbidity.

4. Transfer 5 ml to a cuvette.

5. Insert this cuvette containing the diluted *Escherichia coli* into the sample holder. Be sure to line up the mark on the cuvette with the index marker on the sample holder. Close the cover on the sample holder and observe the position of the needle on the absorbance scale. A slight reading between 0.01 and 0.02 should be observed.

6. If no absorbance reading is observed, pipette another 1 ml of the 24 hour *Escherichia coli* culture into this Ehrlenmeyer flask and swirl this flask again. Observe for any slight turbidity. Select a new cuvette and repeat steps 4 and 5 to obtain a new absorbance reading. This second absorbance reading should be between 0.01 and 0.02.

7. This is now the zero time absorbance reading for the growth curve study.

8. Immediately, place this Ehrlenmeyer flask containing the zero time. *Escherichia coli* into the water bath at 37°C.

9. Frequently swirl this flask throughout the experiment to aerate the bacterial culture.

10. Every 30 minutes, for 2 hours, remove 5 ml of this culture to a fresh unused cuvette to determine the absorbance of the culture during its growth. Follow steps 4 and 5. Note that the absorbance of the culture should increase as the cells reproduce and the culture turbidity increases. Discard all used cuvettes in a proper discard container as directed by the instructor. Periodically, check the 0 percent transmittance and 100 percent transmittance with fresh sterile 5 ml sample of nutrient broth. Correct the machine using the proper knobs if necessary. Refer to

steps 3, 4 and 5 in the section for the procedures for **Use of the Spectrophotometer**.

11. Record all spectrophotometer absorbance readings in a chart for 0 min., 30 min., 60 min., 90 min., and 120 min.

12. Construct a line graph of absorbance values versus time of measurement. Absorbance should be on the vertical axis and time should be noted on the horizontal axis.

Determination of Number of Cells Per ml for Each Time Interval Used in Growth Curve Study

1. If a determination of the actual number of cells present for each absorbance reading is desired, the following procedures listed below should be completed.

Dilutions

1. At 0 time, 30 minutes, 60 minutes, 90 minutes and 120 minutes, remove a 1 ml sample of *Escherichia coli* from the Ehrlenmeyer flask for diluting and plating using the procedures listed below (see Figure 16-1).

2. Select three 99 ml sterile dilution bottles. Label the first dilution bottle 1/100, the second dilution bottle 1/10,000 and the third dilution bottle 1/1,000,000.

3. For each time interval, select a 1 ml pipette and transfer 1 ml of the *Escherichia coli* culture in the Ehrlenmeyer flask to the dilution bottle labeled 1/100. Do not remove the flask from the water bath. Discard this pipette in the pipette discard. Mix the contents of this bottle by swirling.

4. Select a second 1 ml pipette and transfer 1 ml of the 1/100 dilution to the bottle labeled 1/10,000. Discard this pipette in the pipette discard. Mix the contents of this dilution bottle by swirling.

5. Select a third 1 ml pipette and transfer 1 ml of the 1/10,000 dilution to the bottle labeled 1/1,000,000. Discard this pipette in the pipette discard. Mix the contents of this bottle by swirling.

6. Discard the old dilutions and prepare fresh dilutions for each time interval studied.

Pour Plating

7. Select 20 sterile petri dishes. Divide them into 5 groups. Label the first group **zero time:** and 1/10,000, 1/100,000, 1/1,000,000 and 1/10,000,000. Label the second group **30 minutes:** and 1/10,000, 1/100,000, 1/1,000,000 and 1/10,000,000. Label the third group **60 minutes:** 1/10,000, 1/100,000, 1/1,000,000 and 1/10,000,000. Label the fourth group **90 minutes:** 1/10,000, 1/100,000, 1/1,000,000 and 1/10,000,000. Label the fifth group **120 minutes:** 1/10,000, 1/100,000, 1/1,000,000 and 1/10,000,000.

8. Select the four zero time petri dishes. Select the zero time 1/10,000 dilution bottle and a 1 ml pipette. Transfer a 0.1 ml sample to the dish labeled

1/100,000 and a 1 ml sample to the dish labeled 1/10,000. Discard this pipette in the pipette discard. Select the zero time 1/1,000,000 dilution bottle and transfer a 0.1 ml sample to the dish labeled 1/10,000,000 and a 1 ml sample to the dish labeled 1/1,000,000. Discard this pipette in the pipette discard.

9. Select 2 bottles of molten agar and pour 15 ml of agar into each dish. Rotate each dish to evenly distribute the agar and the dilution. Allow the agar to solidify and then invert these dishes.

10. Repeat these plating procedures for each time interval.

11. Incubate all petri dishes at 35°C for 48 hours to permit growth of colonies so that the number of cells per ml can be determined for each time interval studied on the growth curve.

Second Period

1. Divide the petri dishes into the 5 groups. In each group, select those dishes showing between 30–300 colonies per dilution plate and count the colonies.

2. Determine the number of cells per ml by use of the following formula: colonies counted × dilution factor = cells per ml of the *Escherichia coli* culture in the Ehrlenmeyer flask.

3. Record the cells per ml for each time interval in the Results section. Refer to Exercise 15 for further information on a quantitative count.

4. Place the actual number of cells found for each absorbance value for zero time through 120 minutes on your graph of absorbance versus time. Note that any absorbance value represents a distinct number of cells per ml in the culture.

Determination of the Generation Time

1. Find two absorbance values on the vertical axis in the LOG phase that show a doubling. For example, 0.02 to 0.04. Draw two horizontal lines to the graph and then extend two vertical lines from the graph to the horizontal axis. Subtract the lower time from the higher time to determine the generation time for the *Escherichia coli* culture.

Quantitative T-2 Virus Count

Caution: This exercise involves the dilution of bacterial virus and use of an E. coli b host organism. Care must be taken to avoid spills and to properly disinfect any spills that occur.

Objectives

1. Describe unique features of viruses.
2. Define virus titer.
3. List and describe the stages in a lytic virus infection.

Background

Viruses are extremely small infectious agents; small enough that they can pass through filters that retain bacteria. They are composed of an inner nucleic acid core which may be DNA or RNA and an outer protein coat or capsid. Together the nucleic acid and the protein coat make up the nucleocapsid. They are obligate parasites and must reproduce themselves inside a host cell. They use the host cell enzymes for protein synthesis and energy production to make copies of themselves. In the process of infection, they frequently destroy the host cell as they are released and escape to start a new infection cycle. The T-virus used in this exercise specifically infects bacteria and is an example of a bacteriophage (phage). Because this virus infects *Escherichia coli*, it is also known as a coliphage. This virus has a swollen head portion and a thin tail and is shaped somewhat like a human sperm cell. The double stranded DNA genetic material is tightly coiled into the head region. The tail region contains a tail sheath, a core tube and a number of tail fibers.

During a lytic infection cycle, the T-phage destroys the host *E. coli* cell. The first step in the infection cycle is **adsorption**. The virus attaches by its tail region to a lipopolysaccharide receptor in the outer LPS layer of the cell wall. During **penetration**, the tail sheath contracts and the inner tail core tube punctures the cell wall and cell membrane. The phage DNA passes through this tube into the cytoplasm. During **synthesis** a latent period occurs. No fully formed virus particles are seen. The phage directs the synthesis of enzymes that take over the host cell and destroy its DNA by cutting it into small fragments. Phage DNA and phage head and tail proteins are made. During the **assembly (maturation)** phase, the proteins making up the head and tail region are assembled, the DNA nucleic acid is packaged into the head region and the tail is attached to the head region containing the genetic material. During the **release (burst)** phase, a viral lysozyme-like enzyme is produced that lyses or destroys the bacterial cell and numerous viral particles are released. These viruses can then start new cycles of infection in other host cells.

In this exercise, a sample of the virus is serially diluted and samples of each dilution are pipetted into tubes of soft agar containing host *E. coli* b cells. These are then poured over bottom agar in petri plates. After hardening and incubation, the plates are examined for the presence of clear circular areas (virus plaques) appearing in a background of a bacterial lawn. The number of plaques counted when multiplied by the viral dilution factor give an estimate of the number of virus particles in the original sample. This is known as a virus titer. Each plaque is initiated by a single virus particle infecting a host cell and the plaque represents the repeated cycles of lytic infection of adjacent host cells at that site in the agar after the initial infection. These host cells are killed leaving a clear circular area in the agar that contains many virus particles. The plaque count is very similar to the colony count studied in Exercise 15.

Materials

slant stock of *E. coli* b #377

tube containing filtered T-2 virus suspension

tubes of brain heart infusion broth (BHI)

tubes of 3 ml trypticase soy broth without dextrose

bottles containing 30 ml trypticase soy broth without dextrose

tubes containing 9 ml of tryptone broth chilled in a refrigerator

tubes containing 4 ml soft tryptone top agar held at 45°C in a water bath

plates of hard tryptone bottom agar

1 ml pipettes

pipette pumps

Procedures

Preparation of Host *Escherichia coli* b

Pipette 3 ml of brain heart infusion broth (BHI) onto the slant surface of the *E. coli* b. Incubate at room temperature for 2–3 days. As the broth becomes turbid, pipette 1 ml of the turbid BHI broth suspended cells into 3 ml fresh trypticase soy broth without dextrose and maintain the culture in this medium at room temperature. The broth tube should show moderate turbidity. Do not refrigerate. Subculture as necessary. Twenty-four hours before the virus titer experiment, pipette 1 ml of the *E. coli* b into 30 ml of trypticase soy broth and incubate this for 18 hours at 35°C. After incubation, this bacterial culture should be only slightly turbid.

First Period

Virus Dilutions (See Figure 17-1.)

1. Select the tube of T-2 virus and 7 tubes of chilled tryptone broth.

2. Label the tryptone broth tubes 1/10, 1/100, 1/1,000, 1/10,000, 1/100,000, 1/1,000,000, 1/10,000,000.

3. Select a 1 ml pipette and transfer 1 ml of the virus into the 9 ml tryptone broth tube labeled 1/10. Mix the contents by tapping the bottom of the

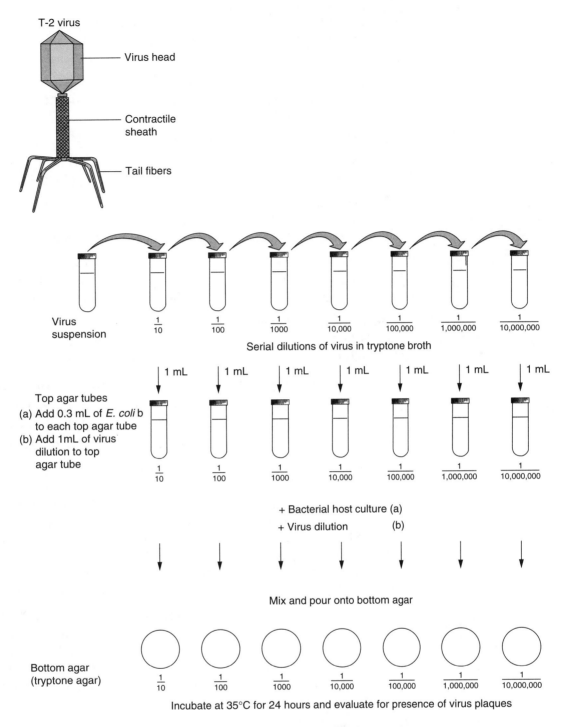

Figure 17-1
Quantitative T-2 Virus Count

Bacterial lawn

Viral plaque

tube and gently swirling the tube contents. Discard this pipette in the pipette discard container. Be absolutely careful not to spill the contents of this or any other dilution tube. Any spills must be immediately covered with disinfectant and any contaminated individuals must scrub their hands with antiseptic soap solution.

4. Select the tube labeled 1/100. Select a second pipette and transfer 1 ml from the 1/10 dilution to the tube labeled 1/100. Gently mix the contents of this tube. Discard the pipette in the pipette discard container.

5. Select the tube labeled 1/1,000. Select a third pipette and transfer 1 ml from the 1/100 dilution to the tube labeled 1/1,000. Gentle mix the contents of this tube. Discard the pipette in the pipette discard.

6. Select the tube labeled 1/10,000. Select a fourth pipette and transfer 1 ml from the 1/1,000 dilution to the tube labeled 1/10,000. Gently mix the contents of this tube. Discard the pipette in the pipette discard.

7. Select the tube labeled 1/100,000. Select a fifth pipette and transfer 1 ml from the 1/10,000 dilution to the tube labeled 1/100,000. Gently mix the contents of the tube. Discard the pipette in the pipette discard.

8. Select the tube labeled 1/1,000,000. Select a sixth pipette and transfer 1 ml from the 1/100,000 dilution to the tube labeled 1/1,000,000. Gently mix the contents of the tube. Discard the pipette in the pipette discard.

9. Select the tube labeled 1/10,000,000. Select a seventh pipette and transfer 1 ml from the 1/1,000,000 dilution to the tube labeled 1/10,000,000. Gently mix the contents of this tube. Discard the pipette in the pipette discard.

Top Agar Tube Inoculation and Pouring on to Bottom Agar

1. Label the top agar tubes in the water bath 1/10, 1/100, 1/1,000, 1/10,000, 1/100,000, 1/1,000,000 and 1/10,000,000. Label the bottom dishes 1/10, 1/100, 1/1,000, 1/10,000, 1/100,000, 1/1,000,000 and 1/10,000,000.

2. Select the 30 ml trypticase soy broth culture of *E. coli* b. Select the 1/10 and 1/100 labeled top agar tubes. Pipette 0.3 ml of the *E. coli* b culture into each top agar tube. Pipette 1 ml of 1/10 and 1/100 virus dilutions to the properly labeled top agar tubes. Roll each tube separately between the palms of the hands to mix the contents and separately pour the contents into the properly labeled bottom agar dish. Separately pick up each covered dish and gently rock the contents to distribute the agar, virus dilution and bacteria evenly throughout the surface of each bottom agar dish.

3. Select the 1/1,000 and 1/10,000 labeled top agar tubes. Pipette 0.3 ml of the *E. coli* b culture into each top agar tube. Pipette 1 ml of the 1/1,000 and 1/10,000 virus dilutions to the properly labeled top agar tubes. Mix the contents and separately pour the contents into the properly labeled bottom agar dish. Gently rock the contents to distribute the agar, virus dilution and bacteria evenly throughout the surface of each bottom agar dish.

4. Select the 1/100,000 and 1/1,000,000 labeled top agar tubes. Pipette 0.3 ml of the *E. coli* b culture into each top agar tube. Pipette 1 ml of the 1/100,000 and 1/1,000,000 virus dilutions to the properly labeled top agar tubes. Mix the contents and separately pour the contents into the properly labeled bottom agar dish. Gently rock the contents to distribute the agar, virus dilution and bacteria evenly throughout the surface of each bottom agar dish.

5. Select the 1/10,000,000 labeled top agar tube. Pipette 0.3 ml of the *E. coli* b culture into the top agar tube. Pipette 1 ml of the 1/10,000,000 virus dilution to the top agar tube. Mix the contents and pour the contents

into the bottom agar dish labeled 1/10,000,000. Gently rock the contents to distribute the agar, virus dilution and bacteria evenly throughout the agar surface of this bottom agar dish.

6. Allow the top agar to harden in all the dishes. Invert the petri dishes and incubate all dishes at 35°C for 24 hours.

Second Period

1. Place the virus titer plates in sequence on the counter from 1/10 to 1/10,000,000. Examine these dishes for the presence of clear circular areas or holes in the bacterial lawn. These are the viral plaques. Select those plates showing between 30–300 plaques and count the number of plaques present.

2. Determine the number of viruses in the original tube by multiplying the number of plaques by the dilution factor. For example, if 180 plaques are counted on a 1/1,000,000 bottom agar virus dilution agar overlay plate, then $180 \times 1,000,000 = 180,000,000$ viruses present in the original sample.

3. Record your observations in the Results section.

4. Answer the questions for the exercise.

Objectives

1. Compare the use of thioglycollate broth versus the GasPak jar system coupled with aerobic growth to determine the oxygen requirements of bacteria.

2. Distinguish between the mechanisms of thioglycollate broth and the GasPak jar system to obtain anaerobic conditions.

3. Define **aerobe, anaerobe** and **facultative anaerobe**.

4. Define **toxic oxygen compounds**.

5. Describe the problem posed by toxic oxygen compounds to bacteria.

6. List a purpose for catalase.

Background

Bacteria vary in their ability to use oxygen as the final acceptor in respiration. Bacteria that only grow in the presence of oxygen are classified as **aerobes**. An example is *Micrococcus luteus*. Those that require the total absence of oxygen for growth are **strict anaerobes**. Examples include *Clostridium sporogenes* and members of the genus *Bacteroides*. Bacteria that can grow in the presence of oxygen but do not use the oxygen for growth and can grow the same in its absence are called **aerotolerant anaerobes**. Examples include some members of the genera *Clostridium* and *Enterococcus faecalis*. **Facultative anaerobes** grow better in the presence than in the absence of oxygen. In the presence of oxygen they use aerobic respiration for energy and growth. In the absence of oxygen they obtain energy for growth by anaerobic glycolysis and fermentation or must use anaerobic respiration. An example is *Escherichia coli*. **Microaerophiles** require small amounts of oxygen for growth and are killed by the amount of oxygen necessary for aerobic growth. Examples include some members of the genus *Streptococcus* and *Treponema pallidum* the cause of syphilis.

Aerobes use the oxygen as the final acceptor for electrons and hydrogens released in respiration. **Toxic oxygen compounds** such as hydrogen peroxide and superoxide are produced during the final stages of electron transport phosphorylation in aerobic respiration. These toxic compounds oxidize cell components such as phospholipids in the cell membrane and kill the cell. The toxic oxygen compounds are eliminated by the enzymes superoxide dismutase and catalase, which are commonly found in aerobic and facultative anaerobic bacteria. Superoxide dismutase converts superoxides into hydrogen peroxide and oxygen, and catalase converts hydrogen peroxide into water and oxygen. Both enzymes work together to eliminate toxic oxygen compounds. Aerotolerant anaerobes may lack catalase but usually have superoxide dismutase. Strict anaerobes lack both protective enzymes and are killed by growth in even small amounts of oxygen. They accumulate large amounts of superoxide and hydrogen peroxide during growth in oxygen and are poisoned by these compounds. Anaerobes must use alternate electron acceptors such as nitrate, sulfate and carbonate in the final stage of respiration as substitutes for molecular oxygen to avoid this lethal effect.

Interestingly, anaerobes play a major role in many infections in the human body. Aerobic and facultative bacteria present in mixed infections use up the oxygen to create reducing conditions that promote the multiplication of the anaerobic bacteria. Examples are abdominal or pelvic infections involving the strict anaerobe *Bacteroides*. The facultative anaerobe *Escherichia coli*, also frequently present, uses up the available oxygen and allows the strict anaerobe to multiply and produce severe septic infections and abscesses, which can spread to organs such as the lungs, liver and the brain. Medical personnel should be certain that all clinical specimens containing possible anaerobes are promptly sent to the laboratory for evaluation and identification.

Determination of Oxygen Requirements: An Overview

Two approaches will be used to determine the oxygen requirements of selected bacteria. They are growth in thioglycollate broth and the GasPak jar system combined with aerobic growth. Thioglycollate broth contains yeast extract, casein, cystine, agar, thioglycollate and resazaurin. The broth supplies essential nutrients and the agar reduces convection currents in this medium to help maintain anaerobic conditions. The thioglycollate combines with oxygen in the broth and creates anaerobic conditions. The resazaurin acts as an oxidation-reduction indicator for this medium. It turns pink at the surface of this medium in the presence of dissolved oxygen. Oxygen is restricted to the top layer of the broth. Any oxygen deeper in the broth is subject to the oxygen-scavenging activity of the thioglycollate, and this portion of the medium becomes anaerobic. If more than 30% of the sterile fluid medium in the tubes shows a pink color due to dissolved oxygen, the tubes should be reheated to expel the gas. The tubes are then cooled and inoculated with pure cultures of the organisms to be studied. Aerobes grow at the surface of the broth. Microaerophiles grow slightly below the surface. Anaerobes grow at the bottom, and facultative anaerobic bacteria grow throughout the broth, but better at the surface. Aerotolerant bacteria grow equally throughout the broth.

In the second approach, a comparison is made of growth in the presence of oxygen with growth under anaerobic conditions in the GasPak jar system. The GasPak jar system includes a foil gas generator envelope, a palladium catalyst contained in a wire mesh cup in the lid and a methylene blue indicator strip to indicate reducing or anaerobic conditions. The inoculated petri dishes are placed inverted into the GasPak jar, 10 ml of water is pipetted into the generator envelope and the indicator package is partly opened to expose the indicator. The lid is placed on the jar and hand-tightened. The generator envelope releases hydrogen gas and carbon dioxide gas. The palladium catalyst combines hydrogen gas with oxygen gas in the jar to form water. Water vapor accumulates on the sides of the jar. The indicator changes from blue to colorless to signify anaerobic conditions. A very clear description of the differences in aerobic growth, facultative growth, aerotolerant, and anaerobic growth can be made by this method. A representative of each of these categories is studied by this method. Single streaks of the four organisms that represent these categories are made on duplicate plates of nutrient agar. One plate is incubated under anaerobic conditions in the GasPak jar at 35°C, while the other is incubated under aerobic conditions at the same temperature. The plates are compared after incubation. Aerobic bacteria only show growth on the aerobically incubated plate, while anaerobes show growth only on the plate incubated in the GasPak jar. Facultative anaerobic bacteria show growth on both plates. The growth on the plate incubated under aerobic conditions is heavier than on the plate incubated under anaerobic conditions. Aerotolerant anaerobes grow the same on both plates. This method can clearly distinguish the four categories from each other.

Materials

20-hour nutrient broth cultures of *Escherichia coli, Micrococcus luteus, Staphylococcus aureus* and *Enterococcus faecalis*

48-hour thioglycollate broth culture of *Clostridium sporogenes*

5 screw cap thioglycollate broth tubes per student

1 GasPak jar system

2 dry nutrient agar petri plates per student

10-ml pipettes

pipette pumps

beaker of distilled water

Procedures

First Period (See Figure 18-1)

1. **Thioglycollate Broth:**

   a. Select five thioglycollate broth tubes.

   b. Examine the thioglycollate broth tubes for a pink zone at the top of the tubes. If the pink zone due to oxidized resazaurin occupies more than 30% of the top of the tubes, place these tubes in a boiling water bath for a few minutes to drive off the dissolved oxygen. Cool the tubes to room temperature before inoculating with bacteria.

   c. The organisms studied are *Escherichia coli, Micrococcus luteus, Staphylococcus aureus, Enterococcus faecalis* and *Clostridium sporogenes*. Label each tube with the initials of a different single organism for this study.

   d. Inoculate a loopful of a single bacterial culture into the appropriately labeled thioglycollate broth tube.

   e. Do not shake the thioglycollate broth tubes.

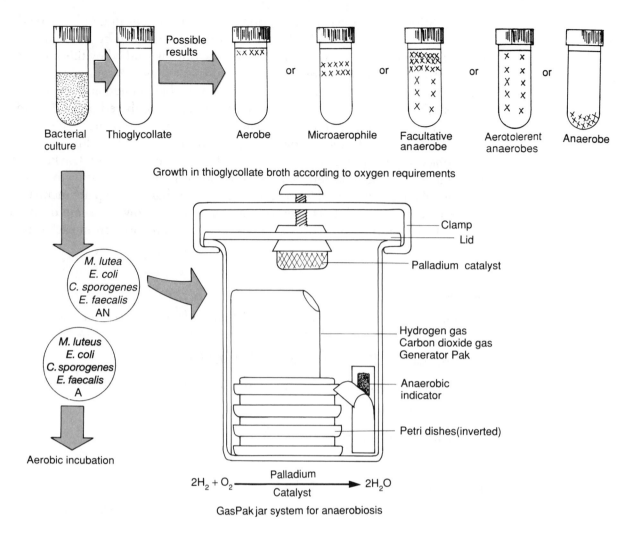

Growth in thioglycollate broth according to oxygen requirements

Bacterial culture → **Thioglycollate** → Possible results → **Aerobe** or **Microaerophile** or **Facultative anaerobe** or **Aerotolerent anaerobes** or **Anaerobe**

M. lutea
E. coli
C. sporogenes
E. faecalis
AN

M. luteus
E. coli
C. sporogenes
E. faecalis
A

Aerobic incubation

Clamp
Lid
Palladium catalyst
Hydrogen gas
Carbon dioxide gas
Generator Pak
Anaerobic indicator
Petri dishes(inverted)

$$2H_2 + O_2 \xrightarrow[\text{Catalyst}]{\text{Palladium}} 2H_2O$$

GasPak jar system for anaerobiosis

Figure 18-1
Determination of Oxygen Requirements

f. Tighten the screw caps tightly to prevent entry of oxygen.

g. Incubate the thioglycollate broth tubes at 35°C for 72 hours.

2. **GasPak Jar Anaerobic System Combined with Aerobic Growth:**

   a. Select two plates of nutrient agar and label one dish "An" for anaerobic and the other "A" for aerobic incubation.

   b. Mark four lines on the bottom of each petri dish and label the first line *"Micrococcus luteus,"* the second line *"Escherichia coli"* and the third line *"Clostridium sporogenes"* and the fourth line *"Enterococcus faecalis."*

   c. Select the "An"-labeled nutrient agar plate first. Flame the loop and streak a single line on the agar above the label for the first culture. Repeat this streaking procedure for the remaining three cultures. Be sure to flame the loop between each transfer to prevent contamination of the cultures and the streaks.

   d. Repeat this procedure for the "A"-labeled nutrient agar plate. See step c above.

e. Incubate the streaked nutrient agar petri dish labeled "A" at 35°C for 72 hours.

f. Place the streaked nutrient agar petri dish labeled "An" inverted in the GasPak jar. Place the gas generator envelope into the GasPak jar. Tear the corner of the gas generator envelope and pipette 10 ml of water into the envelope. Tear open the methylene blue indicator strip and place it in the jar. Place the lid on the jar and hand-tighten snugly. Incubate the sealed GasPak jar at 35°C for 72 hours.

Second Period (Evaluation)

1. Examine the thioglycollate broth for the location of the growth. Classify each bacterial culture for the oxygen requirement by completing the table in the Results section.

2. Open the GasPak jar and remove the nutrient agar plates. Compare the growth patterns in the aerobically and anaerobically incubated dishes and indicate the oxygen requirement in the table in the Results section.

3. Answer the questions for the exercise.

Thioglycollate Broth

Micrococcus luteus—strict aerobe

Escherichia coli—facultative anaerobe

Staphylococcus aureus—facultative anaerobe

Enterococcus faecalis—aerotolerant anaerobe

Clostridium sporogenes—strict anaerobe

Bacteria	Gas Pak Jar (Anaerobic)	Aerobic
Micrococcus luteus	no growth	heavy yellow pigmented growth
Escherichia coli	light to moderate growth	very heavy growth
Enterococcus faecalis	light to moderate growth	light to moderate growth
Clostridium sporogenes	light to moderate filmy spreading growth, fingerlike edges	no growth

Cultural Conditions

Objectives

1. Identify two ways bacteria grow in broth.

2. Differentiate between entire, erose and lobate margins of colonies growing in agar medium in petri plates.

3. Clearly distinguish between three types of growth on slant medium.

4. Distinguish between flat, convex or umbonate elevation that can be found in a colony growing in an agar dish.

5. Explain why an inoculated and incubated nutrient gelatin stab tube must be refrigerated before it is evaluated.

Background

Bacteria can be grown in liquid media such as broth, on solid media in nutrient agar slants or petri dishes and in nutrient gelatin stab tubes. The growth patterns of bacteria present important clues for the identification of the organisms. The observations of cultural characteristics of bacteria is thus useful for the identification of the organisms. The types of growth pattern seen depend on the kind of media used for inoculation. A survey of the observable results on liquid and solid media follows to introduce the wide variety of growth patterns in microorganisms.

Broth Growth   When a nutrient broth tube is inoculated with a loopful of a culture, a variety of growth patterns are possible. (See Figure 19-1.) For example:

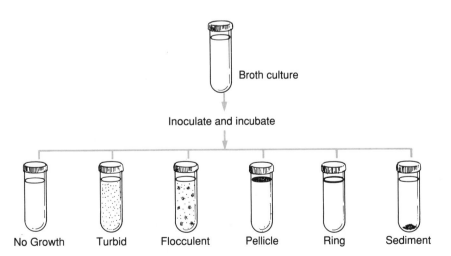

Broth culture

Inoculate and incubate

| No Growth | Turbid | Flocculent | Pellicle | Ring | Sediment |

Figure 19-1
Types of Growth in Broth

Combinations of the broth features can be present in one culture.

In **turbidity** the bacteria grow to produce a uniform cloudiness in the liquid media.

In **flocculent** growth the cloudiness appears as particles suspended in the liquid.

A **pellicle** is a film of growth produced by the microorganisms at the surface.

A **ring** is a line of growth produced by the microorganisms around the inside of the glass tube at the surface of the broth.

A **sediment** is visible when the cells sink and collect as a small mass in the bottom of the tube.

Slant Growth   When a nutrient agar slant is inoculated with a single streak of an organism, a variety of growth patterns are possible. (See Figure 19-2.) For example:

In **filiform** growth the edges of the growth are smooth.

In **echinulate** growth the edges are jagged and appear sharply defined, like teeth on a saw.

In **effuse** growth the entire streak is very fine and filmlike.

In **beaded** growth the lower portion of the growth is heavy, while the upper portion shows fine, grainy growth.

Arborescent   Growth resembles the branches of a tree.

Rhizoid   Growth is finer branches, like thin roots.

Colony Growth on Petri Plates   Streak plates of pure cultures of organisms produce distinctive growth patterns with regard to size, form of the colony, margin, elevation, pigmentation and location. (See Figure 19-3.)

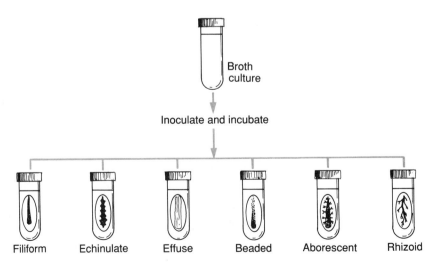

Figure 19-2
Types of Growth on Slants

Filiform   Echinulate   Effuse   Beaded   Aborescent   Rhizoid

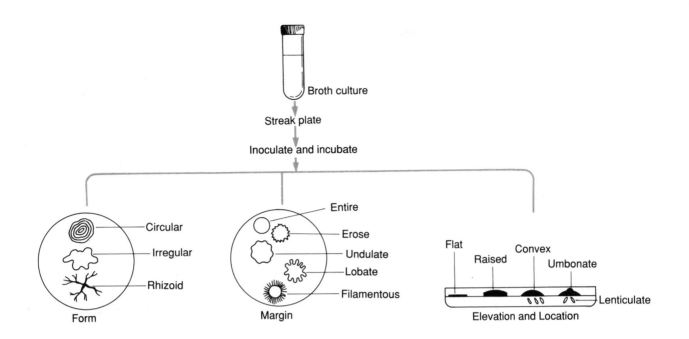

Figure 19-3
Colony Characteristics on
Streak Plates

Size

Very small

Moderate in size

Very large

Form

Circular—round with a smooth edge.

Irregular—round with an uneven edge.

Rhizoid—shows a spreading growth pattern.

Margin

Entire—the outer border is mooth and even around the whole colony.

Erose—the outer border is jagged around the whole colony.

Undulate—a wavy in-and-out outer border is present.

Lobate—the outer border shows fingerlike projections of growth from the main colony. This kind of border is much more irregular than is an undulate margin.

Filamentous—the outer edge has fine, threadlike extensions from the main colony.

Elevation (height)

A **flat** colony is one with no apparent elevation.

A **raised** colony is one with a slight elevation.

A **convex** colony is one that is dome-shaped and is higher in the center than at the edges.

An **umbonate** colony is a dome-shaped colony that has an additional elevation dome in the center of the colony.

Pigmentation   Some colonies have color due to a colored compound made by the bacteria as they grow. The colored compound, or pigment, is readily seen in the colonies growing on agar in petri dishes and in the streak growth on slant cultures. For example, colonies of *Staphylococcus aureus* are yellow, and colonies of *Serratia marcescens* are red when this organism is grown at room temperature. When *Serratia marcescens* is grown in broth, the pigment is excreted by the cells into the medium and the broth is colored pink.

Location   Colonies of bacteria growing on the agar surface in petri dishes will show specific aspects of the characteristics of size, form, margin, elevation and pigmentation. However, colonies growing within the agar appear lens-shaped. They are pointed at either end and swollen in the center. These subsurface colonies are called lens-shaped or lenticulate colonies. Pigmentation is more difficult to discern in these colonies.

Nutrient Gelatin   Nutrient gelatin contains nutrient broth and the protein gelatin. Many bacteria show growth in nutrient gelatin since they metabolize the peptone and beef extract found in the nutrient broth. However, only a select number of organisms are able to digest the fibrous protein gelatin to amino acids. Those that have gelatinase enzyme and digest the gelatin will liquefy this medium. Normally gelatin is a liquid at room temperature and is a solid at refrigerator temperatures. Therefore, the incubated nutrient gelatin stab cultures must be refrigerated before evaluation to distinguish between melting of the gelatin and true digestion of the gelatin protein. Positive digestion of gelatin protein by bacterial cultures should be viewed as an illustration of the ability of many pathogenic bacteria such as staphylococci, streptococci and anaerobes to digest protein such as collagen found in areolar connective tissue in the dermis of the skin and walls of organs, in bone, in cartilage, in ligaments and in tendons. This destructive action by bacterial enzymes could lead to abscesses and gangrene. This **proteolytic** activity in tissue by bacterial enzymes is an example of a **virulence factor**, or a factor that promotes the infection or disease process in humans.

Cultural Conditions: An Overview

In this exercise aerobic and facultative organisms as well as an anaerobe are inoculated into nutrient broth, singly streaked on nutrient agar slants, streaked onto nutrient agar in petri dishes to isolate pure cultures and stabbed into nutrient gelatin. The growth patterns for each of the bacteria observed in these different media illustrate the cultural characteristics described earlier. Each of these organisms should be characterized for its particular growth pattern in nutrient broth, on nutrient agar slants, on nutrient agar petri plates and in nutrient gelatin. A strict anaerobe is included to emphasize that oxygen is toxic to this organism regardless whether it is grown on agar or in broth.

Materials	20-hour broth cultures of *Bacillus subtilis, Escherichia coli, Pseudomonas aeruginosa, Staphylococcus aureus* and *Enterococcus faecalis* and a 20-hour thioglycollate broth culture of *Clostridium sporogenes*

tubes of nutrient broth

nutrient agar slants

nutrient agar petri plates

nutrient gelatin stab tubes kept cold in a refrigerator

Procedures	**First Period**

1. Select six tubes of nutrient broth, six nutrient agar slants, six nutrient agar petri plates and six nutrient gelatin stab tubes.

2. Separate these media into six sets each consisting of a nutrient broth tube, a nutrient slant, a petri plate and a nutrient gelatin stab.

3. Label the first set *"Bacillus subtilis,"* the second set *"Escherichia coli,"* the third set *"Pseudomonas aeruginosa,"* the fourth set *"Staphylococcus aureus,"* the fifth set *"Enterococcus faecalis"* and the sixth set *"Clostridium sporogenes."*

4. Inoculate a loopful of each bacterial culture into the properly labeled nutrient broth tube.

5. Singly streak a loopful of each bacterial culture onto the agar surface of the properly labeled nutrient agar slant.

6. Streak a loopful of each bacterial culture on the properly labeled plates to isolate pure cultures.

7. Stab a nutrient gelatin tube for each organism.

8. Incubate all the tubes and plates at 35°C for 48 hours.

Second Period (See Figures 19-1 through 19-4)

1. Observe and identify the growth responses for each of these organisms on these media. The broth media for these organisms should first be examined, without shaking, for the presence of a pellicle, ring, turbidity or flocculent growth. The presence of sediment should be noted. The tube is then gently shaken to disturb the sediment. Notice whether the sediment rises from the bottom as a powder or as a viscous swirl. Slant cultures of a given organism can show more than one type of growth response. For example, an organism can show filiform or echinulate growth on a slant. Petri plate cultures are somewhat more uniform in their growth response. Note the absence of any growth on any of these media for the strict anaerobe

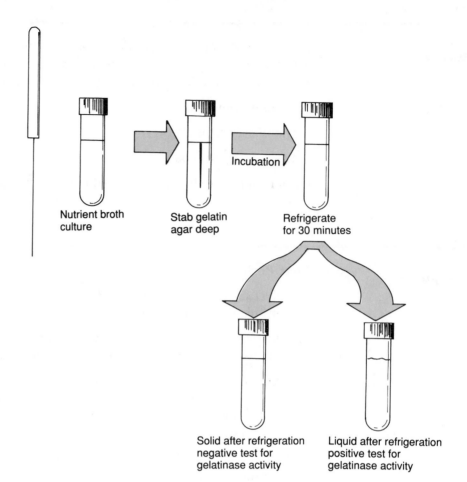

Figure 19-4
Growth and Liquefaction in a
Gelatin Stab

Nutrient broth
culture

Stab gelatin
agar deep

Incubation

Refrigerate
for 30 minutes

Solid after refrigeration
negative test for
gelatinase activity

Liquid after refrigeration
positive test for
gelatinase activity

Clostridium sporogenes. This organism lacks catalase and is poisoned by toxic oxygen compounds produced during growth in the presence of air. Examine the nutrient gelatin stab tubes for cloudiness indicating growth. Place these tubes in the refrigerator for 30 minutes to allow any negative culture results to solidify and to distinguish between true bacterial enzyme-mediated liquefaction and melting.

2. Record the responses of these organisms in the table in the Results section.

3. Answer the questions for this exercise.

Temperature and Bacterial Growth

Objectives

1. Define growth of microorganisms.
2. Define cardinal temperature.
3. Define **psychrophile, mesophile** and **thermophile**.
4. Indicate an unusual feature of psychotrophic bacteria.

Background

Temperature is one of the most important factors that affects the growth of microorganisms. Growth is defined as increase in the number of cells. Bacteria show minimum, optimum and maximum temperatures for growth. These are known as **cardinal temperatures**. The **minimum temperature** represents the lowest temperature at which growth occurs. Below that temperature the cell membrane loses its structural integrity and transport processes into and out of the cell fail. At the **optimal temperature** enzyme reactions occur efficiently so that reproduction proceeds at a maximal rate. The **maximum temperature** is the upper limit at which reproduction is possible. The rate of reproduction is dramatically reduced at this temperature because of protein denaturation, loss of enzyme function and cell death.

Bacteria are classified into distinct groups based on these cardinal temperatures. They are psychrophile, mesophile, thermophile and psychotroph. **Psychrophiles** grow at a range of –5° to 20°C. The optimum temperature is 15°C. **Mesophiles** grow at 20° to 45°C. The optimum temperature for many mesophiles is 37°C, which is the normal temperature of the human body. **Pathogenic**, or disease-producing, bacteria share this same optimal temperature. Some examples include the Group A beta-hemolytic streptococci, species of the *Neisseria* that cause meningitis and gonorrhea, staphylococci, *Mycobacterium tuberculosis* and *Escherichia coli*. **Psychotrophs** represent a special category of mesophiles that can also grow at 0°C; they are frequently responsible for spoilage of refrigerated dairy, meat and vegetable products. **Thermophiles** grow at a range of 45° to 60°C. **Facultative** thermophiles will grow at 37°C but prefer to grow at elevated temperatures. **Obligate** thermophiles will only grow at elevated temperatures. Some examples of thermophiles are found in the spore-forming genera *Bacillus* and *Clostridium*.

This experiment illustrates the differences in temperature requirements of selected microorganisms. Bacteria are inoculated into tubes of nutrient broth and incubated at designated temperatures. These bacteria are classified into temperature categories by the degree of turbidity observed in the nutrient broth tubes. Pigment production by *Serratia marcescens* is studied to determine the temperature dependence of this process. *Serratia marcescens* produces a red-orange pigment called prodigiosin. This pigment is produced at a distinct temperature.

Materials

20-hour cultures of *Pseudomonas fluorescens, Escherichia coli, Staphylococcus aureus, Bacillus stereothermophilus* and *Serratia marcescens*

nutrient broth tubes

refrigerator at 4°C, incubators set at 25°C, 37°C and 55°C

Procedures

First Period

1. For all organisms, mark nutrient broth tubes with the name of the organism and the temperature to be studied. A total of twenty nutrient broth tubes should be labeled. (See Figure 20-1.)

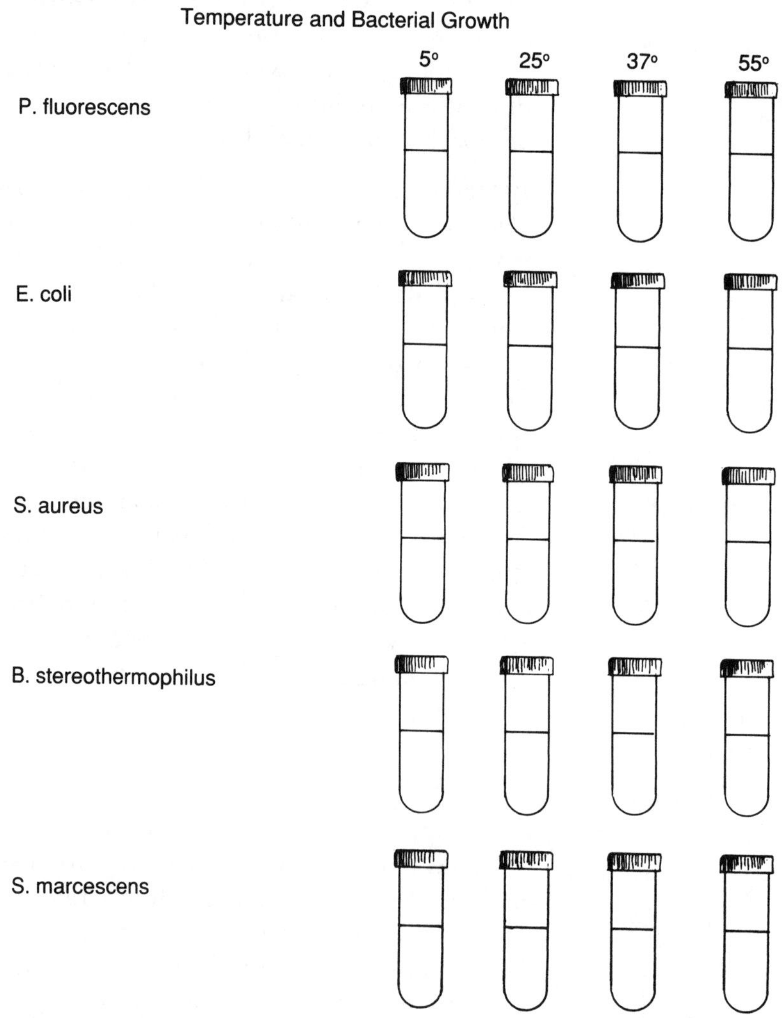

Figure 20-1
Temperature and Bacterial Growth

2. Inoculate each nutrient broth tube with a loopful of the proper bacterial culture.

3. Incubate all the tubes at the proper temperature.

Second Period

1. After incubation gently mix the contents of each broth tube to resuspend the cells. Compare the degree of turbidity at all four temperatures for each organism and record your results in the Results section.

2. Examine each of the broth tubes of *Serratia marcescens* for growth and pigment production. Record the temperature at which each occurs.

3. Answer the questions for the exercise.

Lethal Effects of Temperature

Objectives

1. Define **thermal death time**.
2. Define **thermal death point**.
3. Explain how moist heat kills cells.
4. Define pasteurization.

Background

It has already been established that bacteria have an optimal temperature for growth. The purpose of this exercise is to demonstrate that elevated temperature can have lethal effects on microorganisms. For example, boiling water at 100°C kills bacilli and cocci within 10–15 minutes. Endospores are not killed by this treatment. They tend to survive several hours of boiling at 100°C. Endospores require a higher temperature to kill them. This is achieved in the autoclave, which operates at 15 pounds steam pressure and 121°C for a period of 15 minutes. The autoclave is routinely used to sterilize microbiological media, discard cultures and experimental materials. Liquid media that are heat-sensitive are sterilized by filtration. The moist heat produced by the super-heated steam of the autoclave readily penetrates into cells and endospores and kills them by denaturation of the proteins and enzymes. It also coagulates proteins and breaks the base pairing in the nucleic acids and damages the lipids in the cell membranes in the cells. Dry heating in a hot air oven also sterilizes. However, this method is restricted to glassware and requires about 2 hours at 180°C. Dry heat kills by dehydrating the cells or incinerating them. **Pasteurization** is another method of heating that kills microorganisms. This treatment is used to eliminate pathogens present in dairy products and juices. For example, when raw milk is heated at 72°C for 15 seconds, the pathogenic streptococci, salmonellae, tuberculosis bacilli, Q fever rickettsiae and brucellosis organisms that are present from the cow or handlers are killed. Nonpathogens such as the lactobacilli in milk are not killed. These organisms are **thermoduric** and can withstand a brief exposure to high heat. Therefore, pasteurization does not mean sterilization.

High heat is used in the canning industry to kill the most heat-resistant organisms present in food. Two concepts that are used to note heat killing are the thermal death time and the thermal death point. The **thermal death time** is the time necessary to kill a suspension of microorganisms at a definite temperature. In thermal death time the time varies and the temperature is constant. **Thermal death point** is the temperature necessary to kill a suspension of microorganisms in 10 minutes. In thermal death point the temperature varies and the time is constant. The autoclave is an important application of thermal death time.

Lethal Effects of Temperature: An Overview

These concepts of thermal death are examined in this exercise by determining the differences in heat sensitivities of three microorganisms, *Escherichia coli, Staphylococcus aureus* and sporulated culture of *Bacillus subtilis*. Thermal death for *Bacillus stereothermophilus*, a strict thermophilic spore former, is also studied. This organism is used to evaluate the effectiveness of the autoclave for sterlization (see Exercise 22). These bacteria are heated for 40 minutes in thermostat-controlled water baths set at 80°C and 100°C. Samples are pour plated at 5-minute intervals and incubated. The presence or absence of survivors is noted for each time interval. The first set of platings for a given temperature that just kills all the organisms is the thermal death time. The thermal death time is determined for each organism, and the comparative sensitivity of each organism is determined. Those organisms demonstrating lethality in 10 minutes illustrate the concept of thermal death point.

Materials

20-hour nutrient broth culture of *Escherichia coli*

20-hour nutrient broth culture of *Staphylococcus aureus*

72-hour nutrient broth culture of *Bacillus subtilis* containing endospores

72-hour nutrient broth culture of *Bacillus stereothermophilus* containing endospores

temperature-controlled water bath set at 80°C

temperature-controlled water bath set at 100°C

tubes of nutrient broth containing 9 ml of medium

sterile petri plates

bottles of sterile molten nutrient agar held at 50°C in a water bath

rack of tubes

sterile 1-ml pipettes

pipette pumps

thermometers

large plastic Ziplock bags or plastic bags with ties

Procedures

First Period (See Figure 21-1)

1. Fill the two water baths with distilled water.

2. Set the temperature of one bath to 80°C and the other to 100°C.

3. Place a tube rack in each water bath. Place a tube of nutrient broth in each rack. Insert a thermometer in the tube in each water bath. These tubes are used to establish the temperature of the water baths.

4. Select eight nutrient broth tubes. Label two of the tubes "*E. coli*," two of the tubes "*S. aureus*" and two of the tubes "*B. subtilis*" and two of the tubes *B. stereothermophilus*.

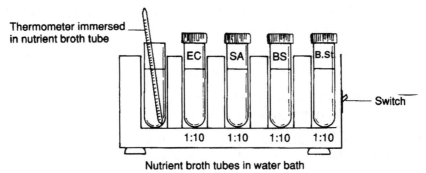

Determining Lethal Effects of Temperatures

Thermometer immersed in nutrient broth tube

EC SA BS B.St

Switch

1:10 1:10 1:10 1:10

Nutrient broth tubes in water bath

Each nutrient broth tube has 1:10 dilution of the original bacterial culture.

"B.St" is *Bacillus stereothermophilus*

Heating Time   Pour plates made for each organism

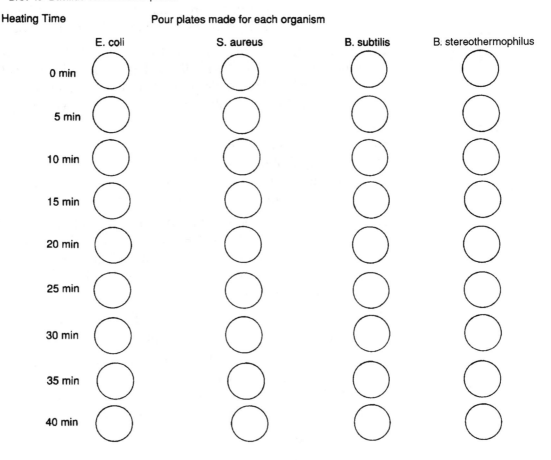

	E. coli	S. aureus	B. subtilis	B. stereothermophilus
0 min	○	○	○	○
5 min	○	○	○	○
10 min	○	○	○	○
15 min	○	○	○	○
20 min	○	○	○	○
25 min	○	○	○	○
30 min	○	○	○	○
35 min	○	○	○	○
40 min	○	○	○	○

Figure 21-1
Determining Lethal Effects
of Temperatures

5. Separate the tubes into two sets. One set is labeled "80°C" and includes a nutrient broth for each organism. The second set is labeled "100°C" and includes a nutrient broth for each organism.

6. Place the two sets of labeled tubes in the proper water bath. Leave the tubes in the water baths in order for them to reach the temperature of the water in the bath.

7. Select 72 petri dishes. Divide them into four equal sets of 18 dishes.

8. Divide each set of 18 dishes into two smaller subsets of 9 petri dishes.

9. Label the first subset of 9 petri dishes "*Escherichia coli*, 80°C." Label the second subset "*Escherichia coli*, 100°C."

10. Label the third subset of 9 petri dishes "*Staphylococcus aureus*, 80°C." Label the fourth subset of 9 petri dishes "*S. aureus*, 100°C."

11. Label the fifth subset of 9 petri dishes "*Bacillus subtilis*, 80°C." Label the sixth subset of 9 petri dishes "*B. subtilis*, 100°C."

12. Label the seventh subset of 9 petri dishes "*Bacillus stereothermophilus*, 80°C. Label the eighth subset of 9 petri dishes *B. stereothermophilus*, 100°C.

13. Label each petri dish in a subset with a heat exposure time. The exposure times for this experiment are: 0 minutes, 5 minutes, 10 minutes, 15 minutes, 20 minutes, 25 minutes, 30 minutes, 35 minutes and 40 minutes.

14. Select a culture tube of *Escherichia coli*, *Staphylococcus aureus*, *Bacillus subtilis* and *B. stereothermophilus*. Pipette 0.1 ml of the culture into the properly labeled 0-minute plate. Pour molten agar over this sample. Rotate the dish to distribute the bacteria in the agar. Allow the agar to solidify.

15. When the temperature in the nutrient broth tubes reach 80°C and 100°C, pipette 1 ml of the bacterial culture into the properly labeled nutrient broth tube in the water bath. Mix the contents in the tube gently. This is a 1:10 dilution of the original bacterial culture.

16. A 5-minute intervals, pipette a 0.1-ml sample of the heated bacterial culture into the properly labeled petri dish. Pour cooled agar into the dish. Rotate the dish to distribute the agar, and allow the agar to harden. Use separate pipettes and continue this sampling for 40 minutes. Discard all used pipettes in a pipette discard.

17. When the agar has solidified, invert all the petri dishes and incubate all **except** for *B. stereothermophilus* petri dishes at 35°C for 48 hours.

18. Place the inverted petri dishes of *B. stereothermophilus* in a plastic Ziplock bag or other plastic bag that can be sealed. Incubate at 55°C for 24 to 72 hours. Check for growth after each 24 hours. After 72 hours the plates may be refrigerated till the next laboratory session.

Second Period

1. Examine all the plates for the presence or absence of growth.

2. Record the time interval at 80°C and 100°C of heating at which no colonies appear on the incubated petri plates. This time represents the thermal death at 80°C and 100°C for each organism. (Note: If the heat killing occurs at 10 minutes, then a thermal death point can be determined.)

3. Record all observations in the table in the Results section.

4. Answer the questions for the exercise.

Steam Sterilization:
The Autoclave

Objectives

1. Define sterilization.
2. Describe how steam sterilization kills cells.

Background

Sterilization is the absolute and complete killing of all microorganisms in a culture, sample, or material. Steam sterilization uses a large pressure cooker or autoclave to achieve this goal. Regular air is removed and replaced with steam. As the steam pressure rises, the temperature also rises proportionally. The temperature in the autoclave rises to 121°C at a steam pressure of 15 pounds per square inch. The samples undergoing sterilization are exposed to the super heated steam for 20 minutes. This moist heat penetrates cells and spores, killing these by irreversibly denaturing proteins. Endospores, capable of surviving boiling water treatment at 100°C for several hours, are killed after superheated steam exposure in the autoclave. Vegetative cells, which can be killed by exposure to boiling water for a few minutes, are more rapidly killed in the autoclave. The extra exposure time in the autoclave allows the steam to adequately penetrate samples for sterilization so that killing can occur. Autoclaves can be used to sterilize microbial media, instruments, rubber gloves and heat stable liquids.

Overview

In this exercise, a *Bacillus stereothermophilus* broth culture containing endospores is used to evaluate the effectiveness of the autoclave. This organism is an obligate thermophile. It grows at a temperature of 56°C and will not grow at 37°C. Ampules containing broth suspensions of *B. stereothermophilus* endospores and the pH indicator bromcresol purple are commercially available from Becton Dickinson Microbiology Systems to evaluate the effectiveness of an autoclave. After autoclaving these ampules are placed in a 56°C incubator. If the endospores survive autoclaving, they will germinate during incubation and the bacilli produced will multiply in the broth producing turbidity. These bacteria will produce acid end products that will cause a color change of the bromcresol purple indicator from purple to yellow. If this is seen, then the autoclaving is inadequate. In this exercise an endospore containing culture of this organism is autoclaved at 121°C for 20 minutes. After autoclaving, the culture is swabbed on nutrient agar plates which are incubated at 56°C for 72 hours in a sealed package. Lack of growth demonstrates sterilization.

Materials

72 hour nutrient broth culture tubes of *Bacillus stereothermophilus* incubated at 56°C. One set of these tubes must be autoclaved at 121°C for 20 minutes prior to the class meeting. The other set should be labeled control-nonautoclaved.

nutrient agar petri plates

packets of sterile swabs

plastic bags

Procedures

First Period

1. Select 2 nutrient agar plates. Label one autoclaved and the other control-nonautoclaved. (See Figure 22-1.)

2. Swab the control and autoclaved cultures on the appropriate prelabeled nutrient agar plates.

3. Incubate these plates at 56°C for 72 hours and examine for growth.

Second Period

1. Observe the autoclaved and control-nonautoclaved plates for the presence of growth. Lack of growth on the autoclaved labeled plates indicates that sterilization has occurred. Growth is expected on the control plates and represents germination of endospores and subsequent colony formation as well as multiplication of vegetative cells to form colonies.

2. Record the responses of *B. stereothermophilus* to these treatments in the table in the Results section.

3. Answer the questions for the exercise.

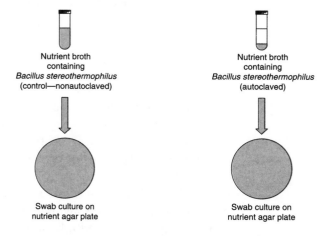

Nutrient broth containing *Bacillus stereothermophilus* (control—nonautoclaved)

Nutrient broth containing *Bacillus stereothermophilus* (autoclaved)

Swab culture on nutrient agar plate

Swab culture on nutrient agar plate

Incubate all plates at 56°C for 72 hours in a sealed package

Results

Colonies seen

No colonies seen

Figure 22-1
Steam Sterilization:
The Autoclave

Osmotic Pressure and Bacterial Growth

Objectives

1. Define **osmosis**.

2. Distinguish between hypertonic and hypotonic solutions.

3. Describe the purpose of a solute used for survival by halotolerant or halophilic bacteria in high salt environments.

4. Describe the purpose of salt for the growth of extreme halophiles.

5. Define **nonhalophile, halotolerant** and **extreme halophile.**

Background

Bacteria can live in a variety of solute concentrations. Frequently the external environment around the cell has a lower solute concentration than the cell itself. Under these circumstances the concentration of water around the cell is greater than that inside the cell, and water will flow into the cell. The cell membrane then swells against the cell wall. The rigid outer cell wall can expand slightly but will not burst, and the cell will survive. This movement of water from an area of higher water concentration to one of lower water concentration is called **osmosis**. The pressure exerted by this excess water in the cell, pressing the cell membrane against the cell wall, is described as an **osmotic pressure**. In this example the external environment, with the higher water concentration and lower solute concentration, is called the **hypotonic** environment, while the cell with the higher solute concentration and lower water concentration is called the **hypertonic** environment. Water, therefore, flows from the hypotonic external environment to the hypertonic inside environment of the cell. Bacterial cells can survive and divide in this hypotonic environment because the rigid cell wall barrier prevents lysis and death of the cell. In contrast, bacterial cells immersed in an environment in which the external solute concentration exceeds that of the living organism's are subject to different problems. In this environment the water concentration is greater within the cells than outside of them. In this example the cell contents are hypotonic, while the external environment is hypertonic. Water will flow out of the cells to the external environment. The cell membrane shrinks from the cell wall and the cell protoplast becomes dehydrated. This dehydration, called **plasmolysis**, causes cell death.

The solute and water concentrations inside and outside of bacterial cells are frequently different. Very rarely are the solute and water concentrations inside and outside the cell the same, but when this does occur, the cells and outside environment are isotonic and there is no net movement of water.

This exercise examines osmotic effects due primarily to changes in salt concentration, because salt is the major environmental influence affecting microorganisms. Bacteria can be classified in terms of their responses to increasing salt concentrations in the following manner: They are nonhalophilic, halotolerant or extreme halophilic. **Nonhalophilic** bacteria are sensitive to the effects of increasing salt concentrations outside of the cell. This category includes coliform bacteria and the pseudomonads. In contrast, some **halotolerant** (osmotolerant) bacteria can survive in higher salt concentrations such as 7.5% to 10% salt. These include gram-positive cocci such as *Staphylococcus aureus*. These bacteria must work to increase their internal solute concentration so that water will flow into the cells. *Staphylococcus aureus* increases the concentration of the water-soluble amino acid called proline. When grown in a medium of high salt concentration, this organism synthesizes proline and accumulates this amino acid in high concentrations in the cell cytoplasm. This excess solute makes the internal cytoplasm hypertonic to the environment, and water flows into the cells. Some compounds that are used to regulate the internal water concentration in the cell include proline, betaine and choline. The use of these solutes explains why staphylococci are readily isolated from mixed cultures streaked onto mannitol salt agar (which has a 7.5% salt concentration) since this medium inhibits salt-sensitive bacteria. This adaptation of staphylococci is medically important because this organism normally grows on skin; the skin usually has a high salt concentration because of the sodium chloride released in perspiration from the sweat glands. Staphylococci are responsible for skin infections and are transmitted to others after contact of hands to mouth or nose. Other microorganisms, called **extreme halophiles**, require high salt concentrations for survival. An example is the gram-negative non–spore forming, bacillus-shaped *Halobacterium salinarium*. This microbe requires salt to stabilize the cell wall and the enzymes of the cell. Halobacteria use potassium ions to survive in high salt environments. They transport potassium ions from the external environment into the cells and accumulate them in large quantities in the cell cytoplasm. Water then flows into the cells. In this way they prevent dehydration of the cells in the extremely saline environments in which they grow. Endospores also resist high concentrations of salt.

A practical application of the concept of osmotic pressure can be found in the food processing industry, which uses the high concentrations of sugar in fruit preserves and the drying of foods to create hypertonic conditions that inhibit bacteria. The spoilage agents of these foods commonly are molds and yeast. These microorganisms can grow at high concentrations of sugar or at high osmotic pressures that are inhibitory to most bacteria.

This exercise studies the comparative resistance to increasing osmotic pressure of the coliform *Escherichia coli*, the skin flora resident *Staphylococcus aureus* and the obligate halophile *Halobacterium salinarium*.

Osmotic Pressure and Bacterial Growth: An Overview

In this exercise the student singly streaks cultures of *Escherichia coli*, *Staphylococcus aureus* and *Halobacterium salinarium* on four plates differing in salt concentration and osmotic pressure. These plates are incubated at 35°C for 1 week and the 25% salt plate again for another week and examined for the presence of growth or absence of growth.

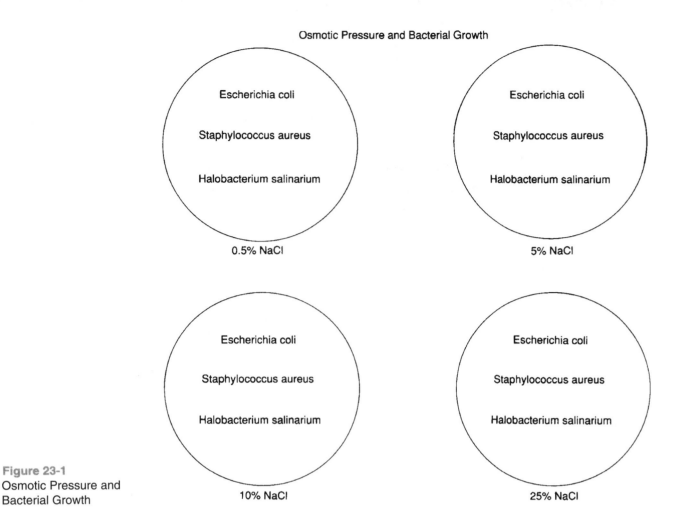

Osmotic Pressure and Bacterial Growth

Figure 23-1
Osmotic Pressure and
Bacterial Growth

Materials

20-hour individual nutrient broth cultures of *Escherichia coli* and *Staphylococcus aureus*. *Halobacterium salinarium* is grown on a *Halobacterium* 25% salt agar slant and resuspended in a sterile 25% salt solution before use.

nutrient agar petri plate with 0.5% salt

nutrient agar petri plate with 5% salt

nutrient agar petri plate with 10% salt

Halobacterium salt agar petri plate with 25% salt

Procedures

First Period

1. Select one plate each of 0.5%, 5%, 10% and 25% salt. Mark the bottom underside of each dish with three lines and label each line with *"Escherichia coli," "Staphylococcus aureus"* and *"Halobacterium salinarium,"* respectively. (See Figure 23-1.)

2. Streak single line inoculations of each culture on the agar over the properly labeled line.

3. Invert all dishes and incubate at 35°C for 1 week and examine for the presence or absence of growth. The 25% salt agar plate may require an additional week of incubation to see growth of the extreme halophile.

Second Period

1. Record your observations in the Results section.

2. Answer the questions for the exercise.

pH and Microbial Growth

Objectives

1. Identify the optimal pH range for the growth of most bacteria.

2. Give an example of how a distinct pH in the body can favor growth of distinct microorganisms.

3. Contrast the optimal pH for growth of bacteria and fungi.

Background

pH measures the concentration of hydrogen ions in a solution. The pH scale extends from 0 to 14. A **neutral** pH is 7. Solutions with a pH less than 7 are acidic, and those with a pH greater than 7 are **alkaline**. The pH is a factor that influences the growth of microorganisms. Most microorganisms grow well in a pH range of 6 to 9 and are called **neutrophiles**. Fungi can tolerate a wider range of pH than bacteria since they can grow well in a pH range of 4 to 9. An unusual group of bacteria called the **obligate acidophiles** only grow at the low pH of 2 to 3. When these cells are grown in a neutral pH environment, the cell membrane lyses and the cells die. Apparently the hydrogen ions are necessary to stabilize the cell membranes of these cells. Some bacteria, called **alkalophiles**, grow at a pH range of 10–12.

pH also can exert inhibitory influences on bacteria. Strong acids and alkalis such as hydrochloric acid and sodium hydroxide, respectively, are bactericidal to many microorganisms. Very low and high pH interfere with enzyme activity, denature proteins and can block transport of substances into cells. Organic acids such as sorbic acid and benzoic acid are commonly used as preservatives in medicines and foods.

The human body shows regional differences in pH and environment that favor the development of a distinct microbial flora. In the mouth, formation of dental caries depends on the production of large amounts of acid by streptococci and lactobacilli. This acid removes minerals from the tooth enamel and promotes caries formation. The pH is reduced to 5 or less. In the stomach the hydrochloric acid inhibits many microorganisms. Unfortunately, many enteric pathogens are protected since they are coated with food particles and are not destroyed by stomach acid. When present in the alkaline small and large intestine, these organisms produce gastrointestinal infections. Human skin has a pH of 5 due to fatty acids released by the sebaceous glands. This low pH inhibits many microorganisms. However, the osmotolerant microorganism *Staphylococcus aureus* survives in this pH and is an example of the transient flora of the skin. In another example, lactic acid bacteria commonly found in the vagina maintain the acid pH of the reproductive tract by fermenting glycogen found in the vaginal mucosa to acids. The normal pH in the vagina is about 3–4. The acids produced by these normal flora lactobacilli help to suppress uropathogens such as *Escherichia coli*,

Klebsiella, Proteus and the yeast *Candida albicans*. When these lactobacilli are suppressed by antibiotics used for other medical problems, the pH rises, the urinary pathogens can increase in number and cause infection. Specific antibiotic therapy is frequently necessary to eliminate these urinary pathogens. In addition, vinegar (acetic acid) douches are sometimes used to restore the acidic pH and to treat vaginal infections.

pH and Microbial Growth: An Overview

The purposes of this exercise are to emphasize the optimal pH for growth of selected microbes, to seek a pH that inhibits microbes and to consider the relationship between pH of particular body regions and distinct medical problems by comparing the growth responses in broths of differing pH for a series of microorganisms. The microbes used are *Alcaligenes faecalis, Escherichia coli, Staphylococcus aureus* and the yeast *Saccharomyces cerevisiae*. Overnight cultures of the bacteria are singly inoculated into nutrient broths adjusted to a pH of 3, 5, 7 and 9. The yeast culture is inoculated into sabouraud dextrose broth tubes at the same three pH values. These tubes are examined for turbidity after incubation, and the growth response is recorded.

Materials

20-hour nutrient broth cultures of *Alcaligenes faecalis, Escherichia coli* and *Staphylococcus aureus*

20-hour sabouraud dextrose broth culture of *Saccharomyces cerevisiae*

tubes of nutrient broth adjusted to pH 3, 5, 7 and 9

tubes of sabouraud dextrose broth adjusted to pH 3, 5, 7 and 9

Procedures

First Period (See Figure 24-1)

1. Select three tubes of pH 3, of pH 5, pH 7 and of pH 9 nutrient broth.

2. Label a single tube of pH 3, pH 5, pH 7 and pH 9 nutrient broth *"Alcaligenes faecalis."* Label the second set of three different pH broth tubes *"Escherichia coli"* and the third set of pH broth tubes *"Staphylococcus aureus."*

3. Select a tube of pH 3, of pH 5, of pH 7 and of pH 9 sabouraud dextrose broth and label each *"Saccharomyces cerevisiae."*

4. Inoculate the labeled tubes with the proper bacterial or yeast culture.

5. Incubate the bacterial cultures at 37°C for 1 week. Incubate the yeast culture at 30°C for 1 week.

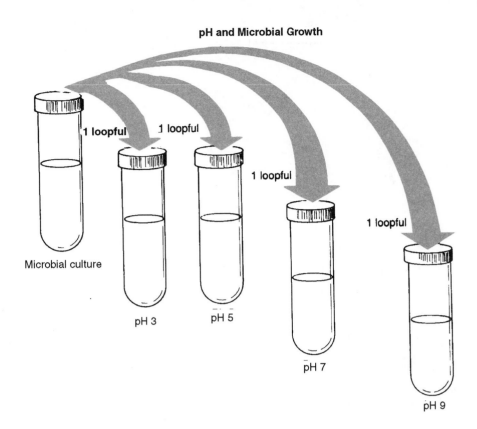

Figure 24-1
pH and Microbial Growth

pH and Microbial Growth

1 loopful   1 loopful

1 loopful

1 loopful

Microbial culture

pH 3   pH 5

pH 7

pH 9

Second Period

1. Mix the contents of the tubes by gently tapping each tube to resuspend the cells. Examine all the tubes for turbidity and record the results observed in the table in the Results section.

2. Answer the questions for the exercise.

The Importance of Handwashing

Objectives

1. Complete the handwashing exercise and distinguish between the results observed on the **before** and **after** plates.

2. Distinguish between resident flora and transient flora on the skin.

3. Explain why only certain microorganisms can grow on TSA agar plates.

Background

Bacteria that are commonly found on the skin include **transient flora**, which are temporary in nature, and **resident flora**, which are more permanent. Transient flora are readily eliminated by handwashing or killed by bodily secretions such as lysozyme from sweat glands, fatty acids from sebaceous glands and the low pH of the skin. Resident flora are not easily removed by washing. Both groups of organisms are found on the skin, adjacent mucous membranes such as the mouth, the pharynx, large intestine, urethra and vagina. The resident microflorae of the skin include diphtheroids such as *Corynebacterium* and *Propionibacterium* and staphylococci such as *Staphylococcus epidermidis*. Transient florae include *Staphylococcus aureus*, gram-negative coliforms, clostridia and aerobic spore-forming bacilli commonly found in air, water and soil.

Historically, Ignaz Semmelweis in the mid-1800s established the importance of handwashing by medical staff in reducing the incidence of puerperal sepsis, or "childbed fever," in patients after childbirth. Before then, handwashing was not routine practice—doctors went from autopsies in a mortuary directly to the maternity ward! Today it is established practice for medical personnel to wash their hands before and after examination of any patient and for surgeons to scrub before surgery to remove and kill disease microorganisms and to prevent their spread to patients.

The Importance of Handwashing: An Overview

This exercise emphasizes the importance of handwashing in removing transient and resident microorganisms from skin surfaces. The students in the class are divided into three groups. Each group is then sub-divided into teams consisting of two students. In the first group the students scrub their hands for thirty seconds; in the second group the students scrub their hands for two minutes and those in the third group scrub their hands with a scrub brush for two minutes. All groups use an antiseptic scrub solution such as Betadine® scrub solution. Each team marks a line on the underside of a trypticase soy agar dish dividing it in half. Half of the dish is labeled **before** and the other half is labeled **after**.

One student scrubs the hands, while the other student swabs their partner's wet hands before and after scrubbing with separate sterile swabs and transfers the swabbings to the appropriate section of the trypticase soy agar plate. The plates are then incubated at 35°C under aerobic conditions till the next laboratory period. This exercise only measures microorganisms able to grow in air. The numbers of colonies on the **before** and **after** halves of the plates are compared and an explanation is derived to explain the results.

Generally, the brief thirty second period of scrubbing removes transient organisms from the skin. The longer two minute period of scrubbing removes transient and some resident organisms. Those that scrub for the thirty seconds and two minutes times generally find fewer colonies on the **after** than on the **before** sections. The surgical scrubs used also have some antiseptic effect on skin microbes. The use of the scrub brush simulates the vigorous scrubbing practiced by surgeons prior to surgery. In this group, fewer microbes can be found on the **after** section since skin cells together with adherent microorganisms are removed and rinsed off the hands. This exercise demonstrates that reasonable handwashing removes transient and some resident microorganisms from the skin and reduces the chances of transmission of disease organisms to others. Handwashing is a major way to reduce the fecal-oral transmission of disease organisms by food handlers and is part of community sanitary codes. This practice of handwashing reduces the incidence of transmission of nosocomial infections from patients to staff and to other patients in medical facilities.

Materials

packets of sterile cotton swabs

surgical scrub solutions—Betadine® or Hibiclens®

trypticase soy agar plates

scrub brush

Procedures

First Period

1. Select a trypticase soy agar plate and mark a line on the bottom of the dish with a wax marking pencil dividing the dish in half. Label one half of the dish **before** and the other half **after**. Label the plates thirty seconds or two minutes. If a scrub brush is used, label the plate **brush** also. (See Figure 25-1.)

2. Partner #1 in each team will scrub their hands and partner #2 in each team will transfer the swabbings before and after scrubbing to the proper portion of the agar surface of the trypticase soy agar plate.

3. Partner #1 wets his or her hands with water.

4. Partner #2 obtains a sterile swab and swabs the wet hands of the first partner. This swab is rolled on to the surface of the entire half of the trypticase

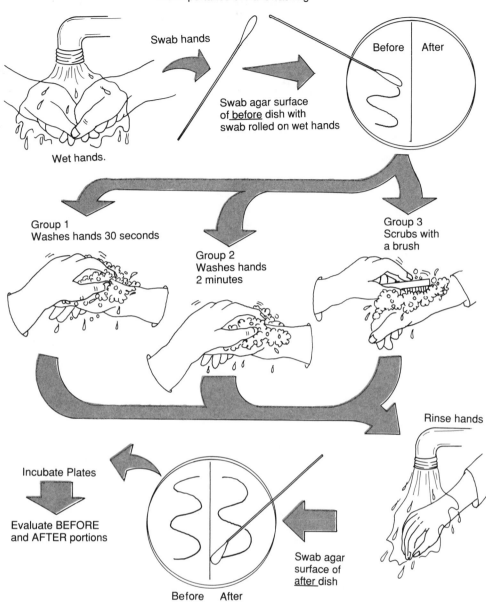

The Importance of Handwashing

Figure 25-1
The Importance of
Handwashing

soy agar plate labeled **before**. This swab must be disposed of in a pipette discard filled with disinfectant.

5. Partner #2 pours a small quantity of surgical scrub on to the hands of partner #1. The first team member then scrubs their hands thoroughly for either thirty seconds or two minutes with or without a scrub brush. Be sure to scrub the palms, fingers and nails thoroughly. Hold the palms and fingers downward while rinsing the hands to prevent any splatter. Rinse thoroughly with tap water. Do not touch any object.

6. Partner #2 obtains a sterile swab and swabs the hands of partner #1 and rolls the swab on the agar surface of the half of the trypticase soy agar plate labeled **after**. This swab must be disposed of in a discard container filled with disinfectant.

7. Incubate these trypticase soy agar plates at 35°C in inverted fashion until the next laboratory class.

Second Period

1. Compare the numbers of colonies found on the **before** and **after** portions of these plates and account for these results. Indicate your findings in the Results section.

2. Answer the questions for the exercise.

Case Study 3

An outbreak of scalded skin syndrome occurs in a pediatric intensive care nursery. Several babies are affected and show severe peeling of skin and skin inflammation. The causative agent is *Staphylococcus aureus*. The infection control committee obtains nasal swab cultures and hand swab cultures from the staff assigned to this unit. These cultures are streaked to mannitol-salt agar plates. The results are listed below:

Staff Member	Mannitol Salt Agar	
	nasal swab	*throat swab*
A	no growth	no growth
B	growth, red agar	growth, red agar
C	yellow halos around colonies	yellow halos around colonies

1. Decide which staff member is the source of the outbreak.

   _____

   _____

2. Devise an explanation for the observed results for each staff member.

   A _____

   _____

   B _____

   _____

   C _____

   _____

3. List procedures that should be practiced to prevent any future oubreaks of this infection.

   _____

   _____

Unit IV

Microbial Relationships and Disease

26   **Commensalism**   **125**

simulates a mixed culture infection that demonstrates that anaerobes can become dominant species present in many infections in the body.

27   **Synergism**   **129**

simulates the cooperative actions of bacteria in mixed infection to produce more severe infections than could be produced by the single organisms alone.

28   **Antagonism**   **133**

demonstrates that selected microbes can produce antibiotic agents that inhibit other test bacteria.

Case Study 4   **137**

Commensalism

Objectives

1. Define **commensalism**.

2. Describe an example in which commensalism can favor growth of anaerobes present in a mixed culture with facultative bacteria.

Background

A number of interactions are possible between bacteria present in a mixed culture. One of these is called **commensalism**. In this interaction one microorganism is helped, while the other is neither helped nor harmed. Illustrations include the resident microorganisms that compose the normal flora in the human body, particularly facultative gram-negative bacilli such as *Escherichia coli* and anaerobic gram-negative bacilli of the *Bacteroides fragilis* group found in the intestinal tract. These anaerobic bacteria tend to become more prevalent than the facultatives or aerobes that are also present in mixed infections of the abdomen.

Clinically, contamination of the peritoneum after a ruptured appendix, after a stabbing wound or because of intestinal surgery can result in the introduction of a variety of facultative and anaerobic microorganisms into the body cavity. The facultative bacteria use up the oxygen present to create anaerobic or reducing conditions so that the *Bacteroides fragilis* bacilli can multiply and produce purulent and septic infections. Frequently these infections are life threatening. In addition, the encapsulated varieties of these anaerobes are more virulent than those lacking a capsule. The presence of a capsule makes the cells more resistant to phagocytosis and promotes attachment to mucous membranes. These cells tend to produce severe abscesses, suppurative infections, extensive tissue damage and sepsis.

**Commensalism:
An Overview**

A model illustrating commensalism is studied by using the facultative organism *Staphylococcus aureus* and the anaerobic organism *Clostridium sporogenes*. A mixed culture of these two organisms in nutrient broth is prepared along with separate pure cultures of each organism. All three tubes are incubated at 35°C for 1 week and then examined for turbidity or growth. Gram stains are prepared from each culture for comparison. The student should note that the anaerobe *Clostridium sporogenes* should not grow in the nutrient broth tube inoculated with this culture because strict anaerobes are inhibited by the presence of toxic oxygen compounds produced when these microorganisms are grown in the presence of oxygen. (Further information regarding this problem can be found in Exercise 18, "Determination of Oxygen Requirements.") The Gram stain of the mixed culture illustrates commensalism by the presence primarily of the gram-positive bacilli of the anaerobic organism.

Materials

20-hour nutrient broth culture of *Staphylococcus aureus*

20-hour thioglycollate broth culture of *Clostridium sporogenes*

tubes of nutrient broth

1-ml pipettes

pipette pumps

Procedures

First Period (See Figure 26-1)

1. Select three tubes of nutrient broth. Label the first tube *"Staphylococcus aureus,"* the second tube *"Clostridium sporogenes"* and the third tube "mixed culture."

2. Pipette 0.1 ml of *Staphylococcus aureus* into the first tube. Discard the pipette in the pipette discard bin containing disinfectant.

3. Pipette 0.1 ml of *Clostridium sporogenes* into the second tube. Discard this pipette in the pipette discard bin.

4. Pipette 0.1 ml of *Staphylococcus aureus* into the third tube of nutrient broth. Discard this pipette in the pipette discard bin. Select another 1-ml pipette and pipette 0.1 ml of *Clostridium sporogenes* into the same third tube. The third tube then contains 0.1 ml of each culture.

5. Incubate all the nutrient broth tubes at 35°C for 1 week.

Second Period

1. After incubation for 1 week examine these tubes for turbidity or growth. **Do not mix these tubes.** Sample the regions of heaviest turbidity and prepare Gram stains from all tubes showing growth.

2. Record your observations for turbidity and the Gram stains in the Table in the Results section.

3. Answer the questions for the exercise.

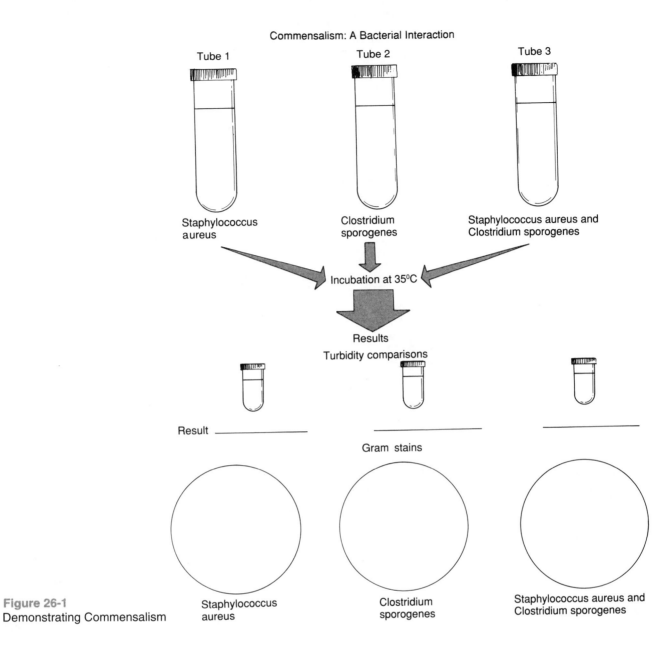

Figure 26-1
Demonstrating Commensalism

Synergism

Objectives

1. Define synergism.

2. Describe an example of a synergistic infection process in the human body.

Background

Synergism is an interaction between bacteria present in a mixed culture in which both benefit. Synergistic interactions in metabolism create a new substance that neither organism can produce by itself. For example, *Escherichia coli* by itself cannot produce the compound putrescine from the amino acid arginine. However, when grown with *Enterococcus faecalis*, which converts arginine to ornithine, *Escherichia coli* then converts the ornithine to putrescine. In another example, the microorganisms *Lactobacillus arabinosus* and *Enterococcus faecalis* complement one another and grow together on minimal medium as separate pure cultures. *Lactobacillus arabinosus* produces the B-vitamin folic acid that is required for growth of *Enterococcus faecalis*, and the *Enterococcus faecalis* produces the amino acid phenylalanine that is required for growth of the lactobacillus. Since each organism supplies a nutrient needed by the other organism, they both are able to grow on the minimal agar. This process of producing the necessary or complementary nutrient needed for growth of the other organism allows for the growth of both microorganisms on this medium. Normally neither organism could grow on this minimal medium.

Synergistic interactions in infection cause more severe tissue damage in the human host than can be produced by the separate individual organisms. In the oral cavity of humans a number of spirochetes in the genus *Borrelia* are present, together with the cigar-shaped fusobacteria. In the presence of a *Herpes* virus infection, injury to the mucous membranes or other mouth trauma these two bacterial organisms cooperate to produce serious necrotic lesions on the tonsils, the gums or in the oral cavity. Many anaerobic infections are polymicrobic in nature and typically produce necrotic tissue damage and abscesses. Combinations of anaerobes are involved in the production of almost half of the cases of severe liver and lung abscesses. In these and other anaerobic infections the combinations of organisms are more destructive to the human body than the separate organisms. For example, the combination of species of *Bacteroides* with other gram-negative anaerobic bacteria can produce more severe liver abscesses than produced by either organism alone.

Synergism: An Overview

Synergism is demonstrated in this exercise by studying the results of fermentation of separate and mixed cultures inoculated into bromthymol blue lactose broth with Durham tubes to detect acid and gas production. Bromthymol blue is blue at a pH of 7.6 and yellow at a pH of 6.0. The cultures used are *Staphylococcus aureus* and *Proteus vulgaris*. *Staphylococcus aureus* ferments lactose to acids so that the lactose broth in the tube and the Durham tube turns yellow. *Proteus vulgaris* does not ferment lactose so the broth remains blue after incubation. The inoculum in the mixed culture tube contains four times more *Proteus vulgaris* than *Staphylococcus aureus*. The additional *Proteus* culture is due to the fact that the organism does not ferment lactose and grows less well in this medium. The synergistic response illustrated in the mixed culture by gas production results in partial emptying of broth from the Durham tube. The bacteria in the mixed culture share their individual enzyme abilities to produce gas from fermentation of lactose. The formation of gas represents the cooperative efforts in a synergistic fashion to produce a new product that neither organism can produce alone. The student should note that this new and unique gas product only appears if acids are produced.

Materials

20-hour nutrient broth culture of Staphylococcus aureus

20-hour nutrient broth culture of Proteus vulgaris

Tubes of lactose broth and bromthymol blue indicator with Durham tubes

Sterile 1-ml pipettes

pipette pumps

Procedures

First Period (see Figure 27-1)

1. Select three tubes of lactose broth. Label the first tube *"Staphylococcus aureus,"* the second tube *"Proteus vulgaris"* and the third tube "mixed culture."

2. Pipette 0.1 ml of the *Staphylococcus aureus* culture into the first tube. Discard this pipette in the pipette discard bin containing disinfectant.

3. Pipette 0.4 ml of the *Proteus vulgaris* culture into the second tube. Discard this pipette in the pipette discard bin.

4. Pipette 0.1 ml of the *Staphylococcus aureus* culture into the third tube. Discard this pipette in the pipette discard bin. Select another 1-ml pipette and pipette 0.4 ml of the *Proteus vulgaris* culture into the same third tube. The third tube contains 0.1 ml of the *Staphylococcus aureus* culture and 0.4 ml of the *Proteus vulgaris* culture.

5. Incubate all lactose broth tubes at 35°C for 1 week.

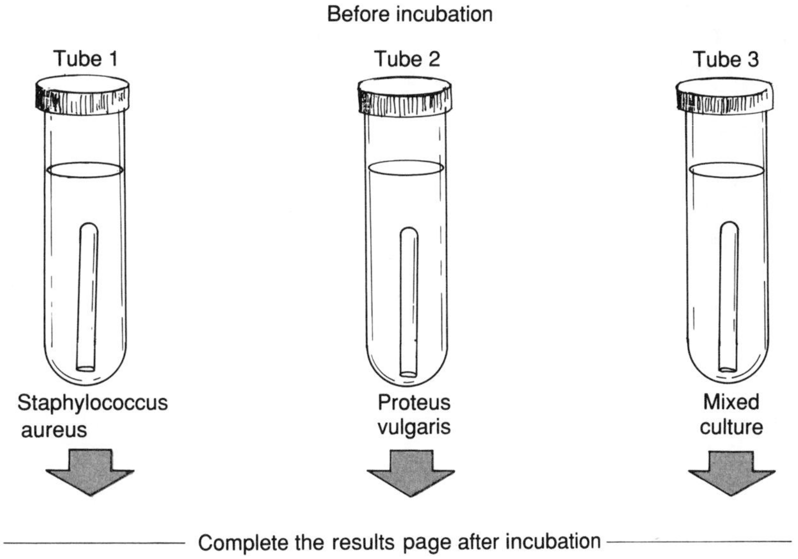
Before incubation
Tube 1
Tube 2
Tube 3
Staphylococcus aureus
Proteus vulgaris
Mixed culture
Complete the results page after incubation

Figure 27-1
Demonstrating Synergism

Second Period

1. Examine the first and second lactose broth tubes for any color change to yellow indicating fermentation of lactose. Examine the third tube for color change and any evidence of gas production. Recall that gas is indicated by any loss of fluid from the Durham tube.
2. Record your results in the chart in the Results section.
3. Answer the questions for the exercise.

Reference

Nurmikko, V. (1956) Factors Affecting Symbiosis Among Bacteria. *Experientia*, 12:245–249.

Antagonism

Objectives

1. Define **antagonism**.

2. Explain how antibiotic activity illustrates antagonism.

Background

Some microorganisms produce substances that inhibit or prevent the growth of other microbes. This process, called **antagonism**, was first observed in 1928 by Fleming, who noticed that a mold contaminant on a petri dish culture of *Staphylococcus aureus* showed a zone of no growth of the bacterial culture around it. This mold was a variety of *Penicillium* and was later shown to be responsible for the production of penicillin. Subsequent to this discovery, other microorganisms were also found to produce antimicrobial substances. For example, the mold *Acremonium* produces the antibiotic cephalothin. The actinomycete *Streptomyces* found in soil produces a variety of antimicrobials. *Streptomyces venezuelae* produces chloramphenicol, *Streptomyces erythraeus* produces erythromycin, *Streptomyces noursei* produces nystatin and *Streptomyces griseus* produces streptomycin. Gram-positive bacilli commonly found in soil also produce antimicrobial substances. *Bacillus polymyxa* produces polymyxin, and *Bacillus subtilis* produces bacitracin.

In this exercise the two antagonists studied are *Streptomyces griseus* and *Bacillus subtilis*. The streptomycin produced by the mold *Streptomyces* is frequently used in combination therapy with isoniazid, pyrazinamide and rifampin against *Mycobacterium tuberculosis*, which causes tuberculosis. Although streptomycin is sometimes used against enteric pathogens, resistance to this antibiotic is common among many of the enteric gram-negative pathogens. This antibiotic interferes with protein synthesis in the cell and is bactericidal. The bacitracin produced by the gram-positive bacillus is used alone or in combination with polymyxin and neomycin in topical application to the skin. It is effective against many gram-positive cocci found on human skin as well as other gram-positive bacteria. Bacitracin interferes with cell wall formation and is bactericidal to microorganisms. (We will further investigate antibiotics in Exercise 41, "Antibiotic Sensitivity Testing.")

As another illustration of the relationship of antagonism, many of the enteric bacteria, some *Clostridium* and some *Streptomyces* produce lethal proteins known as **bacteriocins**. These bacteriocins are proteins that are released into the environment of the bacteria and kill other microorganisms closely related to the producer organism. The most well-known are the colicins produced by *Escherichia coli*. These are toxic to other enteric bacteria.

Antagonism: An Overview

In this exercise the effectiveness of the antimicrobial substances produced by *Streptomyces griseus* and *Bacillus subtilis* against a series of test organisms is studied. Single streaks of the antagonist organisms are made on separate trypticase soy agar plates, which are then incubated at 30°C for 7 days. This allows time for the production and diffusion of the antimicrobial substances into the agar. The test organisms are then singly streaked at right angles to the antagonist organisms. All the plates are then incubated at 30°C for 48 hours and then examined for any evidence of inhibition along the test organism streak lines. Any degree of inhibition indicates sensitivity to the antimicrobial substance of the antagonist organism.

Materials

20-hour trypticase soy broth culture of the antagonists. *Streptomyces griseus* and *Bacillus subtilis*. These cultures must be grown at 30°C.

20-hour trypticase soy broth cultures of the test organisms. (These are made available the second week of this exercise.) The test organisms are: *Enterobacter aerogenes, Escherichia coli, Klebsiella pneumoniae, Proteus vulgaris, Staphylococcus aureus, Staphylococcus epidermidis, Enterococcus faecalis* and *Streptococcus pyogenes.*

trypticase soy agar plates

Procedures

First Week

Antagonist Organism Labeling (see Figure 28-1):

1. Select four trypticase soy agar plates. Label two plates "gram-positive" and two plates "gram-negative."

2. Select one set of "gram-positive" and "gram-negative" labeled plates and draw a single line with a wax marking pencil in the left corner of the underside of each dish. Label each line with the antagonist "*Streptomyces griseus.*"

3. Select the second set of "gram-positive" and "gram-negative" labeled plates and draw a single line with a wax marking pencil in the left corner of the underside of each dish. Label each line with the antagonist "*Bacillus subtilis.*"

Test Organism Labeling (see Figure 28-1):

1. Mark four separate lines in sequence on the bottom of the gram positive petri plates at a right angle to the antagonist line.

2. Label these lines in sequence with these organisms. They are: *Staphylococcus aureus, Staphylococcus epidermidis, Enterococcus faecalis* and *Streptococcus pyogenes.*

3. Mark four separate lines in sequence on the bottom of the gram negative petri plates at a right angle to the antagonist line.

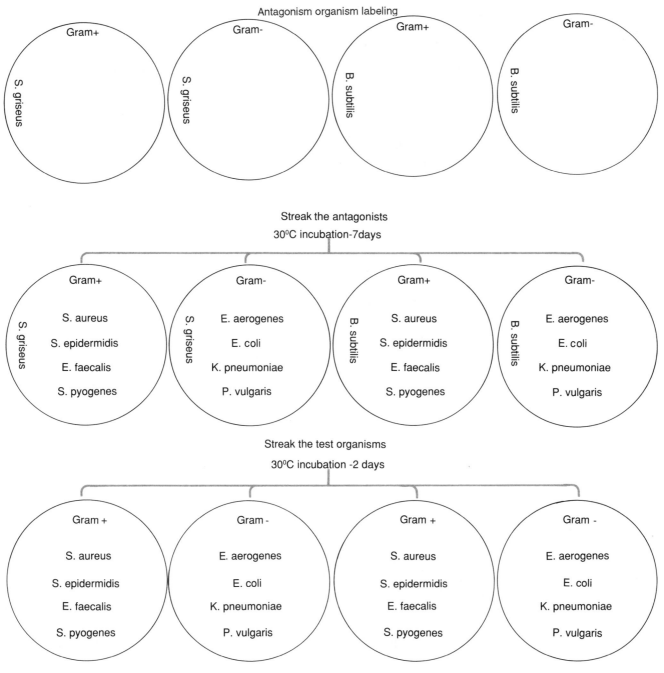

Antagonism organism labeling

Gram+   S. griseus

Gram-   S. griseus

Gram+   B. subtilis

Gram-   B. subtilis

Streak the antagonists
30°C incubation-7days

Gram+   S. griseus
S. aureus
S. epidermidis
E. faecalis
S. pyogenes

Gram-   S. griseus
E. aerogenes
E. coli
K. pneumoniae
P. vulgaris

Gram+   B. subtilis
S. aureus
S. epidermidis
E. faecalis
S. pyogenes

Gram-   B. subtilis
E. aerogenes
E. coli
K. pneumoniae
P. vulgaris

Streak the test organisms
30°C incubation -2 days

Gram +
S. aureus
S. epidermidis
E. faecalis
S. pyogenes

Gram -
E. aerogenes
E. coli
K. pneumoniae
P. vulgaris

Gram +
S. aureus
S. epidermidis
E. faecalis
S. pyogenes

Gram -
E. aerogenes
E. coli
K. pneumoniae
P. vulgaris

Record Results: inhibition (+) or no inhibition (-)

Antagonism: A Bacterial Interaction

Figure 28-1
Demonstrating Antagonism

4. Label these lines in sequence with these organisms. They are: *Enterobacter aerogenes, Escherichia coli, Klebsiella pneumoniae* and *Proteus vulgaris.*

Streaking of Antagonist Organisms:

1. Streak a single line of each antagonist on the appropriately labeled plates. Incubate all plates at 30°C for 1 week.

Second Week

Streaking of Test Organisms and Evaluation:

1. Streak a single line of each test organism on the appropriately labeled lines on the trypticase soy agar plates. Start each streak inoculation at a distance of 1 mm from the right edge of the antagonist growth and continue to the right edge of the agar.

2. Incubate all the petri plates at 30°C for 48 hours and then examine the plates for the presence of complete growth (no inhibition) or any reduction in growth on the test organism streak lines (inhibition). Record your observations in the Results section.

Third Period

1. Record your observations in the Results section.

2. Answer the questions for the exercise.

Reference

Amin, N. A. (1990). Let's Stop the Comeback of Tuberculosis: Best Drug Regimens for Prevention and Treatment. *Postgraduate Medicine* 88(6), 107–124.

Case Study 4

A patient enters the hospital with complaints of weight loss, coughing up of a bloody sputum and fatigue. An acid-fast stain done on a smear from a sputum sample shows acid-fast tubercle bacilli. The chest X-ray is positive for tuberculosis. The physician orders isoniazid and rifampin. Therapy is started and faithfully continued by the patient with incomplete recovery. Later, pyrazinamide and ethambutol are added to the treatment regimen and recovery eventually occurs.

Answer the following:

1. Devise an explanation why the patient did not recover with the first two drugs alone.

_____

_____

_____

_____

_____

2. Devise a model to explain how the 4 drug combination therapy was successful in treatment.

_____

_____

_____

_____

_____

_____

_____

_____

29   **Microbiology of Water**   **141**

uses EPA approved technologies to evaluate drinking water for the presence of coliforms and the risk of the presence of viral, protozoan, and bacterial pathogens.

30   **Food Microbiology**   **151**

evaluates the bacterial content of different foods by plate counts and the medical problems associated with food borne gastrointestinal diseases.

31   **Microbiology of Milk**   **159**

verifies the federal standards for microbial quality of milk and the risks that contaminated milk can be a vehicle for the transmission of disease organisms.

32   **Reductase Activity in Milk**   **163**

uses decolorization time of methylene blue indicator to evaluate milk quality or the numbers of bacteria in milk.

Case Study 5   **166**

Microbiology of Water

Objectives

1. Name three pathogens found in water and the diseases they produce.

2. Describe the steps in the multiple tube fermentation test for analysis of coliforms in water.

3. Describe the Colilert test for analysis of water for the concentration and presence or absence of coliforms.

4. List the advantages of the Colilert test.

5. Describe the significance of the presence/absence approach for water analysis established by the Federal Environmental Protection Agency.

Background

Water may contain a variety of microorganisms. The sources of many of these microbes include sewage or fecal contamination and runoff from soil or vegetation into bodies of water. The organisms commonly found and tested for in water microbiology are the total coliforms and fecal coliforms. **Total coliforms** include facultative gram-negative, non–spore-forming bacilli that ferment lactose to produce gas at 35°C in 24 to 48 hours. These include the genera *Escherichia, Enterobacter, Citrobacter* and *Klebsiella. Escherichia* species are found in the intestines and feces, while the others can also be found in these areas and in runoff from vegetation and soil. Fecal coliforms, a portion of the total coliform group, are found in the intestines of humans and other mammals. They are gram-negative non–spore-forming bacilli that ferment lactose to produce gas at 44.5°C in 24 hours. The typical example is *Escherichia coli*. The presence of fecal coliforms in water strongly suggests that the rarer or less common pathogens such as members of the genera *Salmonella* and *Shigella*, gastroenteritis viruses, hepatitis virus and protozoa such as *Giardia lamblia* and *Entamoeba histolytica* also can be present. *Salmonella typhi* causes typhoid fever; other salmonellae are commonly involved in gastroenteritis. Species of *Shigella* cause dysentery, and *Vibrio cholerae* causes cholera. The pathogenic protozoa cause severe gastroenteritis. *Entamoeba* infections, common in areas of poor water sanitation and sewage treatment, can be carried to the liver, where amebic abscesses are produced. *Giardia lamblia* is commonly found in wilderness areas in the United States. This organism is frequently excreted in the urine of beavers. It affects hikers, campers and others who drink improperly treated water.

Because many of the fecal pathogens are present in water in small numbers, they are difficult and costly to identify and use as indicators of microbial contamination of water. Instead, *Escherichia coli*, a coliform commonly found in human and animal feces, is used to indicate sewage pollution of water. In the *Federal Register* (Vol. 54, No. 124/Thursday, June 29, 1989/Rules and Regulations/40

CFR Parts 141 and 142) the Environmental Protection Agency presents "Drinking Water and National Primary Drinking Water Regulations." These include procedures for identifying total coliforms including fecal coliforms and *Escherichia coli*. This is a final rule. As of December 31, 1990, the maximum contaminant level goal of zero total coliforms, fecal coliforms and *Escherichia coli* was established for all public water systems. In addition, the U.S. Environmental Protection Agency in the *Federal Register* (Part II Environmental Protection Agency 40 CFR Parts 141 and 142) presents "Drinking Water Regulations; Filtration, Disinfection, Turbidity, *Giardia lamblia*, Viruses, *Legionella*, and Heterotrophic Bacteria; Final Rule." This regulation stipulates that all community and noncommunity public water systems that use a surface water source must achieve at least a 99.9% removal and/or inactivation of *Giardia lamblia* cysts and at least a 99.99% removal of viruses, including those of fecal origin known to produce water-borne disease. The procedures adopted to achieve these goals also remove *Legionella pneumophila*, known to produce pneumonia, as well as a variety of heterotrophic bacteria and the turbidity found in untreated water. This standard is in addition to the new standards for total coliforms and fecal coliforms in drinking water. The goals of these standards are to eliminate microbial diseases transmitted through water.

Generally the water treatment technology employing filtration and disinfection is suitable to meet these goals. The Environmental Protection Agency (EPA) specifies the stricter December 31, 1990 standards for drinking water for reasons of health and safety. The EPA indicates that water-transmitted disease pathogens have been found in water samples containing less than 1 coliform per 100 ml even though these water samples met earlier guidelines of no more than 2.2 coliforms per 100 ml of drinking water. The EPA suggests that the coliform-free water ruling should reduce the incidence of fecal coliforms and water-transmitted diseases to even lower levels.

The rules specify the use of a **presence/absence approach** to determine maximum contaminant levels in drinking water. This eliminates the need for a determination of coliform density by the **most probable number (MPN)** analysis, although the MPN determination still remains an option. The new methodology is easier to perform and is less subject to error. The permissible methods for water analysis include the multiple tube fermentation technique, the membrane filter technique and the Colilert Test. Regardless of the method used, the standard volume of water for coliform analysis is 100 ml. In the **multiple tube fermentation** (MTF) technique 10 fermentation tubes are used. Each has a 10-ml portion of water. An alternative allows 5 tubes with 20-ml portions or a single culture bottle containing 100 ml of the water sample. The MTF test requires the performance of presumptive, confirmed and completed tests. In the **presumptive test** the water samples are inoculated into lauryl tryptose broth. This broth favors the growth of coliforms. A positive test is the presence of gas in 24–48 hours incubation at 35°C from fermentation of lactose. The **confirmed test** is used to determine definitely that the positive results of the presumptive test are due to the presence of coliforms and not to any synergistic reaction of other organisms present in the presumptive test water sample. Positive presumptive test samples are inoculated into brilliant green bile lactose (BGBL) broth and EC broth. The BGBL broth is highly selective for total coliforms, and the EC broth is selective for the fecal coliform Escherichia coli. The BGBL broth is incubated at 35°C for 24 hours. The EC broth is incubated in a water bath set at 44.5°C for 24–48 hours. The presence of gas is a positive result in both media. The **completed test** involves streaking a plate of EMB agar followed by incubation for 24 hours and examination for nucleated reddish purple colonies or colonies with a green metallic sheen. These results indicate Escherichia coli. An inoculum from the EMB plate is inoculated into lauryl tryptose broth to test for gas production and is streaked onto a nutrient agar slant. The broth and slant are incubated at 35°C for 24 hours. Any amount of gas production constitutes a positive completed test for coliforms. Gram stains are then made and examined for the presence of typical coliforms.

The multiple tube fermentation has some disadvantages. This series of tests is time consuming, requiring 5 days for completion and evaluation. It requires extensive glassware, media preparation and sterilization. In the **membrane filter technique**, 100 ml of water are filtered and the bacteria are retained on the filter. This filter pad is then placed on selective media such as endo LES agar to isolate coliforms. The number of coliform colonies is counted and expressed as coliform colonies per 100 ml. This method is only useful when the water samples are not too cloudy. It is subject to errors in interpretation. The **Colilert test** avoids these problems. Colilert is a special blend of salts, nitrogen compounds and organic compounds as well as specific indicator nutrient compounds that can be used for the simultaneous detection, identification and confirmation of the presence of total coliforms and fecal coliforms in the same vessel of the water sample that is tested. The two available formats of this test, known as the Colilert MPN and the presence/absence approach, are described in the next section. Colilert is the newest EPA-approved test for microbiological analysis of water.

Microbiology of Water: An Overview

Since coliforms are the most common indicator of fecal pollution, only these organisms are used to study this problem. The Colilert test, recently approved by the EPA, is presented in a multiple tube/MPN format and in a presence/absence format in this exercise. This is the preferred method.

Colilert contains two indicator-nutrient compounds. One is ONPG (orthonitrophenyl-beta-d-galactopyranoside) and MUG (4-methyl-umbelliferyl-beta-d-glucuronide). Total coliforms contain a continuously made enzyme known as beta-galactosidase. This enzyme splits the ONPG compound to liberate the ortho-nitrophenyl indicator and the nutrient galactopyranoside. As the bacteria grow and reproduce on the galactopyranoside compound, they accumulate the indicator ortho-nitrophenol, which turns the medium yellow. The yellow color in the liquid of the tube indicates the presence of total coliforms. Heterotrophic noncoliforms that can use this nutrient and yeasts and molds are killed or suppressed by this medium during the 24-hour incubation time. The fecal coliform *Escherichia coli* contains an enzyme called glucuronidase. This enzyme splits the MUG compound to liberate the glucuronide nutrient portion, which it uses for growth, from the indicator methylumbelliferone portion. The indicator portion fluoresces when the tube is illuminated with an ultraviolet light source of 366 nm. The identification of total coliforms and the confirmation of fecal coliforms is performed in 24 hours on the same water sample Colilert vessel.

The Colilert system has additional advantages over other methods used to detect coliforms in water. It is sensitive enough to detect and confirm the presence of

No. of Tubes Giving Positive Reaction Out of 5 of 10 ml Each	MPN Index/100 ml	95% Confidence Limits (Approximate)	
		Lower	Upper
0	less than 2.2	0	6.0
1	2.2	0.1	12.6
2	5.1	0.5	19.2
3	9.2	1.6	29.4
4	16.0	3.3	52.9
5	greater than 16.0	8.0	Infinite

1 colony-forming unit of total coliforms and the fecal coliform *Escherichia coli* in 100 ml of a water sample. It is available for use with the dry reagent already dispensed in tubes for the MPN format. One need only add the water samples to the tubes, incubate for 24 hours and record the results. In the presence/absence format the dry reagent is available for addition directly to 100 ml of the water sample. The water sample containers are then incubated and the results are recorded. The Colilert reagent is stable for at least 1 year from the date of manufacture. The method is easily used to detect the number of coliforms and the presence/absence of coliforms and conforms to the format for the new federal guidelines for drinking water.

The multiple tube fermentation format is offered as an alternative to the Colilert format. The MTF format requires at least five laboratory class meetings to finish the presumptive, confirmed and completed tests. This method is included as another EPA-approved approach for the analysis of coliforms in water. While the ruling of the EPA specifies use of 100-ml water samples, this laboratory manual suggests a 50-ml water sample for greater safety and ease of performing the MPN experimental approach. (The presence/absence approach retains the testing of a single 100-ml water sample for coliforms.) The use of this smaller MPN sample size is still in accord with the zero coliform approach recommended by the EPA and is also found in the text *The Standard Methods for the Examination of Water and Wastewater*, 17th edition (1989), published by the American Public Health Association. The MPN table for this exercise (Table 29-1) is based on 5 tubes each receiving 10 ml of water sample and is used with the permission of the American Public Health Association.

Materials

sterile screw-capped bottles containing 100 ml of sewage-organism treated water

Colilert MPN:*

Cat. #W100-1 box of disposable tubes of predispensed reagent in carrier trays. There are 10 tubes per tray. Each tray can be used to complete two 5-tube tests.

*Colilert supplies are available from:
Idexx Laboratories
1 - Idexx Drive
Westbrook, ME 04092
Tel. number 1-800-321-0207 (in CT 1-481-3073)

Cat. #WRP25-sterile disposable transfer pipettes. 25/pkg.

Cat. #W102-Comparator (MPN) 1 tube containing 10 ml of Colilert color and fluorescence comparator for use in determining positive from negative test samples

Presence/Absence Test:

Cat. #WPK020-Colilert P/A Kit 1 box of 20 unit doses reagent for twenty 100-ml water samples and 20 sterile garduated disposable vessels for the water samples. These items can be purchased separately by ordering cat. #WP020 and WSV20.

Cat. #WP102-Comparator P/A 1 vial containing 50 ml of Colilert color and fluorescense comparator

sterile 10 ml pipettes if disposable pipettes are not purchased

Cat. #WL200-Pocket Fluorescent UV (366 nm) Light. Batteries not included.

tubes of double-strength lauryl tryptose broth with Durham tubes

tubes of brilliant green bile lactose (BGBL) broth with Durham tubes

tubes of *Escherichia coli* (EC) broth with Durham tubes

plates of eosin methylene blue (EMB) agar

nutrient agar slants

Gram stain reagents

incubator set at 35°C and a water bath set at 44.5°C

Procedures

First Period

1. *Colilert MPN* (See Figure 29-1):
   a. Place a 10-tube carrier and its tubes on the laboratory counter. Crack the carrier along the perforation in front, bend it along the back crease line and separate it into two 5-tube carriers.

   b. Use the sterile disposable popettes or sterile 10-ml pipettes to aseptically fill each Colilert tube in a carrier with 10 ml of the water sample.

   c. Cap each of the tubes tightly.

   d. Place one hand on top of the carrier and the other hand on the bottom. Mix the contents of the tubes vigorously by inversion to dissolve the reagent.

   e. Incubate the inoculated tubes in the carrier at 35°C for 24 hours by placing the carrier and tubes in the incubator. The incubation must start within 30 minutes of inoculating the tubes.

2. *Colilert Test: Presence/Absence Format* (See Figure 29-2):
   a. Select a presterilized container and label it "water sample."

   b. Add a unit dose of the Colilert reagent to the container.

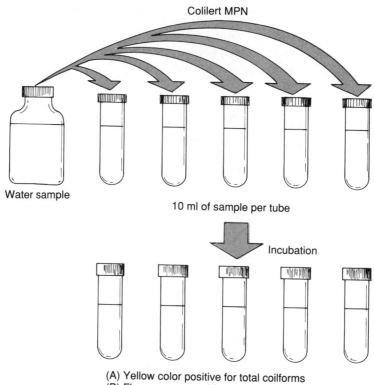

Colilert MPN

Water sample

10 ml of sample per tube

Incubation

(A) Yellow color positive for total coilforms
(B) Fluorescence positive for fecal coliforms
(C) Number of positive tubes used to determine MPN

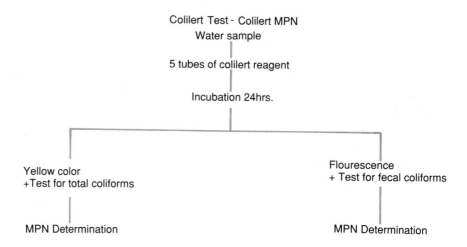

Colilert Test - Colilert MPN
Water sample

5 tubes of colilert reagent

Incubation 24hrs.

Yellow color
+Test for total coliforms

Flourescence
+ Test for fecal coliforms

MPN Determination

MPN Determination

Figure 29-1
Colilert MPN

c. Aseptically transfer 100 ml of the water sample to be tested into the labeled container. Close the container securely and mix the contents.

d. Incubate the container immediately at 35°C for 24 hours.

Second Period (Interpretation of Results):

1. Colilert MPN: Total Coliform Determination:
   a. Compare each tube to the color comparator. If the inoculated water sample has a yellow color equal to or greater than that of the comparator, the presence of total coliforms is confirmed.

b. If no yellow color is seen after 24 hours, then these samples are negative for total coliforms.

c. If the color is less yellow than the comparator, incubate the tube another 4 hours. If coliforms are present, the color will become brighter yellow. If it does not, then coliforms are not present. See the *"MPN Determination for Total Coliforms and Fecal Coliforms"* section below to obtain the most probable number of total coliforms and fecal coliforms per 100 ml of water sample.

2. *Presence/Absence Format: Total Coliform Determination:*
   a. Transfer the comparator chemical to a presterilized empty container. Examine the incubated 100-ml water sample for a yellow color. Compare the color in the water sample to that in the comparator container. If the color is equal to or greater than that in the comparator, then interpret the sample as a positive result. If the color is slightly less than in the comparator, incubate the sample up to 4 more hours. If coliforms are

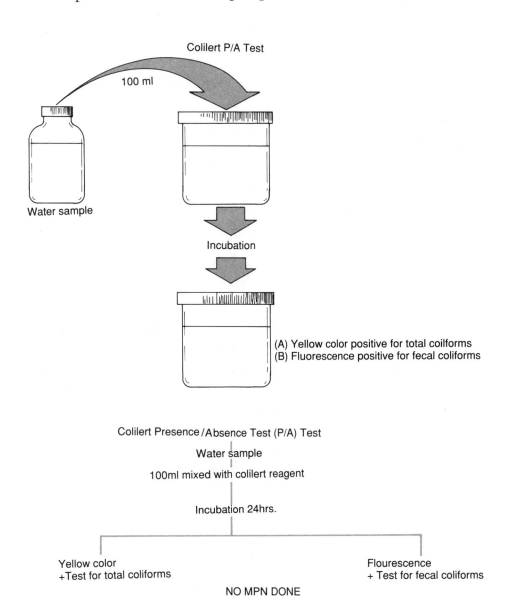

Figure 29-2
Colilert P/A Test

present, the color will increase. This indicates the water sample contains total coliforms.

3. *Fecal Coliform Determination for Both Formats:*
   a. Illuminate the water sample with the ultraviolet light source that supplies 366 nm UV light by placing it 2 inches from the water sample. Fluorescence indicates the presence of fecal coliforms.

4. *MPN Determination for Total Coliforms and Fecal Coliforms: Optional Determination:*
   a. Find the line in the MPN Index table (Table 26-1) that corresponds to the number of tubes showing positive results out of 5 of each of the 10-ml samples inoculated and incubated to determine statistically the number of total coliforms or *Escherichia coli* per 100 ml of the water sample. Read the MPN Index per 100 ml for this sample from the proper MPN table.

   b. Consult *The Standard Methods for the Examination of Water and Wastewater,* 17th edition (1989), published by the American Public Health Association, for further information.

Alternative Method: The Multiple Tube Fermentation Test

First Period (See Figure 29-3)

1. *Presumptive Test:*
   a. Select 5 double-strength lauryl tryptose broth tubes. Label each broth tube "10 ml."

   b. Pipette 10 ml of the contaminated water sample into each double-strength lauryl tryptose broth tube.

   c. Incubate the broth tubes at 35° C for 24 hours and then examine them for gas production. If negative, incubate an additional 24 hours and re-examine.

Second Period

2. *Confirmed Test:*
   a. Obtain a tube of BGBL broth for each tube of lauryl tryptose broth showing gas production.

   b. Transfer a loopful from each positive presumptive test broth tube to the respectively labeled BGBL broth tube.

   c. Incubate the BGBL broth tubes at 35° C for 24 hours and then examine them for gas production, which is a positive result for total coliforms. If negative, incubate an additional 24 hours and re-examine.

3. *Fecal Coliform Test:*
   a. Obtain a tube of EC broth for each tube of lauryl tryptose broth showing gas production.

   b. Transfer a loopful from each positive presumptive test broth tube to the respectively labeled EC broth tube.

   c. Incubate the EC broth tubes in a water bath at 44.5° C for 24 hours and then examine them for gas production, which is a positive result for fecal coliforms.

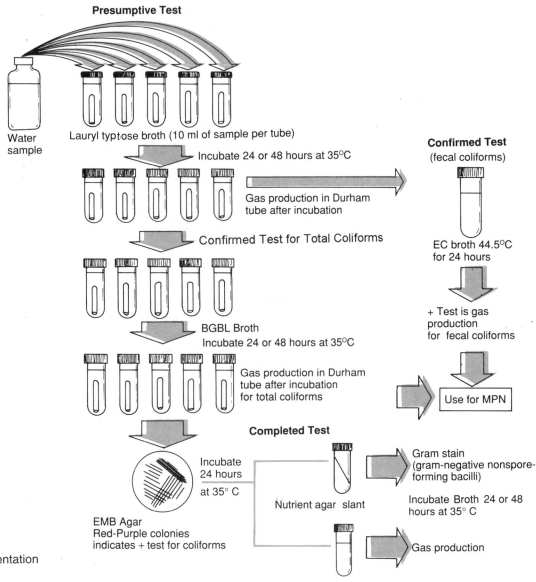

Presumptive Test

Water sample

Lauryl tryptose broth (10 ml of sample per tube)

Incubate 24 or 48 hours at 35°C

Gas production in Durham tube after incubation

Confirmed Test (fecal coliforms)

EC broth 44.5°C for 24 hours

+ Test is gas production for fecal coliforms

Use for MPN

Confirmed Test for Total Coliforms

BGBL Broth
Incubate 24 or 48 hours at 35°C

Gas production in Durham tube after incubation for total coliforms

Completed Test

Incubate 24 hours at 35° C

Nutrient agar slant

Gram stain (gram-negative nonspore-forming bacilli)

Incubate Broth 24 or 48 hours at 35° C

EMB Agar
Red-Purple colonies indicates + test for coliforms

Lauryl tryptose broth

Gas production

Figure 29-3
Multiple Tube Fermentation Test

Third Period

1. *MPN Index Determination: Optional Determination:*
   a. Obtain all the BGBL and EC broth tubes. Record which tubes show positive and negative results from the 10-ml original water samples.

   b. Find the line in the MPN Index table (Table 29-1) that corresponds to the number of tubes showing positive results for any 5 of the tubes receiving 10 ml of the water sample to determine statistically the number of total and fecal coliforms per 100 ml of the water sample.

   c. Consult *The Standard Methods for the Examination of Water and Wastewater*, 17th edition (1989), published by the American Public Health Association, for further information.

2. *Completed Test:*
   a. Streak a plate of EMB agar from a positive BGBL broth tube. Incubate this plate at 35° C for 24 hours.

1. *Completed Test.*
   a. Examine the EMB plate for reddish purple nucleated colonies or a green metallic sheen from the surface of the growth by reflected light. This is a typical growth pattern for *Escherichia coli*. Atypical coliforms may look pink or mucoid. These may be *Enterobacter aerogenes*.

   b. Transfer a loopful from a typical colony into lauryl tryptose broth and streak a slant of nutrient agar from the EMB plate.

   c. Incubate the lauryl tryptose broth tube and the nutrient agar slant at 35° C for 24-48 hours.

Fifth Period

1. *Completed Test:*
   a. Examine the lauryl tryptose broth for gas production.

   b. Prepare a Gram stain from the nutrient agar slant. Examine the Gram stain for the presence of gram-negative non–spore-forming bacilli.

   c. The combination of gas production in the lauryl tryptose broth and the presence of gram-negative non–spore-forming bacilli in the Gram stain finishes the completed test, verifies the definition of coliforms and completes the identification of coliform bacteria as the agents responsible for pollution of water.

2. Answer the questions for the exercise.

Food Microbiology

Objectives

1. Name three common methods of food preservation.

2. Describe the influence of each method on the process of controlling microorganisms present in food.

3. Define **water activity**.

4. Name three microorganisms that cause food poisoning.

5. Describe an unusual feature of food poisoning caused by *Clostridium perfringens*.

Background

The food industry deals with a number of microbiological problems. One is to detect microbial contamination in food. A second is to develop methods of food processing to control microbial contamination. A third is to use adequate processing to eliminate microorganisms from foods and prevent spoilage and food poisoning.

Detection of Microorganisms in Foods   A common method for detection of microorganisms in foods is the **standard plate count**, or SPC. Small samples of the food are blended, diluted, plated and incubated for a period of time to allow for growth of microorganisms. Unusual microorganisms such as thermophiles or psychrophiles can be assayed for by incubating some platings at high and low temperatures. Specific groups of organisms or specific organisms can also be identified. For example, additional platings on MacConkey agar can detect coliforms. *Salmonellae* or *Shigellae* can be isolated on selective media such as Hektoen agar or SS agar. *Staphylococcus aureus* can be concentrated by growth in broth containing 7.5–10% salt, followed by platings on selective media such as mannitol-salt agar medium. *Enterococci* can be isolated by direct plating on selective media such as KF agar.

Spoilage of Foods by Microorganisms   The type of food spoilage encountered in foods depends on the kinds of nutrients present. For example, dairy products and some fruits and vegetables are rich in carbohydrates. These are frequently spoiled by fermentative organisms such as lactobacilli and streptococci. Protein-rich foods such as meat, fish and poultry are spoiled by proteolytic bacteria such as species of *Pseudomonas* Citrus fruits and other acid fruits tend to be spoiled by yeasts and molds.

Controlling, Microorganisms in Foods   The food industry uses a variety of methods to control the numbers of microorganisms in foods. Some of the common methods of food preservation are low temperature, high temperature and drying. Low temperature slows the metabolism of microorganisms. Many of the bacteria that spoil refrigerated foods are **psychotrophic**. These have a maximum temperature for growth of 37° C but also can grow at 5° C, which is a temperature commonly found in the household refrigerator.

Freezing further reduces the capacity of microorganisms to grow and kills some but not all microorganisms. Freezing reduces the **water activity**, or a_w, which is a measure of the availability of water for growth of microorganisms. Water activity is defined as the ratio of the relative humidity of the air over a test solution compared with the relative humidity over distilled water. For example, a lower relative humidity or available water is found for solutions of high osmotic pressure than for distilled water. Most bacteria require a water activity of 0.95. Molds and yeasts can survive in a lower water activity of 0.80. Because of the reduction of water in the cells, freezing tends to slow the metabolism in cells. Bacteria differ in their response to freezing.

Food processors further reduce the microbial content in foods by briefly immersing foods in hot water prior to freezing. The hot water treatment, called **blanching**, inactivates the enzymes in the foods and kills some of the microorganisms.

High temperatures are also used to preserve foods. Examples of heat treatment of foods include pasteurization and thermal death time. In **pasteurization** of milk the temperature is raised to 72° C for 15 seconds. This serves to kill the tuberculosis bacillus, salmonellae, brucellosis bacteria, streptococci and the rickettsia *Coxiella burnetii*. **Thermoduric bacteria** are mesophiles that can survive a brief exposure to high heat. These include the lactobacilli and some of the streptococci. These organisms can spoil milk that is not properly refrigerated. The **thermal death time** is defined as the time it takes at a given temperature to completely kill all the organisms in a given population. The thermal death time in foods is determined by heating the food for a sufficient time at a definite temperature to kill the most heat-resistant microorganism present. Thermal death time is influenced by a number of factors. Foods with a low water content tend to show a high heat resistance in the microbial cells. Fats, proteins and carbohydrates in foods protect microbes from the effects of high heat. The temperature sensitivity of microorganisms is increased when they are present in foods of low pH or high pH. Stationary phase microbial cells are more heat resistant than log phase cells. Endospores are more heat resistant than vegetative cells. Cocci are more heat resistant than bacilli, and gram-positive cells are more heat resistant than gram-negative cells. The temperature requirement for growth of an organism is related to its heat resistance. For example, psychrophiles are most sensitive to heat, mesophiles are intermediate in their heat sensitivity and thermophiles are the most heat resistant.

Drying, or dehydration, of foods is yet another method used by food processors to reduce the number of microorganisms in foods. Before being dried, foods are subjected to a number of treatments to reduce or prevent microbial growth. Foods are blanched in hot water or sprayed with antimicrobial chemicals such as sulfur dioxide or sorbic acid. Drying of foods serves to reduce the water content of foods and a_w so that the resident microorganisms cannot multiply. Dehydration of foods reduces the water activity below the 0.95 that is typical for most bacteria. Therefore, bacteria generally do not spoil dried foods; molds and yeasts, which can tolerate a lower water activity, are the major spoilage agents of dried foods.

Food Poisoning   Various microorganisms are responsible for different types of food poisoning. A common type of food poisoning involves the accumulation of microbially produced toxins in the food or released into the intestinal tract. These are known as **food intoxications**. Examples of food intoxications are caused by the gram-positive *Staphylococcus aureus, Clostridium perfringens, Bacillus cereus, Clostridium botulinum* and the gram-negative *Escherichia coli.* The gram-positive *Staphylococcus aureus* produces an enterotoxin that has been implicated in food poisonings involving such foods as meat, poultry, custard- and cream-filled pastries and salads. These staphylococci are normal flora in the nasal passages and the skin. Individuals who have upper respiratory infections or skin infections and who handle foods are frequently the sources of food poisoning outbreaks. The symptoms of staphylococcal food poisoning include severe cramps, nausea, vomiting, sweating and headaches. These symptoms usually last 24 hours.

The gram-positive spore-forming bacillus *Clostridium perfringens* produces an enterotoxin that is responsible for gastroenteritis. *Clostridium perfringens* poisoning is an example of a food-borne illness due to a toxin that accumulates in the food, and it is one of the more widespread food intoxications. The foods involved are frequently meat products that are not totally consumed and are refrigerated for consumption in the future. Improper refrigeration and rewarming of foods create risks for this kind of food intoxication. The toxin accumulates in foods as the bacteria form endospores. Thus, this toxin is spore-specific and is produced during sporulation. Ingestion of contaminated food leads to food poisoning if toxin is present in sufficient amounts in the food or if sufficient numbers of ingested bacteria sporulate in the intestinal tract to release the toxin. The symptoms frequently involve diarrhea, abdominal pain and fever. The symptoms usually disappear after one or two days.

Another mild food poisoning is caused by *Bacillus cereus.* This is commonly found in fried rice, corn products and meat products. This organism also produces an enterotoxin, and the symptoms resemble those of *Clostridium perfringens* food poisoning.

A highly fatal form of food poisoning is caused by the gram-positive organism *Clostridium botulinum.* This organism produces an extremely potent exotoxin that is fatal in small quantities. It causes nausea, vomiting, double vision, difficulty in breathing and death by respiratory failure. This type of food poisoning is common in inadequately heat-treated home-canned food products. Commercially canned mushrooms have also been involved in some outbreaks.

Gram-negative organisms are also responsible for outbreaks of food intoxication. For example, *Escherichia coli* is responsible for severe cases of food poisoning associated with traveler's diarrhea. These organisms produce an enterotoxin that causes profuse diarrhea, cramps, fever and vomiting. Various fresh and prepared foods are implicated in this form of food poisoning.

In contrast to the food intoxications are the **food infections**, in which the organisms invade and infect the intestinal lining. Examples of this kind of food infection are caused by gram-negative *Salmonella* and *Vibrio parahaemolyticus.* Fecal contamination of food and water is a common way these organisms are ingested. Foods that are commonly involved in salmonellosis include eggs, meats, meat products and poultry. Symptoms of *Salmonella* food poisoning include nausea, vomiting, muscular weakness, abdominal pain and fever. These symptoms last for two to three days.

The gram-negative halotolerant marine organism *Vibrio parahaemolyticus* is an unusual source of food poisoning. Food poisoning with this organism occurs after ingestion of contaminated seafood. Ingestion of clams, shrimps, crabs and lobsters contaminated with this organism have caused food poisoning. Symptoms of this form of food poisoning include severe diarrhea, cramps, nausea and vomiting.

Food Microbiology: An Overview

This exercise examines the microbial content of a protein-rich food, a frozen food and a dried food. Typically, fresh ground meat or boneless chicken, frozen mixed vegetables and dried prunes or mixed fruit are used. Standard plate counts of a small sample of each food are prepared. A duplicate set of platings is made for the ground meat or chicken. One set of plates is incubated at 35°C and the other is incubated at 5°C to detect psychrophiles and psychrotrophs, which are also spoilage agents. Psychrophiles grow at refrigerator temperatures. Psychrotrophs grow well at 35°C but can also grow at refrigerator temperatures. Selective media such as MacConkey agar can also be streaked with a dilution of the meat or chicken to detect coliforms such as *Escherichia coli* that ferment lactose and organisms that do not show lactose fermentation. The latter include species of the genera *Salmonella*, *Proteus* and *Pseudomonas*. Lactose fermenters show red colonies, and lactose nonfermenters show clear to colorless colonies on this medium. The materials and procedures for this exercise are presented in great detail to emphasize the importance of asepsis in all phases of the standard plate count process. The goal is to prevent the introduction into the foods of any additional microorganisms from the environment and to prevent any cross-contamination from one food to another.

Materials

20-gram samples of fresh chopped meat wrapped in aluminum foil. An alternative is samples of boneless chicken. These samples must be kept frozen prior to use.

one carton of dried fruit (This can be dried prunes or mixed fruit.) one package of frozen mixed vegetables. (This must be kept frozen prior to use.)

4" × 4" squares of aluminum foil. (These should be wrapped in additional aluminum foil and sterilized in the steam sterilizer.)

3 sets of sterile equipment each consisting of a scalpel and forceps for handling foods during weighing

blender base and 3 sterile blender jars

3 sterile wide mouth jars with covers, containing 180 ml sterile distilled water

triple beam balance

bottles of 80 ml of plate count agar stored in a water bath at 50°C

sterile petri dishes

sterile 1-ml pipettes

pipette pumps

dilution bottles containing 99-ml sterile distilled water

sterile forceps

Procedures

First Period (See Figure 30-1)

1. Obtain a sample of each kind of food (ground meat or chicken, frozen mixed vegetables and dried fruit). Select three wide mouth jars with 180 ml of sterile distilled water. Label the first "meat" or "chicken," the second "vegetables" and the third "fruit."

2. Using sterile forceps, place a 4" × 4" square of sterile aluminum foil on the pan of the triple beam balance. Be sure to discard the aluminum foil weighing papers in a microbiological discard bin when all weighing are completed.

3. Use the sterile scalpel and forceps to aseptically weigh 20 grams of the meat or chicken on the aluminum foil weighing paper. Place the food

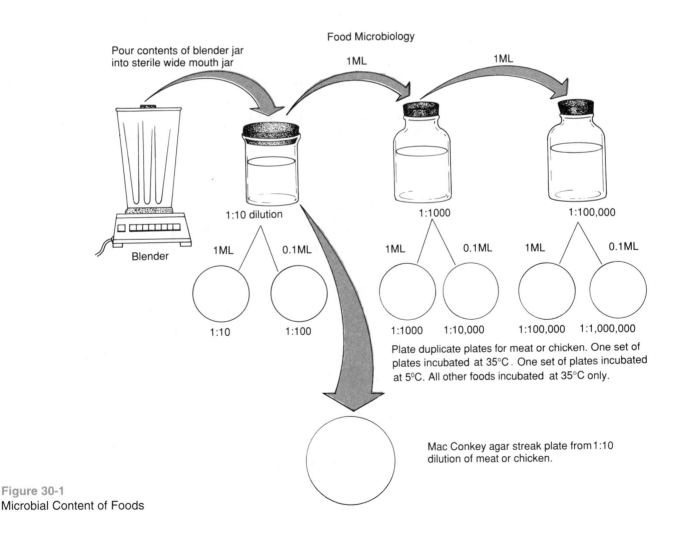

Figure 30-1
Microbial Content of Foods

sample in a labeled wide mouth jar containing 180 ml of sterile distilled water.

4. Select a second sheet of sterile aluminum foil weighing paper and aseptically weigh 20 grams of vegetables with the second set of sterile implements.

5. Transfer the vegetables to the properly labeled wide mouth jar.

6. Select a third sheet of sterile aluminum foil weighing paper and aseptically weigh 20 grams of dried fruit with the third set of sterile implements. Discard the three sets of weighing implements in the microbiological discard bin.

7. Transfer the dried fruit to the properly labeled wide mouth jar.

8. Cap and swirl each wide mouth jar and transfer the contents to a separate blender jar.

9. Blend each food sample for 5 minutes. This blended food sample is a 1:10 dilution of the original food sample.

10. Pour the contents of each blended jar back into the properly labeled wide mouth jar.

11. Select two 99-ml sterile water bottles for each food and label them "1:1000" and "1:100,000" and with the name of each food.

12. Swirl separately each food sample in the wide mouth jar.

13. Dilute each food sample as follows: Select a sterile 1-ml pipette and transfer 1 ml of the 1:10 dilution in the wide mouth jar to the water bottle labeled "1:1000." Place the pipette in the pipette discard. Mix this dilution by swirling. Select a sterile 1-ml pipette and transfer 1 ml from the 1:1000 dilution to the water bottle labeled "1:100,000." Discard this pipette in the pipette discard.

Mesophile Studies in Foods:

14. Select six petri dishes for each food. Label them with the name of each food and "35°C." Label the separate dilutions as follows: "1:10," "1:100," "1:1000," "1:10,000," "1:100,000" and "1:1,000,000."

15. Transfer the food sample dilutions to the dishes as follows:
    a. Select sterile 1-ml pipettes for each dilution set.

    b. Transfer 0.1 ml from the 1:10 dilution to the dish labeled "1:100."

    c. Use the same pipette to transfer 1 ml from the 1:10 dilution to the dish labeled "1:10." Place this pipette in the pipette discard.

    d. Transfer 0.1 ml from the 1:1000 dilution to the dish labeled "1:10,000."

    e. Use the same pipette to transfer 1 ml from the 1:1000 dilution to the plate labeled "1:1000." Place this pipette in the pipette discard.

    f. Transfer 0.1 ml from the 1:100,000 dilution to the plate labeled "1:1,000,000."

g. Use the same pipette to transfer 1 ml from the 1:100,000 dilution to the plate labeled "1:100,000." Place this pipette in the pipette discard.

16. Pour melted and cooled plate count agar into all the dishes. Rotate the dishes to distribute the agar and the dilution sample uniformly. Allow the agar to harden.

17. Then invert the dishes and incubate them at 35°C for 48 hours.

Psychrophile/Psychrotroph Studies in Ground Meat or Poultry:

18. Select six sterile petri dishes and label them with "meat" or "chicken" and "5°C." Label them with the following dilutions: "1:10," "1:100," "1:1000," "1:10,000," "1:100,000" and "1:1,000,000."

19. Use 1-ml pipettes to repeat the transfers of meat or chicken dilutions described in steps 15 and 16.

20. Then invert the dishes and incubate them for 2 weeks in a refrigerator at 5°C.

Selective Media Studies:

21. Streak a loopful of the 1:10 dilution of the meat or chicken on MacConkey agar to isolate single colonies. Invert this dish and incubate at 35°C for 48 hours.

Second Period and Two Weeks Later

1. Examine all the dilution plates of the three foods incubated at 35°C for 48 hours. Count those dilution plates showing between 30 and 300 colonies.

2. Calculate the number of bacteria per gram of food by the following formula: colonies counted × dilution factor = number of bacteria per gram of original food sample.

3. Examine the MacConkey agar streak plate. Red colonies are coliforms and are lactose fermenters. Clear or pale white colonies are lactose non-fermenters. These may suggest the presence of *Proteus*, *Pseudomonas* or *Salmonella*. If the instructor desires, the students can use the procedures of the exercises on morphological unknown and clinical unknown (Exercise 13 and Exercises 30–35) to identify selected, well-isolated colonies on this plate.

4. After 2 weeks of incubation at 5°C, count the numbers of colonies on the ground meat or chicken dilution plates and determine the numbers of psychrophiles and psychrotrophs; per gram of the food by the formula in step 2 above.

5. Compare the numbers of bacteria per gram for low-temperature growing organisms to those for organisms growing at 35°C.

6. Record all the findings in the Results section

7. Answer the questions for the exercise.

Microbiology of Milk

Objectives

1. List the names of organisms that can be found in raw milk.
2. Define the term **thermoduric**.
3. List the microbial standards permissible for pasteurized Grade A milk.
4. Explain why pasteurization of milk is important.

Background

Milk is a superb fluid medium for the growth of microorganisms. Milk contains the carbohydrate lactose, which can be fermented by a variety of microorganisms; the protein casein, which can be digested by proteolytic bacteria and lipids, which can be digested by lipolytic bacteria. Milk also contains minerals such as calcium and phosphorus and vitamins. The pH of milk is near neutrality, which is also favorable for the growth of a variety of organisms. Raw milk can be contaminated from bacteria on the udder of the cow, from utensils used in milking and from dust or dirt that can enter during any handling procedure. Some of the organisms found in raw milk are members of the genera *Bacillus*, *Streptococcus* and *Lactobacillus*. Other organisms that may be present in raw milk are: *Mycobacterium tuberculosis*, which causes tuberculosis; species of *Brucella*, which cause brucellosis; *Salmonella typhi*, which causes typhoid fever; coliforms and Q Fever rickettsias.

During pasteurization, milk is exposed to 72.5°C for 15 seconds. This heat treatment eliminates all the disease-producing organisms and only allows the thermoduric organisms to survive. **Thermoduric** bacteria are those organisms that can withstand a brief exposure to high heat such as is found in pasteurization. The thermoduric organisms in milk generally include members of the genera *Streptococcus*, *Lactobacillus* and some of the spore formers in the genus *Bacillus*. *Streptococcus lactis* and other species of *Lactobacillus* are frequently involved in the spoilage of milk that is not properly refrigerated. These organisms ferment the lactose sugar in the milk to produce acids. The organisms in the genus *Bacillus*, when present, digest the proteins of the milk. The standard plate count is used to determine the numbers of bacteria in milk. The U.S. Department of Health and Human Services, Public Health Service, Food and Drug Administration established a Grade A Pasteurized Milk Ordinance, 1985 Revision, which states the following:

Grade A Raw Milk for Pasteurization:

Individual producer Grade A milk and milk products can contain up to 100,000 bacteria per ml prior to co-mingling (mixing).

Grade A milk and milk products after commingling can contain up to 300,000 bacteria per ml.

Grade A Pasteurized Milk and Milk Products:

Pasteurized milk should not exceed a count of 20,000 bacteria per ml and should not have more than 10 coliforms per ml.

Bulk transport tank shipments of pasteurized milk can contain up to 100 coliforms per ml.

Microbiology of Milk: An Overview

In this exercise the standard plate count is used to evaluate good and poor quality milk. The good quality milk is fresh pasteurized milk that is properly refrigerated. The poor quality milk can be pasteurized milk allowed to spoil or good quality milk inoculated with a variety of organisms typically found in spoiled milk. These can include coliforms, lactobacilli and some streptococci. The milk samples are diluted and pour plated in plate count agar and incubated at 35°C. The number of bacteria per ml are determined from the dilution factor multiplied by the number of colony-forming units in the agar. The numbers of bacteria found per ml are compared with the standards for raw and pasteurized milk.

Materials

sterile screw-cap bottles containing 100 ml of good quality milk

sterile screw-cap bottles containing 100 ml of poor quality milk (All milk samples should be kept refrigerated prior to use.)

sterile 99-ml distilled water bottles for dilutions

sterile petri dishes

sterile 1-ml pipettes

pipette pumps

bottles of plate count agar held at 50°C in a temperature-controlled water bath

Procedures

First Period (See Figure 31-1)

1. *Dilutions of Good Quality Milk:*
   a. Select a bottle of good quality milk from the refrigerator.

   b. Select one 99-ml dilution bottle. Label this water bottle "1:100" and "good milk."

   c. Select a sterile 1-ml pipette and transfer 1 ml of the milk to the dilution bottle labeled "1:100." Place this pipette in a pipette discard containing disinfectant.

   d. Mix the contents by swirling.

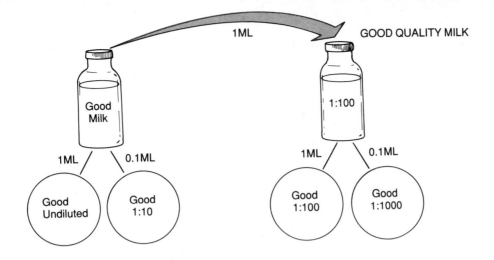

GOOD QUALITY MILK

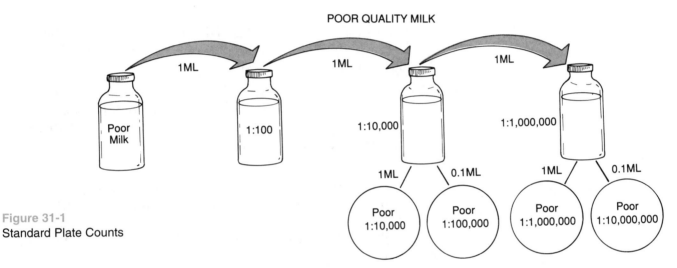

POOR QUALITY MILK

Figure 31-1
Standard Plate Counts

2. *Dilution of Poor Quality Milk:*
   a. Select a bottle of poor quality milk from the refrigerator.

   b. Select three 99-ml dilution bottles. Label the first "1:100," the second "1:10,000" and the third "1:1,000,000." Label these three dilution bottles "poor milk."

   c. Select a sterile 1-ml pipette and transfer 1 ml of the poor quality milk to the dilution bottle labeled "1:100." Place this pipette in the pipette discard. Mix the contents by swirling.

   d. Select a sterile 1-ml pipette and transfer 1 ml from the 1:100 dilution bottle to the second dilution bottle labeled "1:10,000." Place this pipette in the pipette discard. Mix the contents by swirling.

   e. Select a sterile 1-ml pipette and transfer 1 ml from the 1:10,000 dilution bottle to the third dilution bottle labeled "1:1,000,000." Place this pipette in the pipette discard. Mix the contents by swirling.

3. *Plating of Good Quality Milk:*
   a. Select four sterile petri dishes. Label the first dish "undiluted," the second dish "1:10," the third dish "1:100" and the fourth dish "1:1,000." Label all these dishes "good milk."

b. Select the original bottle of good milk. Select a sterile 1-ml pipette. Transfer 0.1 ml from the good milk bottle into the petri dish labeled "1:10." Using the same pipette, transfer 1 ml from the good milk bottle to the petri dish labeled "undiluted." Place this pipette in the pipette discard.

c. Select the dilution bottle of good milk labeled "1:100." Select a sterile 1-ml pipette. Transfer 0.1 ml from the dilution bottle labeled "1:100" to the petri dish labeled "1:1000." Using the same pipette, transfer 1 ml from the 1:100 dilution bottle to the petri dish labeled "1:100." Place this pipette in the pipette discard.

d. Select two bottles of cooled and melted plate count agar from the water bath. Pour 15 ml of agar into each petri dish dilution of good quality milk. Rotate the dishes gently to evenly distribute the agar and the dilution. Allow the agar to solidify, and then invert these dishes.

4. *Platings for Poor Quality Milk:*
   a. Select four sterile petri dishes. Label the first dish "1:10,000," the second dish "1:100,000," the third dish "1:1,000,000" and the fourth "1:10,000,000." Label all these dishes "poor milk."

   b. Select the 1:10,000 dilution bottle. Select a sterile 1-ml pipette. Transfer 0.1 ml from the 1:10,000 dilution bottle to the petri dish labeled "1:100,000." Using the same pipette, transfer 1 ml from the 1:10,000 dilution bottle to the dish labeled "1:10,000." Place this pipette in the pipette discard.

   c. Select the 1:1,000,000 dilution bottle. Select a sterile 1-ml pipette. Transfer 0.1 ml from the 1:1,000,000 dilution bottle to the petri dish labeled "1:10,000,000." Using the same pipette, transfer 1 ml from the 1:1,000,000 dilution bottle to the plate labeled "1:1,000,000." Place this pipette in the pipette discard.

   d. Select two bottles of cooled and melted plate count agar from the water bath. Pour 15 ml of agar into each petri dish dilution of poor quality milk. Rotate each dish gently to evenly distribute the agar and the dilution. Allow the agar to solidify, and invert the dishes.

   e. Incubate all the good quality and poor quality milk dilution pour plates at 35°C for 48 hours.

Second Period

1. *Colony Counting and Determination of the Number of Bacteria per ml in Good Quality and Poor Quality Milk:*
   a. Obtain all the incubated good quality and poor quality milk pour plates.

   b. Count only those plates showing between 30–300 colonies for the good quality and poor quality milk dilutions.

   c. Multiply the number of colonies counted by the dilution factor to determine the number of bacteria per ml for good quality and poor quality milk.

   d. Record the findings in the Results section.

   e. Answer the questions for the exercise.

Exercise 32

Reductase Activity in Milk

Objectives

1. Describe what happens during the reduction of methylene blue dye in a sample of milk.

2. Explain why the results for this test should differ for good quality and poor quality milk.

Background

The **dye reduction test** can be used to measure milk quality. This test is usually reserved for raw milk. If large numbers of microorganisms are present in milk, they will use up the oxygen and create anaerobic conditions. If a dilute solution of a dye such as methylene blue is added to this milk, the bacteria will transfer hydrogens and electrons to the dye and chemically reduce it to a colorless compound. The milk changes color from light blue to white. The reduction of the dye becomes a convenient tool to assay the microbial quality of a milk sample. Since raw milk is not readily available, a sample of Grade A pasteurized refrigerated milk and a sample of Grade A pasteurized milk to which coliforms have been added are used for this study. The noninoculated milk substitutes for good quality raw milk, and the inoculated milk substitutes for poor quality raw milk, which normally contains coliforms. Therefore, this exercise represents a simulation of the testing of the microbial quality of two samples of raw milk.

Reductase Activity in Milk: An Overview

Each milk sample of differing bacteriological quality is in a separate sterile screw-capped tube. The milk samples are labeled "A" and "B." Sample A or B may be good or poor quality. These two samples are treated as unknowns. One ml of a 1:25,000 dilution of methylene blue dye is added to each milk sample. The samples are sealed and inverted to mix the contents. Then they are placed in a 35°C water bath. Each sample is examined at half-hour intervals for decolorization. Samples of milk that decolorize in 30 minutes to 2 hours are of poor quality. They have large numbers of bacteria that rapidly use the methylene blue dye as an acceptor for the electrons and hydrogens released during respiration and decolorize the dye. Samples of milk that require 2 to 6 hours for a color change are of fair quality and contain fewer bacteria that respire at this temperature and need a longer time for reduction of the dye and decolorization. Samples of milk that require 6 to 8 hours to undergo decolorization are of good quality and have an even lower bacterial population that can respire at this temperature and transfer hydrogen atoms to methylene blue to form the colorless reduced dye. Thus, the greater the microbial population in the milk, the faster is the decolorization.

| **Materials** | sterile screw-cap tubes containing 10 ml of a good milk sample (Grade A pasteurized milk to stimulate a good quality raw milk sample) |

sterile screw cap tubes containing 10 ml of a poor milk sample (Grade A pasteurized milk with added coliforms to simulate a poor quality raw milk)

The milk samples are labeled "A" and "B." The microbial quality of each milk sample is unknown and must be determined.

sterile 1:25,000 methylene blue solution. (The dye solution should contain 8.8 mg of methylene blue per 200 ml of sterile distilled water. This stock solution will contain the proper dilution of the dye.)

sterile 1-ml pipettes

pipette pumps

temperature-controlled water bath set at 35°C

| **Procedures** | 1. Select a milk sample from group A and group B. (See Figure 32-1) |

2. Select a sterile 1-ml pipette and transfer 1 ml of the methylene blue dye solution to milk sample A. Discard this pipette in the pipette discard.

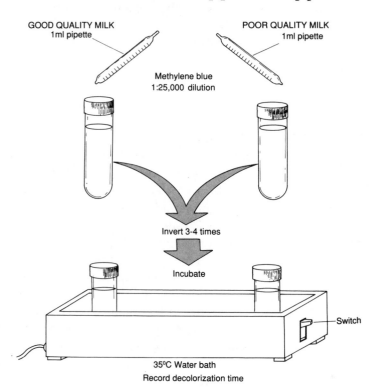

Figure 32-1
Demonstrating Reductase
Activity in Milk

3. Select a sterile 1-ml pipette and transfer 1 ml of the methylene blue dye solution to milk sample B. Discard this pipette in the pipette discard.

4. Tighten the cap securely on each tube and invert each tube 3 to 4 times to mix the contents.

5. Place each tube in the 35°C water bath.

6. Record the exact time these tubes are placed in the bath. After 5 minutes' incubation, remove the tubes from the bath and invert them only one time. Replace the tubes in the bath to incubate.

7. Check the tubes every 30 minutes for evidence of decolorization. Record the time during the laboratory session required for the tubes to become white. This is a measure of the number of bacteria in the milk and of the milk quality. Record this finding in the Results section.

8. Answer the questions for the exercise.

Case Study 5

An infant develops a case of infant botulism. This is caused by the spore forming anaerobic bacillus *Clostridium botulinum* that produce toxin types A and B. Symptoms of this disease include generalized muscle weakness, listlessness, difficulty in swallowing and sucking and sometimes death. Infants less than a year old are most susceptible. Their intestinal tracts lack the variety of flora that should inhibit these clostridia. These spores are commonly found in the environment and foods. For example, the spores for this bacillus are found in honey, household dust, vacuum cleaner dust, and dirt. The toxin that is released from the digestive tract is absorbed into the bloodstream and transported to neuromuscular junctions where it interferes with the release of the neurotransmitter called acetylcholine. This results in weak excitation of muscles and poor contraction of muscles. Treatment includes mechanical and nasogastric feeding. Antibiotics are not used in uncomplicated cases because they would promote further release of toxin on death and lysis of the bacilli in the intestinal tract.

Answer the following.

1. Describe practices in the home to minimize the development of this disease in infants.

   _____

   _____

2. Describe any dietary practices to minimize development of this disease in infants.

   _____

   _____

Reference

Midura, T. (1996). Update: Infant botulism. *Clinical Microbiology Reviews*, 9, 2: 119–125.

33   **Clinical Unknown**   **169**

presents the need for the Gram stain and a variety of tests to identify major bacterial organisms that cause nosocomial infections.

34   **Fermentation of Carbohydrates**   **173**

describes different fermentation patterns that can be used in the presumptive differential identification of a clinical unknown.

35   **The Oxidation Fermentation (O-F) Test**   **181**

distinguishes between fermentative, non-fermentative and non-saccharolytic behavior in bacteria that can be used in the identification of a clinical unknown.

36   **Differences in Respiratory Behavior**   **184**

presents a variety of respiratory patterns in bacteria that can be used to identify, clinical unknowns and place them into specific groupings.

37   **Differential Identification I: Amino Acid and Specialty Tests**   **195**

uses specific amino acid metabolism tests to make a differential identification of the gram-negative clinical unknowns which also are responsible for major nosocomial infections.

38   **Differential Identification II: Macromolecule and Specialty Tests**   **205**

uses macromolecule and specialty tests to make a differential identification of the gram-positive clinical unknown and to support the identification of the gram-negative clinical unknown as well as to demonstrate simulations of virulence factors in bacteria. Summary diagnostic charts in this exercise are used to confirm the final decision.

39   **Rapid Multimedia Test: Enterotube II®**   **215**

illustrates a procedure for the rapid identification of the gram-negative enteropathogens and uropathogens in comparison to the more laborious traditional methods.

Case Study 6   **223**

Clinical Unknown

Objectives

1. Define **clinical unknown**.

2. Distinguish between respiratory, enteric and urogenital infections.

3. Define nosocomial infection and list two reasons for its appearance in patients.

Background

Traditionally, in microbiology courses a project involving the identification of a **clinical unknown**, or a culture of an unknown organism, is completed. In this sequence of exercises the pure cultures used for the unknown will be presumed to represent clinical specimens from initial infections obtained from patients in hospitals, doctor's offices, or from nosocomial infections. **Nosocomial**, or hospital-acquired, infections frequently occur after inhalation therapy, during use of indwelling catheters or during use of chemotherapeutic or immunosuppressive drugs Wound and burn infections are often nosocomial in nature. The organisms used in this study include a spectrum of microbes that are found in respiratory, enteric, and urogenital infections, as well as skin infections and burn infections. Very young and very old patients frequently have impaired resistance and are more susceptible to these kinds of infections. These disease-causing organisms include gram-positive and gram-negative bacteria. Some of the organisms commonly found are listed here by the area of the body involved. In **respiratory** infections, *Staphylococcus aureus*, *Streptococcus pyogenes*, *Klebsiella pneumoniae*, *Pseudomonas aeruginosa* and *Moraxella (Branhamella) catarrhalis* are commonly found. Occasionally *Alcaligenes faecalis* or *Bacillus subtilis* can be found in weakened or immunocompromised patients. In **enteric** infections, enterotoxigenic *Escherichia coli*, *Salmonella* and *Shigella* can be found. In **urogenital** infections, *Escherichia coli*, *Enterobacter aerogenes*, *Proteus vulgaris*, *Klebsiella pneumoniae*, *Pseudomonas aeriginosa*, and occasionally *Alcaligenes faecalis* can be found. In **skin infections**, *Staphylococcus aureus* and *Streptococcus pyogenes* can be found. Infections of burns frequently involve Staphylococcus aureus and *Pseudomonas aeruginosa*.

One of the critical problems faced in clinical microbiology laboratories is the identification of these organisms, which is necessary for any differential diagnosis and treatment plan for the patient. Once the unknown pathogen in the clinical specimen is identified, the laboratory can complete an antibiotic sensitivity survey to indicate which antibiotics are useful to eliminate the microbial cause of the medical problem. The organisms listed above represent sources of the initial infections or hospital-acquired infections in patients. In the exercises that follow, a series of laboratory procedures are presented that permit the identification of these organisms. These laboratory procedures are divided into a series of distinct metabolic tests. They include fermentation, other carbohydrate catabolism tests, respiratory behavior tests, protein metabolism, amino acid metabolism, lipid hydrolysis and use of selective or differential media and other specialized tests. One of the goals of this exercise is to acquaint the allied health student with the difficulties involved in ruling out the various possible causes of infection and disease and ruling in a distinct cause of the problem. While completing this problem, it is hoped that the health career student will have a greater awareness of the possible errors in reasoning and interpretation that can occur, which can delay effective treatment and can make the patient susceptible to infection by other nosocomial and community-acquired organisms.

Clinical Unknown: An Overview

Each student will receive a pure culture of the clinical unknown isolate to identify. The student will complete a Gram stain of the clinical unknown and will inoculate and incubate the unknown in specific test media to rule out all the unwanted organisms and identify the cause of the medical problem. The student must also inoculate a trypticase soy broth and streak a nutrient agar slant of the unknown. Each of these cultures will be incubated at 35°C for 24 hours. The broth culture represents a working culture for inoculating test media. The slant culture represents a reserve stock culture for subculturing of the unknown. This reserve slant should be kept in the refrigerator when not used. A fresh working culture should be made for each session involving work on the clinical unknown.

The following list of microorganisms and the problems caused by them represents a selection of bacteria that can be used for the clinical unknown problem.

Alcaligenes faecalis: urinary tract and respiratory tract infections

Bacillus subtilis: meningitis and pneumonia in immunocompromised patients

Enterobacter aerogenes: urinary tract infections

Enterococcus faecalis: peritonitis, urinary tract infections and endocarditis

Escherichia coli: urinary tract infection, traveler's diarrhea, pelvic inflammatory disease, food poisoning, infant meningitis and sepsis

Klebsiella pneumoniae: necrotizing pneumonia, urinary tract infection, sepsis and meningitis

Moraxella (Branhamella) catarrhalis: pneumonia and otitis media

Proteus vulgaris: urinary tract and abdominal infections

Pseudomonas aeruginosa: infections of burns, urinary tract infections, pneumonia, nosocomial infections and infections in immunocompromised patients

Salmonella typhimurium: severe gastroenteritis

Staphylococcus aureus: pneumonia, toxic shock syndrome, food poisoning, osteomyelitis, cellulitis, boils and impetigo

Materials

20-hour nutrient broth culture of the clinical unknown

tubes of trypticase soy broth

nutrient agar slants

Caution:
The student will be given an actively growing culture of the clinical unknown and must use extreme care and caution during all studies involved in its identification.

Procedures

1. Select a clinical unknown, record the number in your notebook and inform your instructor of this number.

2. Obtain a tube of trypticase soy broth and inoculate a working culture of your unknown.

3. Obtain a slant of nutrient agar and inoculate a reserve stock culture of your unknown.

4. Incubate both tubes at 35°C for 24 hours.

5. After incubation, place the reserve culture in the refrigerator. The working culture can be used for inoculation of all test media.

6. Prepare a Gram stain of your clinical unknown. Record the Gram reaction, shape and arrangements of the cells.

7. The reserve stock or a trypticase soy broth culture can be used to prepare a fresh unknown culture for chemical control studies (Exercise 40) and antibiotic sensitivity testing (Exercise 41).

8. Answer the questions for the exercise.

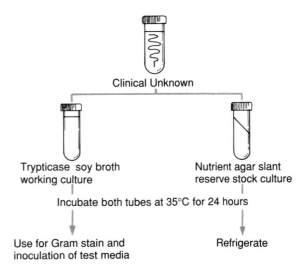

Figure 33-1
Procedures for Clinical Unknown

Fermentation of Carbohydrates

Objectives

1. Define **fermentation**.

2. Distinguish between the observed results seen for fermentation of sugar in phenol red sugar broth with Durham tubes and fermentation in glucose broth to mixed adds or to 2,3 butanediol.

3. Describe how fermentation can be used to control glycolysis.

Background

The process of energy release in cells first involves the anaerobic breakdown of sugar: a process called glycolysis. Glycolysis can be viewed as a two-stage pathway leading to the formation of ATP and pyruvic acid. In the first, or preparatory stage, the six-carbon compound glucose is phosphorylated and then split to yield two three-carbon compounds called glyceraldehyde phosphate and dihydroxyacetone phosphate. The dihydroxyacetone phosphate is converted to another glyceraldehyde phosphate. In the next step each glyceraldehyde phosphate is phosphorylated to form 1,3 diphosphoglyceric acid. This oxidation reaction also involves reduction of a dehydrogenase coenzyme NAD to NADH. In the second, or ATP production stage, pairs of high-energy phosphorus are sequentially removed from the two three-carbon sugars and added to ADP to form ATP. A net production of two ATP is gained by the cell in this process. The final three-carbon compound remaining is pyruvic acid. In the process of fermentation the reduced coenzyme NADH formed earlier in glycolysis transfers the hydrogen to pyruvic acid to form lactic acid. Therefore, **fermentation** involves oxidation and reduction of organic compounds in a biochemical pathway in which no added electron acceptor is present. This process is anaerobic—no oxygen is used. No electron transport phosphorylation system is used, and the oxidation of the reduced coenzyme NADH to NAD restores the dehydrogenase enzyme to the proper oxidized state so that glycolysis, can continue to change glyceraldehyde phosphate to 1,3 diphosphoglyceric acid. Fermentation is therefore a vital controlling switch for restoring the oxidized state of the coenzyme NAD, which is necessary for glycolysis to occur.

Fermentative bacteria can, by reduction of pyruvic acid, produce a variety of end products. Some streptococci and lactobacilli carry out a **homolactic** fermentation and produce primarily lactic acid from pyruvic acid. Other streptococci and lactobacilli carry out a **heterolactic** fermentation and produce lactic acid, ethanol and carbon dioxide. Bacteria found in the family *Enterobacteriaceae* typically ferment sugars to a variety of end products. These enteric bacteria found in the genera *Escherichia, Salmonella, Proteus, Shigella* and *Yersinia* produce a mixture of acids from pyruvic acid fermentation. The **methyl-red test** measures the production of a variety of mixed acids by fermentation of glucose. These acids include lactic acid, acetic acid, succinic acid and formic acid. Four times as much acids as neutral products are produced in this mixed acid fermentation, so that the pH is reduced below 4.4. In the presence of the enzyme formic hydrogenylase the formic acid produced is split into hydrogen gas and carbon dioxide gas. In contrast, bacteria in the genera *Enterobacter, Serratia* and *Klebsiella* ferment pyruvic acid to the neutral end products acetoin and 2,3 butanediol. The **Voges-Proskauer** test measures the production of the neutral end product acetoin by fermentation of glucose. The pH drops as the pyruvic acid is produced by glycolysis of sugar, then rises to 6.2 as the neutral end products are excessively produced. Fermentation can thus produce acidic or neutral end products.

Other bacteria are nonfermenters. These bacteria include aerobic, non–spore-forming bacilli that are nonsaccharolytic and do not use carbohydrate or oxidize carbohydrates in a strictly oxidizing fashion. *Alcaligenes faecalis* is non-saccharolytic, and *Pseudomonas aeruginosa* uses sugars in an oxidative fashion. This species of *Pseudomonas* changes glucose to pyruvic acid by a pathway that does not use the three-carbon compound intermediates found in glycolysis. Instead, very weak acids are produced in this pathway that would not cause a change in the indicators commonly used to study fermentation. The pyruvic acid formed in this pathway is oxidized in the Krebs cycle and electron transport phosphorylation to carbon dioxide and water.

Fermentation of Carbohydrates: An Overview

The Gram stain of the clinical unknown isolate demonstrates the shape and arrangement of the cells and whether the organism is gram-positive or gram-negative. The unknown organism is inoculated into phenol red glucose, lactose and mannitol broth containing Durham tubes to study fermentation behavior. Phenol red has a red color at a pH of 8.4 and is yellow at a pH of 6.8 or less. After incubation, a yellow color in the broth tube and in the Durham tube indicates an **acidic fermentation**. If the bacteria are capable of producing gas, then a yellow color is seen in the broth tube and some liquid empties out of the Durham tube. The space in this tube is filled with gas produced during fermentation. Gas is produced only in the presence of an acidic fermentation reaction. This reaction is called **acid and gas**.

The pattern of fermentation reactions seen for the Durham tube fermentations is helpful in their identification. Enteric bacteria found in the genera *Escherichia, Enterobacter* and *Klebsiella* produce acid and gas from all three sugars. Others, such as members of the genus *Salmonella* and *Proteus,* produce acid and gas from glucose and show different reactions with the other sugars. *Proteus* and most *Salmonellae* do not ferment lactose and show differing reactions on mannitol. Gram-positive cocci such as *Staphylococcus aureus* or *Enterococcus faecalis* produce acid-only reactions with these sugars. Other streptococci only ferment glucose. Other aerobic non–spore-forming gram-negative bacilli do not ferment any of these sugars. The Durham tube sugar broths remain red when inoculated and incubated with *Pseudomonas aeruginosa*. The Durham tube sugar broths turn a deeper shade of red when inoculated and incubated with nonsaccharolytic bacteria such as *Alcaligenes faecalis* or *Bordetella pertussis*. These bacteria break down the peptones in this medium to release ammonia. The alkaline ammonia further raises the pH, so a darker red color appears.

The clinical unknown is also inoculated into two tubes of glucose broth for the Methyl-Red test and the Voges-Proskauer test. The Methyl-Red test measures the production of a variety of acids on fermentation of glucose. The pH drops to 4.4 or less. The indicator Methyl-Red is added after incubation. The tube is shaken; a red color indicates a positive test for mixed acids. If a yellow color appears, the test is negative. Mixed acids are not produced.

The Voges-Proskauer test measures the production of the neutral fermentation products acetoin and 2,3 butanediol. The pH is at least 6.2. A 1-ml sample of this broth is pipetted after incubation into a small tube and tested with Barritt's A and B reagents for the presence of acetoin, which is the precursor of 2,3 butanediol. There is no color test for the final end product of this pathway. The tube is shaken to mix the contents with oxygen. A reaction occurs between oxygen, the Barritt's reagents and acetoin to form a red-colored compound. This compound usually forms at the surface where oxygen is present. This red color is a positive test for the presence of acetoin and indirectly for 2,3 butanediol.

Collectively, the Durham insert sugar broth fermentation tubes distinguish between organisms that can ferment sugars and those that do not. This test also differentiates between those organisms that ferment sugars to acids or acid and gas. The Methyl-Red test and Voges-Proskauer test allow one to distinguish between members of *Enterobacteriaceae* that produce mixed acids from glucose and those that produce the neutral 2,3 butanediol fermentation. Bacteria in the genera *Escherichia*, *Proteus*, *Salmonella* and *Shigella* give positive Methyl-Red reactions and negative Voges-Proskauer reactions. Bacteria in the *Enterobacter*, *Klebsiella* and *Serratia* group give a positive Voges-Proskauer test and a negative Methyl-Red test. These enteric organisms are responsible for urinary tract infections, abdominal infections after surgery, diarrhea, dysentery, hospital-acquired infections and pneumonias. Therefore, these fermentation tests are important tests for the presumptive identification of fermentative and nonfermentative bacteria and for distinguishing between members of the *Enterobacteriaceae* that can cause significant medical problems.

Materials

20-hour nutrient broth pure cultures of *Alcaligenes faecalis*, *Enterobacter aerogenes*, *Escherichia coli*, *Pseudomonas aeruginosa*, *Staphylococcus aureus*, *Proteus vulgaris* and unknown.

tubes of phenol red glucose (dextrose) broth with Durham tubes

tubes of phenol red lactose broth with Durham tubes

tubes of phenol red mannitol broth with Durham tubes

tubes of MRVP glucose broth for the Methyl-Red test and Voges-Proskauer test

Methyl-Red reagent

Barritt's reagent A: 5% alpha naphthol in 95% ethanol in dropper bottles

Barritt's reagent B: 40% aqueous potassium hydroxide in dropper bottles small test tubes

sterile 1-ml pipettes

pipette pumps

Procedures

First Period (See Figure 34-1)

1. *Phenol Red Sugar Broth Durham Tube Fermentation:*
   a. Select six phenol red glucose, lactose and mannitol broth tubes. Properly label each fermentation tube with the appropriate initial "G,"

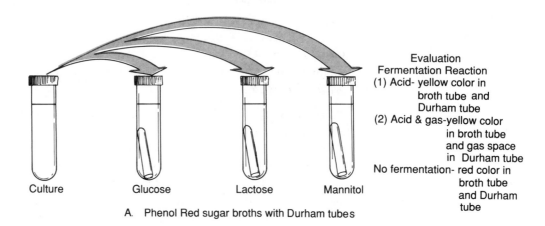

Culture   Glucose   Lactose   Mannitol

Evaluation
Fermentation Reaction
(1) Acid- yellow color in
      broth tube and
      Durham tube
(2) Acid & gas-yellow color
      in broth tube
      and gas space
      in Durham tube
No fermentation- red color in
      broth tube
      and Durham
      tube

A. Phenol Red sugar broths with Durham tubes

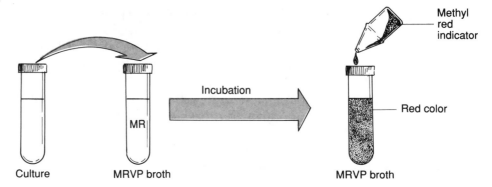

Culture   MRVP broth   Incubation   Methyl red indicator   Red color   MRVP broth

B. Methyl red test (mixed acids)

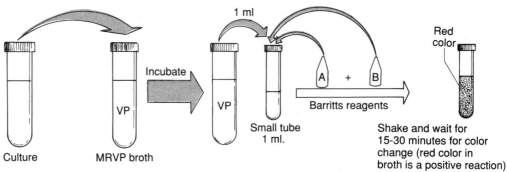

Culture   MRVP broth   Incubate   VP   Small tube 1 ml.   Barritts reagents   1 ml   A + B   Red color   Shake and wait for 15-30 minutes for color change (red color in broth is a positive reaction)

Figure 34-1
Fermentation of Carbohydrates

C. Voges-Proskauer test (2,3 butanediol formation)

Compare unknown results to these test results and identify type of reaction present

"L" or "M" for the respective sugars. Be careful since all these fermentation broth tubes are the same color.

b. Separate the labeled fermentation tubes into six sets so that each contains glucose, lactose and mannitol broth.

c. Label the first set "*Alcaligenes faecalis*," the second set "*Escherichia coli*," the third set "*Pseudomonas aeruginosa*," the fourth set "*Staphylococcus aureus*," the fifth set "*Proteus vulgaris*," and the sixth set "unknown."

d. Inoculate each tube with a loopful of the proper bacterial culture.

2. *Methyl-Red Fermentation Test:*
   a. Select three tubes of MRVP broth.

   b. Label all tubes "MR."

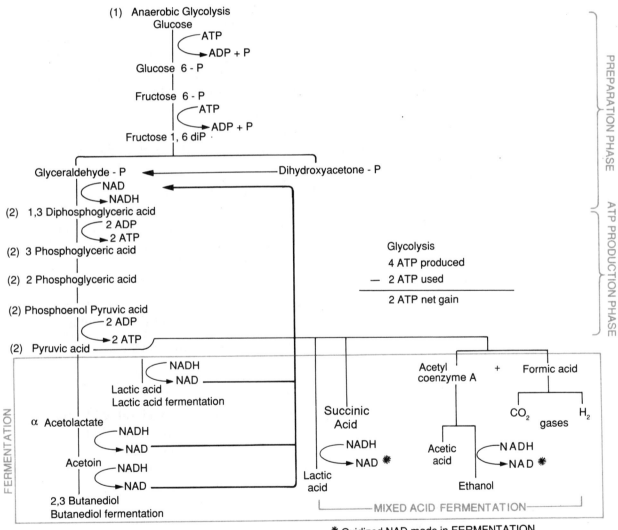

Figure 34-2
Fermentation

c. Label the first tube *"Enterobacter aerogenes,"* the second *"Escherichia coli"* and the third "unknown."

d. Inoculate each tube with a loopful of the proper bacterial culture.

3. *Voges-Proskauer Fermentation Test:*
   a. Select three tubes of MRVP

   b. Label all tubes "VP."

   c. Label one tube *"Enterobacter aerogenes,"* the second *"Escherichia coli"* and the third "unknown."

   d. Inoculate each tube with a loopful of the proper bacterial culture.

   e. Incubate the phenol red sugar broth fermentation tubes, the Methyl-Red broth and the Voges-Proskauer broth tubes at 35°C for 24 hours and then complete the evaluation.

Second Period Evaluation:

1. *Phenol Red Sugar Broth Durham Tube Fermentation:*
   a. Examine these broth tubes for the presence of a yellow color, which indicates acid, or a yellow color in the tube and a loss of some of the fluid from the Durham tube, which indicates acid and gas. These are positive results. A red color in the tube and the Durham tube indicates no fermentation.

2. *Methyl Red Fermentation Test:*
   a. Add 5 drops of the indicator Methyl-Red to each of the tubes labeled "MR."

   b. Mix the tubes gently and examine. A red color indicates a pH less than 4.4. This is due to the production of large amounts of a variety of acids. This is a positive test. A yellow color indicates a higher pH and is a negative test. Very little acid is produced and neutral products such as butanediol and acetoin predominate.

3. *Voges-Poaskauer Fermentation Test:*
   a. Select three small tubes. Label the first tube *"Enterobacter aerogenes,"* the second tube *"Escherichia coli"* and the third tube "unknown."

   b. Pipette 1 ml of the Voges-Proskauer broth from an organism into the tubes.

   c. Add 18 drops of Barritt's reagent A to each tube.

   d. Next, add 18 drops of Barritt's reagent B to each tube. Mix the contents of each tube to add oxygen to the broth. Oxygen is essential for a positive test. The oxygen reacts with the Barritt's reagents and the acetoin to form a red-colored complex at the top of the tube. These tubes should be mixed periodically, since the reaction may require 15–30 minutes to occur.

4. Record the results for all fermentation tests in the Results Section.

5. Answer the questions for the exercise.

6. See Summary Table.

Summary Table of Results: Fermentation Tests

Bacteria	Phenol Red Sugar Broth Durham Tube Fermentation			Methyl-Red Fermentation	Voges-Proskauer Fermentation
	Glucose	**Lactose**	**Mannitol**		
Alcaligenes faecalis	−	−	−	−	−
Enterobacter aerogenes	A/G	A/G	A/G	−	+
Escherichia coli	A/G	A/G	A/G	+	−
Pseudomonas aeruginosa	−	−	−	−	−
Proteus vulgaris	A/G	−	−	+	−
Staphylococcus aureus	A	A	A	+	+/− or +

Key for Table:

A	=	acid
A/G	=	acid + gas
−	=	negative
+/−	=	weakly positive

Exercise 35

The Oxidation-Fermentation (O-F) Test

Objectives

1. Distinguish between the results of oxidative metabolism and fermentative metabolism of sugars.

2. List three metabolically different groups identified by the oxidation-fermentation test.

3. Compare the reactions seen for members of the family *Enterobacteriaceae* and the gram-negative nonfermentative bacilli in the O-F Test.

Background

In Exercise 34, fermentation of sugars was studied as a tool to help identify clinical isolates of unknown bacteria. Some gram-positive bacteria showed fermentative ability. Gram-negative bacteria in the family *Enterobacteriaceae* ferment sugars to acids, or acid and gas. Other gram-negative bacilli showed no fermentation of glucose, lactose and mannitol. These bacteria are clearly distinct from the *Enterobacteriaceae* and are members of the gram-negative nonfermentative bacilli. This grouping includes bacteria in the genera *Alcaligenes, Bordetella, Flavobacterium* and *Pseudomonas.* These organisms are commonly involved in a variety of infections in the human body. *Alcaligenes faecalis* is commonly found in clinical isolates in hospitals. It is involved in nosocomial, urinary and respiratory tract infections. *Bordetella pertussis* causes whooping cough. Species of *Flavobacterium* are associated with infant meningitis and can produce infections in immunocompromised hosts. *Pseudomonas aeruginosa* is involved in urinary tract and respiratory tract infections, infections of burns, meningeal infections, and wound infections. This organism is resistant to many antibiotics.

The oxidation-fermentation test (the O-F test) is used to easily distinguish these bacteria from members of the family *Enterobacteriaceae*. These nonfermentative bacilli break down sugar in an oxidative fashion or do not metabolize sugar. Those bacteria that do not utilize sugar are **nonsaccharolytic**. In both cases, these bacteria produce negative results for fermentation of phenol red sugar broths with Durham tubes. Those bacteria that oxidize sugars produce very weak acids that are not detected by the pH indicators used for fermentation studies. The O-F medium of Hugh and Leifson is used to characterize these bacteria. In contrast to the 2:1 ratio of peptone to sugar found in conventional fermentation media, this medium has a 0.2:1 ratio of peptone to sugar. The reduced peptone concentration serves two purposes. First, it reduces the concentration of the protein breakdown products ammonia and amines, which could neutralize any weak acids produced during oxidation of sugar. Second, the higher concentration of sugar increases the chances of oxidation of sugar and formation of more weak acids. The indicator bromthymol blue is added into this medium.

It is yellow at a pH of 6.0 and blue at a pH of 7.6. For those bacteria that oxidize the glucose sugar to acids, the indicator turns yellow. In the case of non-saccharolytic bacteria, proteolytic reactions are common, and the indicator turns a deeper shade of blue.

The O-F Test: An Overview

Typically, in the O-F test two agar deep tubes containing the semisolid medium of Hugh and Leifson are inoculated with the same culture by stabbing with an inoculating needle. One tube has its contents covered with a layer of sterile mineral oil that is 1 cm deep. The other tube is left uncovered. The first tube only allows anaerobic breakdown of the sugar, while the second tube allows for aerobic metabolism of sugar. The tubes are incubated at 35°C for a week and then examined. If the organisms show oxidative metabolism of glucose, then only the uncovered or open tube shows the yellow color. The mineral oil-covered tube shows a blue green color, which is an alkaline reaction. Nonsaccharolytic bacteria do not use the sugar, and proteolytic reactions predominate. Both tubes turn a darker shade of blue because of the presence of alkaline amines and ammonia. In contrast to these organisms, fermentative bacteria show a yellow color or acid reaction in the open and covered tubes.

In this exercise, three known organisms will be inoculated into O-F medium to establish the reactions for fermentative, oxidative and nonsaccharolytic bacteria. They include *Escherichia coli*, *Pseudomonas aeruginosa*, and *Alcaligenes faecalis*. The unknown organism, if it is a nonfermenter, should also be inoculated into this medium to identify its action on glucose. The O-F test clearly determines whether an organism that is a nonfermenter is oxidative or nonsaccharolytic. Once the *Enterobacteriacae* have been excluded, a broad variety of microbes are eliminated from consideration. Other tests assume more importance in the final identification of the clinical unknown and differential diagnosis of the nature of the source of the medical problem. These will be discussed in subsequent exercises.

Materials

20-hour nutrient broth cultures of *Alcaligenes faecalis*, *Escherichia coli*, *Pseudomonas aeruginosa* and unknown

Agar deep tubes of O-F medium with glucose

tubes containing sterile mineral oil

sterile 1-ml pipettes

pipette pumps

small metric ruler

Procedures

First Period (See Figure 35-1)

1. Select eight tubes of O-F medium with glucose.

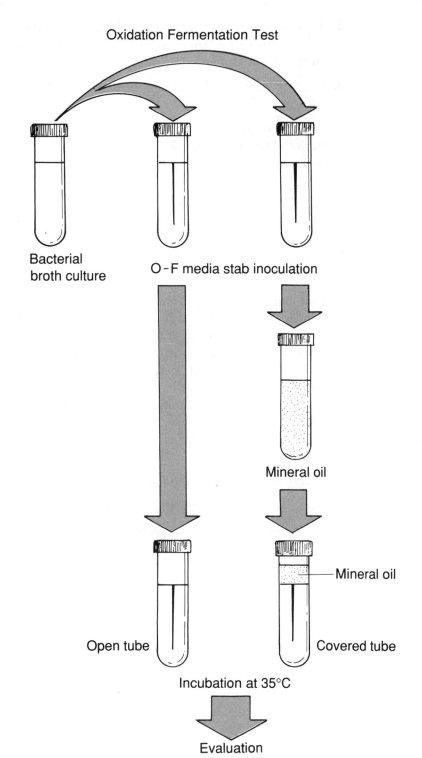

Oxidation Fermentation Test

Bacterial broth culture

O−F media stab inoculation

Mineral oil

Mineral oil

Open tube

Covered tube

Incubation at 35°C

Evaluation

Figure 35-1
Oxidation-Fermentation
(O-F) Test

Bacteria	Open Tube	Closed Tube	Sugar Metabolism
Escherichia coli	Yellow (acid)	Yellow (acid)	Fermentation
Pseudomonas aeruginosa	Yellow (acid)	Blue-green (alkaline)	Oxidation
Alcaligenes faecalis	Blue (alkaline)	Blue (alkaline)	Non-saccharolytic

Compare unknown results to these test results and identify type of reaction present.

2. Separate the tubes into four sets. Label two of the tubes *"Alcaligenes faecalis,"* two *"Escherichia coli,"* two *"Pseudomonas aeruginosa"* and two "unknown."

3. Use a straight needle to stab inoculate each of the tubes with the proper bacterial culture to at least half of the depth of the agar.

4. Select one tube from each set and measure a distance of 1 centimeter up from the surface of the agar. Mark this distance with a wax marking pencil on the glass around the outside of the tube.

5. Pipette sterile mineral oil into each of the tubes in Step 4 to the 1-centimeter line. These four tubes represent the covered tubes. The tubes lacking mineral oil are the open tubes.

6. Incubate all the tubes at 35°C for one week.

Second Period

1. Examine the open tubes and covered tubes for any evidence of a color change. Acid is indicated by a color change from blue green to yellow. Strictly oxidative bacteria only show this change in the open tube. This reaction will first appear at or near the surface where oxygen is present. This acid will gradually spread into the agar on extended incubation and cause a color change within the agar deep. The covered tube remains the same. Fermentative bacteria show this change in the open and covered tube. Nonsaccharolytic bacteria produce a deeper blue color in both tubes during incubation. This is due to release of alkaline products from proteolysis.

2. Record the findings in the table in the Results section

3. Answer the questions for the exercise.

4. See Figure 35-1 for Summary Table.

Differences in Respiratory Behavior

Objectives

1. Describe the purpose of the enzyme catalase.

2. Describe the specific reactions involved in the oxidase test.

3. List two advantages of the Oxoid Identification Sticks-Oxidase method compared to traditional oxidase test methods.

4. List two types of nitrate reduction.

5. Name two different microorganisms identified by specific nitrate reduction tests.

Background

In an earlier exercise, the Gram stain was used to determine the Gram reaction, shape and arrangements of the cells of the unknown. The fermentation tests and the O-F test can be used to place the unknown into major broad categories. For example, many gram-negative bacilli that ferment sugars to acid and gas are members of the family *Enterobacteriaceae*. This family includes *Escherichia coli, Enterobacter aerogenes* and *Klebsiella pneumoniae*. Other gram-negative bacilli that do not ferment sugars at all are members of the non-fermentative gram-negative bacilli. This group includes *Pseudomonas aeruginosa* and *Alcaligenes faecalis*. Many of the gram-positive cocci also show limited fermentation abilities or ferment sugars to acids and no gas. These include *Staphylococcus aureus, Enterococcus faecalis* and *Streptococcus pyogenes*. This exercise provides additional information for making a decision regarding the identity of the unknown. It concerns the terminal stages in respiration and uses the catalase, cytochrome c oxidase and nitrate reductase tests to demonstrate variations in these reactions in different bacteria.

In order to clarify the nature of these different responses, a brief summary of respiratory reactions follows. In aerobic respiration a complex organic compound such as glucose is broken down to carbon dioxide and water. In this process, much ATP is produced. During the Krebs cycle phase, pairs of hydrogen atoms removed by dehydrogenase enzymes are primarily transferred to the coenzyme NAD to form NADH. The hydrogens and electrons are then transferred to a series of carriers bound to the cell membrane, which make up the electron transport phosphorylation system. These carriers in sequence include flavoproteins, quinones and a series of cytochromes. The flavoproteins accept and transfer hydrogen atoms; the quinones accept only hydrogen atoms from the flavoproteins and transfer only electrons to the cytochromes. The hydrogen ions are released outside of the cell. The cytochromes only transfer electrons to each other and to oxygen. The electrons are transferred from the terminal cytochrome to oxygen by the enzyme cytochrome c oxidase to form water. This process of water formation involves the inflow of hydrogen ions and their binding to oxygen and is coupled with the addition of phosphorus to ADP to form ATP. (See Figure 36-1.)

The Catalase Test

Frequently during respiration electrons are directly transferred from flavo-proteins to oxygen to form superoxides. These superoxides react with hydrogen ions and electrons to form hydrogen peroxide. These reactions are summarized as follows:

$$O_2 + e \rightarrow O_2^- \text{ (superoxide)}$$

$$O_2^- + e + 2H^+ \rightarrow H_2O_2 \text{ (hydrogen peroxide)}$$

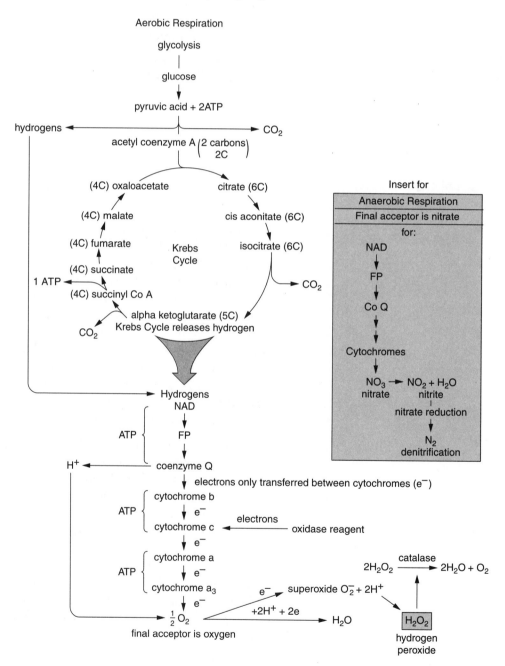

Figure 36-1
Aerobic Respiration

Superoxide and hydrogen peroxide are toxic oxygen compounds that attack organic compounds, splitting chemical bonds to kill the cells. Most aerobic and facultative bacteria have an enzyme called **catalase** that breaks down the hydrogen peroxide to water and oxygen. Streptococci and obligate anaerobes lack catalase. Clinically, the catalase test is important in distinguishing between different gram-positive cocci. Micrococci and staphylococci, in contrast to streptococci, give positive catalase test reactions. Gram positive, endospore producing, aerobic bacilli are all catalase-positive. Obligate anaerobes lack catalase and are readily killed by growth in the presence of oxygen because of the accumulated toxic oxygen compounds.

The Oxidase Test

In aerobic respiration, electrons are transferred by the enzyme cytochrome c oxidase from cytochrome c to oxygen to form water. The **oxidase test** is specific for the presence of cytochrome c. The oxidase reagent (1% solution of dimethyl p-phenylenediamine hydrochloride) is an electron donor and transfers electrons to oxidized cytochrome c. When this reagent is oxidized, it turns pink, then red and finally black. This reagent is colorless in the reduced state. Bacteria in the family *Enterobacteriaceae* lack cytochrome c and give a negative oxidase test. These organisms have a cytochrome o, which is nonreactive in the oxidase test. Gram-negative nonfermentative bacilli such as *Pseudomonas aeruginosa* or *Alcaligenes faecalis* give a positive oxidase test. The diplococci *Neisseria* and *Moraxella (Branhamella) catarrhalis* also give positive oxidase tests. Therefore, the oxidase test is a useful discriminating tool for clearly distinguishing between gram-negative fermentative enteric bacteria and gram-negative nonfermentative bacilli. It is also useful for the identity of *Neisseria* species and *Moraxella (Branhamella) catarrhalis*. Diplococci from the genus *Neisseria* are pathogenic and are responsible for meningitis and gonorrhea. *Moraxella (Branhamella) catarrhalis* is responsible for pneumonia and otitis media (middle ear) infection.

Nitrate Reduction

Microbes sometimes grow in environments lacking oxygen. These organisms must use alternative final electron acceptors when oxygen is not available. The use of final electron acceptors other than oxygen is termed **anaerobic respiration**. These alternative electron acceptors include sulfate, carbonate and nitrate, This section specifically concerns **nitrate reduction**. In the early portion of the dissimilative nitrate reduction pathway, nitrate is used as the alternative electron acceptor and is reduced to nitrite. This reaction only occurs under anaerobic conditions because the enzyme is synthesized only under anaerobic conditions and is inhibited by the presence of oxygen. As a rule, members of the *Enterobacteriaceae* reduce nitrates to nitrites. They also ferment sugars and lack oxidase activity. Nitrate reduction to nitrites is also useful for the identification of *Moraxella (Branhamella) catarrhalis*.

Other microorganisms can carry out the dissimilative reduction of nitrate beyond nitrite to nitrous oxides and finally to nitrogen gas. This process is called **denitrification** and is carried out by the aerobe *Pseudomonas aeruginosa*. The gas produced is readily trapped and seen in a Durham tube present in the nitrate broth.

Differences in Respiration Behavior: An Overview

The catalase, oxidase, and nitrate reductase tests depend on differences in the terminal stages of respiration and are useful in the differential identification of bacteria. The catalase test is performed on a 20-hour bacterial culture grown on a nutrient agar slant. Addition of 3 percent hydrogen peroxide to this growth results in bubbling due to release of oxygen gas. This reaction is immediate and very pronounced with *Staphylococcus aureus*. Lack of bubbling with a culture means no catalase activity.

The oxidase test is performed by the filter paper method or the Oxoid Identification Sticks–Oxidase method. In the filter paper method a bacterial culture is grown overnight on trypticase soy agar. A sheet of Whatman filter paper placed in a petri dish is wetted with oxidase reagent. A heavy inoculum of the bacterial culture is streaked onto this moistened paper with a sterile toothpick. In a positive test the paper turns pink, then red and finally black.

The Oxoid Identification Sticks–Oxidase method represents a modem approach used to distinguish between oxidase-positive and oxidase-negative gram-negative bacteria. Clinically, the sticks are also used to readily distinguish *Neisseria*, which are oxidase-positive, from other gram-negative oxidase-negative diplococci. They are also used to distinguish oxidase-positive *Pseudomonas* from other enteric pathogens that are typically oxidase-negative. The oxidase reagent N,N dimethyl-p-phenylenediamine oxalate is impregnated into one end of a wooden stick. The opposite end is colored red for identification and to ensure that the correct end is held. The bacterial culture to be tested is grown on media lacking fermentable sugar, such as trypticase soy agar. The colony is touched with the reagent end of the stick so that some microbial mass is picked up. In a positive test the reagent end changes to a blue purple color within 30 seconds to 3 minutes. No color change is a negative test.

The Oxoid product has a number of advantages over traditional methods. The product is conveniently supplied in packs of 100 sticks. The shelf life of this product is at least 1 year when stored at 2°C–8°C. In contrast, the liquid reagent must be made up daily, since it loses activity on storage; the Oxoid product avoids the need for frequent preparation of fresh reagent. The Oxoid stick method is also more convenient and easier to do than the filter paper method. The Oxoid stick method also avoids the problem of iron oxidation of the reagent and false-positive results when nichrome wire loops are used to transfer the bacteria. Another advantage is that the student is exposed to a method for oxidase activity testing that is widely used for screening and presumptive identification of bacterial cultures in clinical and scientific laboratories.

Regardless of the method used, the oxidase test depends on the presence of cytochrome c in the cell. All bacteria in the grouping *Enterobacteriaceae* are oxidase-negative. Many of the gram-negative nonfermentative bacilli are oxidase-positive. This includes the genera *Pseudomonas, Alcaligenes, Bordetella* and *Flavobacterium*. The nitrate reduction tests use a broth medium supplemented with potassium nitrate. This broth tube also contains a Durham tube to detect nitrogen gas. The bacterial culture is inoculated into nitrate broth and incubated overnight. During growth the bacteria use up the oxygen in the medium to create anaerobic conditions. Under these conditions, nitrate is reduced to nitrite. The nitrate reductase enzyme removes oxygen from nitrate, leaving nitrite, and adds the oxygen to hydrogen ions and electrons produced in the Krebs cycle, to form water. On the addition of nitrite reagent A (sulfanilic acid) and nitrite reagent B (dimethyl alpha naphthylamine) to the broth, a red color appears. This color change is a positive test. Negative tests mean either that nitrate reduction does not occur or that nitrates may have been reduced farther in the assimilative pathway to ammonia or in the dissimilative pathway to nitrogen gas. The presence of gas in the Durham tube indicates that denitrification has occurred. Zinc powder should be added to those tubes showing negative nitrite results and no gas. Zinc reduces the nitrate present to nitrite. The nitrite reagents react with nitrite and a red color appears. The red color after the addition of zinc demonstrates that nitrate reduction does not occur with this particular bacterial culture. The use of zinc confirms a true negative nitrate reduction test. The majority of enteric bacteria give a positive nitrate reduction to nitrite. Gram-negative nonfermentative bacteria show a variety of responses. For example, *Pseudomonas aeruginosa* denitrifies nitrates to nitrogen gas; *Alcaligenes faecalis* shows variable nitrate reduction reactions and no denitrification. *Moraxella (Branhamella) catarrhalis* shows a positive nitrate reduction to nitrite.

Materials

20-hour nutrient broth cultures of *Escherichia coli*, *Pseudomonas aeruginosa* and *Staphylococcus aureus* and unknown organism

nutrient agar slants

plates of trypticase soy agar

nitrate broths with Durham tubes

3% hydrogen peroxide in darkened dropping bottles

fresh oxidase reagent (1% solution of dimethyl p-phenylenediamine hydrochloride) in darkened dropper bottles. This must be made fresh each time and must be refrigerated.

Whatman filter paper sheets trimmed to fit a petri dish

sterile flat toothpicks stored in glass petri dishes or tubes

sterile plastic or empty glass petri dishes for oxidase test

Oxoid Identification Sticks–Oxidase test. These are supplied in packs of 100 sticks. They must be stored at 2°C–8°C prior to use.

nitrite test reagent A (sulfanilic acid) in darkened dropper bottles

nitrite test reagent B (dimethyl alpha naphthylamine) in darkened dropper bottles

zinc powder (reagent grade)

Procedures

First Period

1. *Catalase Test:* (Figure 36-2)
   a. Select two nutrient agar slants. Label one "*Staphylococcus aureus*" and the other "unknown."

   b. Streak each slant with the proper organism.

   c. Incubate the slants at 35°C for 20 hours.

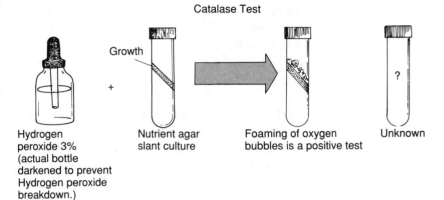

Catalase Test

Growth

+

Hydrogen
peroxide 3%
(actual bottle
darkened to prevent
Hydrogen peroxide
breakdown.)

Nutrient agar
slant culture

Foaming of oxygen
bubbles is a positive test

Unknown

?

Compare unknown results to these test results and identify type of reaction present

Figure 36-2
Tests to Demonstrate
Differences in Respiratory
Behavior

2. *Oxidase Test:* (Figure 36-3)

   a. Select three trypticase soy agar plates. Label the first *"Pseudomonas aeruginosa,"* the second *"Escherichia coli"* and the third "unknown."

   b. Streak each plate with the proper organism.

   c. Incubate the plates at 35°C for 20 hours.

3. *Nitrate Reduction Tests:* (Figure 36-4)

   a. Select three nitrate broth tubes with Durham tubes. Label the first tube *"Escherichia coli,"* the second *"Pseudomonas aeruginosa"* and the third "unknown."

   b. Inoculate each tube with a loopful of the proper bacterial culture.

   c. Incubate all the tubes at 35°C for 48 hours.

Second Period

1. *Catalase Test:* (Figure 36-2)

   a. Add a small quantity of 3% hydrogen peroxide to the slant of *Staphylococcus aureus.* Observe the foaming. This is due to the breakdown of hydrogen peroxide to water and oxygen gas and is a positive catalase test. Use caution to avoid any overflow of the foam, bubbles or liquid from the tube. Any overflow could contaminate the student or the laboratory with staphylococci. Any spills that occur must be promptly disinfected and the student must scrub his or her hands with surgical scrub solution.

   b. Repeat this procedure with the unknown culture and examine for the presence of foaming. The absence of foaming is a negative test for catalase activity.

2a. *Oxidase Test: The filter paper method:* (Figure 36-3)

   a. Select and trim a sheet of Whatman filter paper to the dimensions of a petri dish and place it in the dish. Wet the paper with oxidase reagent. Select a toothpick and streak some of the growth of *Pseudomonas aeruginosa* onto the wetted paper. Place the toothpick in a container of disinfectant. Select separate toothpicks and repeat these streaks for *Escherichia coli* and the unknown on the wetted paper. Be sure to dispose of the toothpicks in a container of disinfectant.

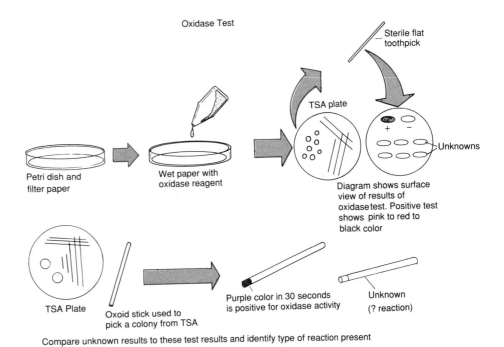

Oxidase Test

Sterile flat toothpick

TSA plate

Unknowns

Petri dish and filter paper

Wet paper with oxidase reagent

Diagram shows surface view of results of oxidase test. Positive test shows pink to red to black color

TSA Plate

Oxoid stick used to pick a colony from TSA

Purple color in 30 seconds is positive for oxidase activity

Unknown (? reaction)

Compare unknown results to these test results and identify type of reaction present

Figure 36-3
Oxidase Tests: Filter Paper Method and Oxoid Identification Stick–Oxidase Test

b. **Several students can complete their oxidase tests in one petri dish containing filter paper wetted with oxidase reagent.**

c. Notice on the *Pseudomonas* section a color change from pink to red to black. This is a positive oxidase test and is due to oxidation of the reagent. The *Escherichia coli* should show no change in color. The absence of this color change is a negative test. Compare the reaction of the unknown to the observed result for these two test organisms and determine whether positive- or negative-oxidase activity is present.

d. Dispose of the petri plate and paper in a discard for microbiological waste materials and not in the waste basket.

2b. *Oxidase Test: Oxoid Identification Sticks–Oxidase Test Method:* (Figure 36-3)

a. Remove the container from the refrigerator and allow it to stand 5 minutes at room temperature.

b. Choose a well-separated representative colony on the trypticase soy agar plate.

c. Remove one stick (color-coded red) from the container, and, holding it by the colored end, touch the colony with the impregnated end of the stick. *Rotate the stick* and pick off a small mass of cells.

d. Place the stick between the lid and the base of the inverted plate.

e. Examine the impregnated end of the stick after 30 seconds. If a color change has not occurred, examine again after 3 minutes.

f. A positive reaction is shown by the development of a blue purple color. No color change is observed with organisms that are oxidase-negative. Dispose of the Oxoid oxidase test stick in a microbiological discard.

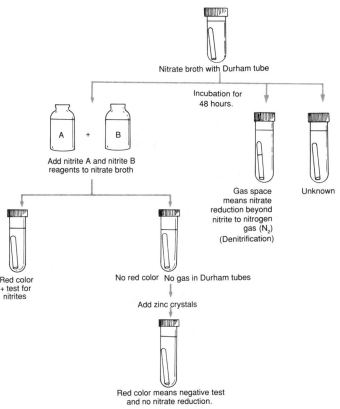

Figure 36-4
Nitrate Reduction Tests

Nitrate broth with Durham tube

Incubation for 48 hours.

A + B

Add nitrite A and nitrite B reagents to nitrate broth

Gas space means nitrate reduction beyond nitrite to nitrogen gas (N_2) (Denitrification)

Unknown

Red color + test for nitrites

No red color No gas in Durham tubes

Add zinc crystals

Red color means negative test and no nitrate reduction.

Compare unknown results to these test results and identify type of reaction present.

3. *Nitrate Reduction Tests:* (Figure 36-4)
   a. Add 3 drops of nitrate A solution followed by 3 drops of nitrate B solution to each nitrate broth bacterial culture. **Caution: Nitrate B is carcinogenic. Do not get any of this reagent on your skin. Wash your hands immediately if you do.** Do not mix this tube. Observe the results.

   b. Notice that the culture of *Escherichia coli* changes to a red color. This reaction indicates reduction of nitrate to nitrite. This red color first appears at the bottom of the broth which is anaerobic and moves upward.

   c. Observe that the nitrate broth of *Pseudomonas aeruginosa* does not turn red. However, a gas space appears in the Durham tube. This is nitrogen gas, which represents additional reduction of nitrates to nitrous oxides and finally to nitrogen gas. This process is called **denitrification**.

   d. Compare the unknown to the above tests. If this culture does not agree with either of the above results, a true negative test may have occurred. Proceed as follows to check this possibility.

   e. Add a pinch of zinc powder to the unknown tube. Mix the contents of this tube and observe for the presence of a red color. The zinc reduces the nitrate to nitrite. This nitrite reacts with the nitrite test reagents to produce a red color. Therefore, these bacteria do not use nitrate.

   f. Record the reaction of the unknown in the nitrate reduction test.

4. Record the results for all respiratory behavior tests in the Results Section.

5. Answer the questions for the exercise.

6. See Summary Table.

Summary Table of Results

Differences in Respiratory Behavior

Catalase Test

Bacteria	Reaction
S. aureus	Bubbling of oxygen gas (Positive reaction)

Oxidase Test

Bacteria	Reaction
E. coli	No reaction (No color change)
P. aeruginosa	Pink color observed (Positive reaction)

Nitrate Reduction

Bacteria	Reaction
E. coli	Reduction to nitrites (red color observed in bottom of broth)
P. aeruginosa	Further reduction to nitrogen gas (denitrification)

Differential Identification I: Amino Acid and Specialty Tests

Objectives

1. Explain the overall major significance of all the tests in this exercise.

2. Explain the differences in the alkaline slant/acid deep, acid slant/acid deep, alkaline slant/alkaline deep reactions seen on Kligler's iron agar.

3. Explain the significance of the IMViC test.

4. Distinguish between deamination and decarboxylation.

5. List the critical reaction necessary for a positive indole, urease, deaminase and decarboxylase test.

6. Name an organism that is responsible for a positive indole, urease, and phenylalanine deaminase test.

Background

Previous exercises on the clinical unknown demonstrated that members of the *Enterobacteriaceae* ferment glucose to acids, or acid and gas, lack oxidase activity and reduce nitrates to nitrites. Failure to show these characteristics excludes the microorganisms from this gram-negative grouping. In this latter case the organism may be a member of the gram-negative nonfermentative bacteria. In this exercise a variety of tests are presented that help the student to further reduce the possible choices in order to make a differential identification of the clinical unknown. These tests include fermentation of sugar with or without hydrogen sulfide production in Kligler's iron agar, indole production, urease activity, use of citrate as a sole carbon source, deamination of the amino acid phenylalanine, decarboxylation of the amino acid lysine, the IMViC test and motility. Gram-positive bacteria frequently give negative results after incubation on these media. These negative test results can be important supporting evidence for the gram-positive unknown. In contrast, these tests are critical in the differential identification of the gram-negative unknown.

Kligler's Iron Agar Reactions

Growth on **Kligler's iron agar** is an important screening medium for identification of members of the *Enterobacteriaceae* and the gram-negative nonfermentative bacteria. This medium contains dextrose, lactose, thiosulfate and ferrous sulfate. The ratio of lactose to dextrose is 10:1. The medium is poured as an agar slant with an agar deep portion of about 1.5 inches. The agar deep portion is thick and relatively anaerobic, while the slant portion is exposed to air and is aerobic. This medium is inoculated with a culture by stabbing the agar deep and streaking the slant portion of the medium. During growth on Kligler's iron agar, a number of reactions are possible. If fermentation of only dextrose occurs, then on early incubation a small amount of acids is produced and a yellow color appears in the medium. However, peptides in the slant portion are decarboxylated in the presence of oxygen to large quantities of alkaline amines, and the slant reverts to a red color. The agar deep portion remains yellow because oxygen is not present in this region. The end result is an alkaline slant and an acid agar deep by 24 hours of incubation. This reaction is typical of lactose nonfermenters such as species of *Salmonella* and *Shigella*. However, bacteria that ferment dextrose and lactose produce a different observable reaction, since this medium contains ten times more lactose than dextrose. These bacteria that also ferment lactose produce large quantities of acid in this medium. The amount of acid produced is sufficient to offset any accumulation of alkaline amines, so the pH remains low. In this case both the slant and the agar deep remain yellow. *Escherichia coli*, *Klebsiella pneumoniae* and *Enterobacter aerogenes* produce this acid slant and acid agar deep reaction on Kligler's iron agar. Bacteria that belong with the gram-negative nonfermentative bacilli produce an alkaline slant and alkaline agar deep reaction on this medium. These organisms do not ferment the dextrose and lactose in this medium. Instead, in this medium these organisms decarboxylate the peptides to alkaline amines, so the slant and agar deep turn a deeper shade of red. The alkaline slant and alkaline deep reaction is another indicator that the unknown does not belong in the *Enterobacteriaceae*. This medium also contains a source of sulfur called sodium thiosulfate, which is used by bacteria for the production of hydrogen sulfide. Bacteria such as *Proteus vulgaris* and species of *Salmonella* metabolize thiosulfate to release hydrogen sulfide. The hydrogen sulfide reacts with ferrous sulfate to yield ferrous sulfide, which forms a black precipitate in the agar deep portion of this medium. This reaction only occurs in an acid medium, so it must be assumed that glucose fermentation preceded the release of hydrogen sulfide from thiosulfate. *Proteus vulgaris* and members of the genus *Salmonella* ferment glucose but not lactose and produce hydrogen sulfide on this medium.

Indole Test

The **indole test** is based on the fact that some bacteria can grow in tryptophan broth and break down this amino acid into indole, pyruvic acid and ammonia. After incubation, Kovac's reagent is added to the broth. In a positive test a red-colored complex forms at the surface as a result of a reaction between the Kovac's reagent and the indole. Enteric bacteria that produce a positive indole test include *Escherichia coli* and *Proteus vulgaris*. *Klebsiella pneumoniae*, *Enterobacter aerogenes* and *Serratia marcescens* yield negative results. The gram-negative nonfermentative bacilli such as *Pseudomonas aeruginosa* and *Alcaligenes faecalis* yield negative indole test results.

Citrate Test

The **citrate test** measures the ability of an organism to use sodium citrate as the sole carbon source for energy. This medium contains sodium citrate, ammonium dihydrogen phosphate and the indicator bromthymol blue. This indicator is yellow below a pH of 6.0 and blue above a pH of 7.6. The medium lacks any other carbohydrate or proteins that could be used as energy sources, Bacteria that metabolize the citrate release ammonia from the ammonium compound and convert it to the alkaline ammonium hydroxide. The indicator turns blue after 24 to 48 hours of growth. This is a positive reaction. This test is very helpful in the differential identification of some of the *Enteobacteriaceae*. It is positive for *Enterobacter aerogenes*, *Klebsiella pneumoniae* and *Serratia marcescens*. It is variable and can show a delayed positive reaction for *Proteus vulgaris*. It is negative for *Escherichia coli*. The gram-negative nonfermentative coccobacillus *Alcaligenes faecalis* shows a positive citrate test.

Urease Test

The **urease test** measures whether or not bacteria can produce the enzyme urease and split urea into ammonia and carbon dioxide. Urea broth contains the substrate urea and the pH indicator phenol red. The indicator is yellow below a pH of 6.8 and is red above a pH of 8.4. In the presence of the alkaline product ammonia the indicator turns a cerise (red) color. This is a valuable test to distinguish *Proteus vulgaris* and *Klebsiella pneumoniae* from other enteric pathogens such as *Escherichia coli*, *Enterobacter aerogenes* and members of the genera *Salmonella* and *Shigella*. *Proteus vulgaris* produces a strong positive urease reaction with a deep cerise color to the broth. *Klebsiella pneumoniae* gives a weaker positive reaction and a paler cerise color to the broth. All the other listed enteric pathogens yield a negative urease test. This test is also one of the few reactions that distinguishes *Klebsiella pneumoniae* from *Enterobacter aerogenes*.

Phenylalanine Deaminase Activity

This test is specific for bacteria in the genera of *Proteus* and *Providencia*. Bacteria in these genera have the enzyme **phenylalanine deaminase**, which can remove an amino group from phenylalanine to yield phenylpyruvic acid and ammonia. Other enteric bacteria lack this enzyme activity and yield negative results. The phenylpyruvic acid is detected by the addition of ferric chloride solution to the slant medium and the observation of a green color in the liquid and in the agar.

Lysine Decarboxylase Activity

In the **decarboxylase reaction**, the bacterial enzyme removes a carboxyl group from an amino acid to create an alkaline amine and carbon dioxide. Decarboxylation of the amino acid lysine forms **cadaverine**. This decarboxylase reaction is used for the identification of members of the *Enterobacteriaceae*. Lysine decarboxylase activity is found in *Enterobacter aerogenes*, *Klebsiella pneumoniae*, *Serratia marcescens* and members of the genus *Salmonella*. *Proteus vulgaris* and members of the genus *Shigella* lack this activity. *Escherichia coli* shows variable activity. For this reaction, Moeller decarboxylase broth is used. This medium contains glucose and the indicator bromcresol purple, which is yellow below a pH of 5.2 and purple above a pH of 6.8. One tube receives the amino acid lysine and the other lacks this amino acid. Each tube is inoculated with the bacterial culture to be tested for decarboxylase activity. Both broth tubes receive a sterile mineral oil overlay. This is necessary to achieve anaerobic conditions required for fermentation of the sugar to mixed acids and a low pH. During incubation the glucose is fermented to acids and a yellow color is seen. The low pH activates the decarboxylase enzymes and decarboxylation of the amino acid lysine occurs, producing the alkaline amine. As the pH rises again, the medium reverts again to the purple color. This reversion to an alkaline pH represents a positive test for lysine decarboxylase activity. The student must compare the results for the medium containing the amino acid to the one lacking the amino acid. The tube lacking the amino acid is the control and establishes that the required fermentation has occurred.

Motility

Motility is another important characteristic for the identification of unknown bacteria. Motile bacteria in the *Enterobacteriaceae* include *Escherichia coli*, *Enterobacter aerogenes*, *Serratia marcescens*, *Proteus vulgaris* and members of the genus *Salmonella*. *Klebsiella pneumoniae* and members of the genus *Shigella* are nonmotile. The gram-negative nonfermentative bacteria *Pseudomonas aeruginosa* and *Alcaligenes faecalis* are also motile. The gram-negative nonfermentative diplococcus *Moraxella (Branhamella) catarrhalis* is nonmotile. Most of the aerobic and facultative gram-positive cocci are nonmotile. In contrast, the aerobic gram-positive bacilli such as *Bacillus subtilis* and *Bacillus cereus* are motile. These two bacilli are commonly studied in courses in microbiology.

The IMViC Test

The **IMViC test** is used to differentiate *Escherichia coli* from *Enterobacter aerogenes*. Both of these organisms are coliforms. Coliforms are gram-negative, non–spore-forming, facultative short bacilli that ferment lactose broth to acid and gas. *Escherichia coli* is found in the human intestinal tract. Pathogenic strains are responsible for traveler's diarrhea, infant meningitis and urinary tract infections. *Escherichia coli* is a standard used to indicate fecal pollution of water. *Enterobacter aerogenes* is found on vegetation and is a sewage pollutant due to runoff into sewers and bodies of water. It also is a source of urinary tract infections. The IMViC test is composed of four tests. They are: indole production (I), Methyl-Red test for mixed acid fermentation (M), Voges-Proskauer test for acetoin and 2,3 butanediol production (V) and the citrate test (C). (The "i" is inserted for ease of pronunciation.) The following tabulated results clearly permit one to distinguish between *Escherichia coli* and *Enterobacter aerogenes*.

	I	M	V	C
Escherichia coli	+	+	−	−
Enterobacter aerogenes	−	−	+	+

Today the IMViC test is used by water, food and dairy microbiologists to test for coliforms, but it has been replaced by rapid multimedia tests such as the Enterotube II in most clinical laboratories.

Differential Identification I: Amino Acid and Specialty Tests: An Overview

The previous exercises concerning the clinical unknown presented information about the Gram reaction, morphology and the fermentative and respiratory abilities of the unknown. This exercise concentrates on specific amino acid tests and specialty tests that can be used to further categorize gram-positive organisms and to identify specific gram-negative organisms. The student must carefully inoculate the clinical unknown into these media, incubate them for the prescribed time and then evaluate the results in a very critical fashion. For example, gram-positive cocci such as *Staphylococcus aureus* and *Enterococcus faecalis* lack any urease, phenylalanine deaminase and lysine decarboxylase enzyme activities. While gram-positive bacteria yield negative results for some of these tests, gram-negative bacteria can be clearly identified with the aid of these tests. A few examples should be sufficient to illustrate how these tests can be used to critically identify gram-negative organisms. *Escherichia coli* can be distinguished from *Enterobacter aerogenes* by the results obtained in the IMViC test. *Klebsiella pneumoniae* and *Enterobacter aerogenes* can be distinguished by two tests. *Klebsiella pneumoniae* is nonmotile and shows positive urease activity. *Enterobacter aerogenes* shows the opposite results for these tests. *Escherichia coli* can be eliminated from consideration by its lack of urease activity. The presence of *Proteus vulgaris* can be confirmed by the presence of a positive urease test, positive phenylalanine deaminase activity, no fermentation of lactose and hydrogen sulfide production in Kligler's iron agar. *Escherichia coli* and *Enterobacter aerogenes* lack positive results for some of these tests. Evidence for the gram-negative nonfermentative bacteria *Pseudomonas aeruginosa* or *Alcaligenes faecalis* as the unknown can be found by the observation of an alkaline slant and alkaline agar deep reaction on Kligler's iron agar and the presence of motility.

Materials

20-hour trypticase soy broth cultures of *Enterobacter aerogenes*, *Escherichia coli*, *Klebsiella pneumoniae*, *Proteus vulgaris*, *Pseudomonas aeruginosa*, *Shigella dysenteriae* and the unknown

slants of Kligler's iron agar

tubes of tryptophan broth

tubes of urea broth

slants of Simmons citrate agar

slants of phenylalanine agar

tubes of Moeller decarboxylase broth (half of the tubes have 1% lysine added and half lack the lysine)

motility test agar deep tubes

Kovac's reagent

10% ferric chloride solution

tubes of sterile mineral oil

10-ml pipettes

pipette pumps

small metric rulers

Procedures

First Period (See Figure 37-1)

1. *Kligler's iron agar:*
   a. Select five slant tubes of Kligler's iron agar. Label the first tube "*Escherichia coli*," the second "*Shigella dysenteriae*," the third "*Proteus vulgaris*," the fourth "*Pseudomonas aeruginosa*" and the fifth "unknown."

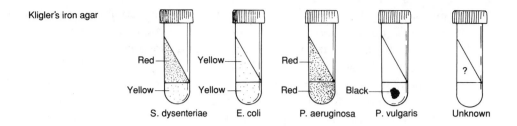

Kligler's iron agar

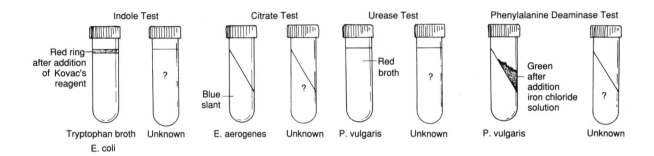

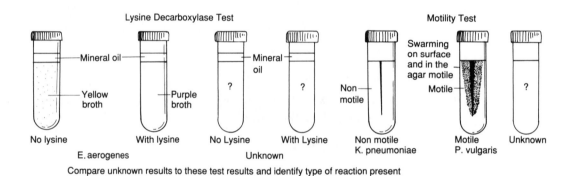

Compare unknown results to these test results and identify type of reaction present

Figure 37-1
Amino Acid and
Specialty Tests

b. Stab the agar deep portion of the tube and streak the slant portion of each tube with the proper culture.

c. Incubate the tubes at 35°C for 48 hours.

2. *Tryptophan Broth (Indole Test):*
   a. Select three tubes of tryptophan broth. Label the first tube *"Escherichia coli,"* the second *"Enterobacter aerogenes,"* and the third "unknown."

   b. Transfer a loopful of the proper culture into the labeled tubes.

   c. Incubate the tubes at 35°C for 48 hours.

3. *Citrate Test:*
   a. Select three slants of citrate agar. Label the first slant *"Escherichia coli,"* the second slant *"Enterobacter aerogenes"* and the third slant "unknown."

b. Streak each slant with a loopful of the proper culture.

c. Incubate all the tubes at 35°C for 48 hours.

4. *Urease Test:*
   a. Select three tubes of urea broth. Label the first tube *"Escherichia coli,"* the second *"Proteus vulgaris"* and the third "unknown."

   b. Transfer a loopful of the proper culture into the labeled tubes.

   c. Incubate all the tubes at 35°C for 48 hours.

5. *Phenylalanine Deaminase Test:*
   a. Select three slants of phenylalanine agar. Label the first tube *"Escherichia coli,"* the second "Proteus vulgaris" and the third "unknown."

   b. Streak each slant with a loopful of the proper culture.

   c. Incubate all the tubes at 35°C for 48 hours.

6. *Lysine Decarboxylase Test:*
   a. For each organism studied, select a tube of Moeller decarboxylase broth with lysine and one without lysine. Three such sets of this medium are used. Label the first set *"Proteus vulgaris,"* the second set *"Enterobacter aerogenes"* and the third set "unknown." Use the small metric ruler to mark a distance of 1 cm up from the surface of the broth. Mark a complete circle around the tube at this location.

   b. For each organism, inoculate a tube of Moeller decarboxylase broth with lysine and one without lysine with a loopful of the proper culture.

   c. Pipette a 1-cm overlay of sterile mineral oil into each tube to the mark on the tube to obtain anaerobic conditions.

   d. Incubate all tubes at 35°C for 48 hours.

7. *Motility Test Agar (motility):*
   a. Select three motility agar deep tubes. Label the first tube *"Proteus vulgaris,"* the second *"Klebsiella pneumoniae"* and the third "unknown."

   b. Use the inoculating needle to stab inoculate each tube with the proper culture.

   c. Incubate all tubes at 30°C for 5 days.

Second Period

1. *Kligler's Iron Agar.*
   a. Observe each incubated tube of Kligler's iron agar for evidence of fermentation. Dextrose fermentation produces an alkaline red slant and an acid yellow agar deep. Lactose fermentation produces sufficient acids to cause the slant and agar deep to turn yellow in color. Absence of fermentation produces a red alkaline slant and agar deep. Hydrogen sulfide production is visible as a blackening in the agar deep portion of the tube. The four organisms used illustrate these reactions. Recall that *Shigella dysenteriae* shows an alkaline slant and acid deep, *Escherichia coli* shows an acid slant and acid deep, *Pseudomonas aeruginosa* shows an alkaline slant and alkaline deep and *Proteus*

vulgaris produces hydrogen sulfide. Compare the unknown to these bacteria and indicate its reaction on Kligler's iron agar.

2. *Tryptophan broth (Indole Test):*
   a. **Kovac's reagent is very volatile and irritating. It is desirable to perform this test in an exhaust hood with disinfectant and an available gas supply. Keep the bottle of Kovac's reagent tightly closed when not in use.** Add 10 drops of Kovac's reagent to the tryptophan broth tubes labeled *"Escherichia coli," "Enterobacter aerogenes"* and *"unknown."* A positive test is indicated by the appearance of a red-colored layer at the top of the broth. This indicates hydrolysis of tryptophan to indole. Recall that *Escherichia coli* gives positive results. Compare the unknown to the control tubes and indicate the proper results.

3. *Citrate Test:*
   a. Observe the citrate slant tubes for *Escherichia coli, Enterobacter aerogenes* and the unknown. A change in color of the slant from green to blue is a positive result. This indicates use of citrate as the sole carbon source and development of an alkaline pH in the medium. Recall that *Enterobacter aerogenes* gives positive results. Compare the unknown to the control tubes and indicate the proper results.

4. *Urease Test:*
   a. Observe the urea broth tubes of *Escherichia coli, Proteus vulgaris* and the unknown. The appearance of a cerise (red) color in the broth indicates hydrolysis of urea to carbon dioxide and the alkaline compound ammonia. Recall that *Proteus vulgaris* gives a positive result. Compare the unknown to the control tubes and indicate the proper results.

5. *Phenylalanine Deaminase Test:*
   a. Add 6 drops of 10% ferric chloride solution to the phenylalanine agar slants for *Escherichia coli, Proteus vulgaris* and the unknown. Observe for the appearance of a green color in the liquid and in the agar. This indicates the presence of phenylpyruvic acid. Recall that *Proteus vulgaris* gives a positive result. Compare the unknown to the control tubes and indicate the proper results.

6. *Lysine Decarboxylase Test:*
   a. Examine the sets of Moeller decarboxylase tubes with and without lysine for *Proteus vulgaris, Enterobacter aerogenes* and the unknown. In a positive test the tube lacking lysine is yellow, which indicates fermentation of the glucose. The tube with lysine reverts to a purple color due to decarboxylation of the lysine to the alkaline amine cadaverine. In a negative test the tubes with and without lysine will be yellow after incubation, which indicates that fermentation of glucose occurred but that there was no decarboxylation of lysine. Recall that *Enterobacter aerogenes* gives a positive result. Compare the unknown culture tubes to the control tubes to determine whether a positive test occurred.

7. *Motility Test Agar (motility):*
   a. Examine the motility agar deep tubes for *Klebsiella pneumoniae, Proteus vulgaris* and the unknown. Motility is indicated by swarming of the bacterial growth on the agar surface and cloudiness extending to the sides of the inoculation stab line in the agar deep. Recall that

Klebsiella pneumoniae is nonmotile and that *Proteus vulgaris* is motile. Determine whether the unknown is motile or not.

8. *The IMViC Test:*

a. The IMViC test distinguishes *Escherichia coli* from *Enterobacter aerogenes*. Recall that *Escherichia coli* gives positive results for the indole test and Methyl-Red mixed acids fermentation only and that *Enterobacter aerogenes* is only positive for the Voges-Proskauer test for acetoin and for the citrate test. Compare the unknown to these two cultures to determine whether it matches the results for *Escherichia coli, Enterobacter aerogenes* or neither of these organisms.

9. Record all results in the appropriate tables in the Results section and evaluate the unknown.

10. Answer the questions for the exercise.

11. See Summary Table.

Summary Table of Results

Amino Acid and Specialty Tests

Bacteria	KIA	TryP-I	CIT	UR	PD	LD	M
Escherichia coli	A/A	+	–	–	–	V	+
Enterobacter aerogenes	A/A	–	+	–	–	+	+
Klebsiella pneumoniae	A/A	–	+	+^{w}	–	+	–
Salmonella typhimurium	H$_2$S	–	V	–	–	+	+
Proteus vulgaris	H$_2$S	+	– to delayed +	+	+	–	+
Pseudomonas aeruginosa	ALK/ALK	–	+	–	–	–	+
Shigella dysenteriae	ALK/A	V	–	–	–	–	–

Key for Table:

KIA	Kligler's iron agar
Tryp-I	tryptophan-indole
CIT	citrate
UR	urease
PD	phenylalanine deaminase
M	motility

A/A	=	Acid/Acid reactions for slant and deep
ALK/ALK	=	alakaline/alkaline reactions for slant and deep
ALK/A	=	alkaline slant/acid deep
V	=	variable
+	=	positive
–	=	negative
H$_2$S	=	hydrogen sulfide

Differential Identification II: Macromolecule and Specialty Tests

Objectives

1. Explain the purpose of the starch, milk protein and spirit blue tests.

2. Explain why refrigeration after incubation is necessary in the evaluation of gelatinase activity.

3. Describe four reactions that are observed in litmus milk.

4. Identify tests that are useful in distinguishing between *Staphylococcus aureus* and *Enterococcus faecalis* and list the results observed.

5. Indicate a major collective value of the tests in this exercise for the differential identification of an unknown.

Background

In the previous exercises on the clinical unknown, the gram-positive or the gram-negative unknown was inoculated into a variety of media to measure respiratory behavior, fermentative abilities, amino acid metabolism and reactions in a variety of specialized tests. Those tests were very helpful in forming a differential decision concerning the identity of the gram-negative enteric clinical unknown. They also provided additional results necessary for identifying the gram-negative nonfermentative unknowns and the gram-positive unknowns.

The present exercise is valuable for completing the identification of the gram-negative nonfermentative bacterial unknown as well as the aerobic and facultative gram-positive bacterial unknowns. The gram-negative enteric bacilli used as unknowns should also be inoculated into these media. In this exercise the clinical unknown is inoculated into a series of specialized media containing different **macromolecules**. The macromolecules studied are the polysaccharide starch, the protein casein and lipid. Those bacteria that yield positive tests produce extracellular enzymes, or enzymes that operate outside of the cell, to digest the macromolecule substrates. This exercise presents an opportunity to study the ability of bacteria to digest large molecular weight compounds typical of those present in cells and tissues of the human body and to mimic in a culture medium environment the action of virulence or disease-producing factors present in bacteria. A brief survey follows to introduce some of the extracellular enzymes and substances that enhance the disease process by destroying macromolecules.

These enzymes typically attack polysaccharides, proteins and lipids. In the human body the ground substance of connective tissue contains a complex polysaccharide called hyaluronic acid, which serves as a cementing substance between cells. Clostridia and staphylococci have an enzyme called **hyaluronidase** that digests this cementing material, enabling the bacteria to spread through the tissue. This enzyme is also called **spreading factor**.

Clostridia such as *Clostridium perfringens* have enzymes that contribute to the tissue destruction found in gas gangrene. One such enzyme is **lecithinase**, which can digest the phospholipid portion of cell membranes and kill the cells. Another such enzyme these bacteria produce is **collagenase**, which digests the collagen protein found in connective tissue, muscle and bone.

Staphylococci and streptococci produce **leukocidin**, a substance that destroys white blood cells such as neutrophils that are active in phagocytosis. Collectively, these bacteria enhance the spreading of disease organisms in the body by destroying the macromolecules found in tissues and by destroying our protective cells.

The ability to digest macromolecules is studied in a simpler fashion in this exercise by streaking starch agar plates, milk protein (casein) agar plates, spirit blue (lipid) agar plates, stabbing nutrient gelatin agar deeps and inoculating litmus milk broth with the clinical unknown. In addition, two optional specialty tests are presented to distinguish between the gram-positive organisms *Staphylococcus aureus* and *Enterococcus faecalis*. Both of these organisms show gram-positive cocci in chains and clusters. Both ferment phenol red dextrose, lactose and mannitol to acids. Both produce an acid reaction with reduction in litmus milk. Staphylococci produce a positive catalase test, while streptococci lack catalase activity.

Two additional tests are included to help resolve any possible confusion or difficulties in the identification of these two organisms. The media used are mannitol-salt agar and bile-esculin agar. Mannitol-salt agar is highly specific for *Staphylococcus aureus*, and bile-esculin agar is very specific for *Enterococcus faecalis*. Mannitol-salt agar contains 7.5% salt, mannitol and the pH indicator phenol red. The high salt concentration is inhibitory to most organisms. The bacteria ferment the mannitol in the agar to acids. The phenol red in the medium changes to yellow, and the white *Staphylococcus aureus* colonies are surrounded by yellow halos. The bile-esculin medium contains esculin and 4% bile salts. The bile salts inhibit gram-positive and gram-negative bacteria. *Enterococcus faecalis* hydrolyzes the esculin compound to esculetin and glucose. The glucose is used by the enterococcus as a source of energy by fermentation or as a source of carbon. The esculetin reacts with iron salts in the medium to form a brown to black colored complex. This results in a brown black to black discoloration of the medium.

Differential Identification II: Macromolecule and Specialty Tests: An Overview

In this exercise the student must streak the unknown onto plates of starch agar, milk protein (casein) agar, spirit blue lipid agar, stab a tube of nutrient gelatin and transfer a loopful of the unknown into litmus milk broth. If the Gram-stain and other results suggest the possibility that the clinical unknown is *Staphylococcus aureus* or *Enterococcus faecalis*, the student should streak a plate of mannitol-salt agar or streak a slant of bile-esculin agar.

This section presents the positive test reactions of bacteria on all these media. The macromolecule plate media are inoculated with *Bacillus subtilis* and incubated for 48 hours at 35°C prior to evaluation. *Bacillus subtilis* produces positive test results for hydrolysis of starch, milk protein and lipid. Starch agar is hydrolyzed by the bacterial enzyme amylase into shorter polysaccharides called

dextrins. These dextrins are in turn split into the disaccharide maltose. The hydrolysis of starch is indicated by a clearing or a halo around the colony when Gram's iodine is poured on the agar surface. If no hydrolysis occurs after incubation, then the color of the agar around the colony turns blue black after addition of the Gram's iodine. This blue black color indicates the presence of starch.

Milk protein agar contains the phosphoprotein called **casein**. This protein is insoluble in water and gives the milk a cloudy white appearance. Bacteria that possess proteinases hydrolyze this protein into peptides and amino acids that are soluble in water. A clearing in the agar or a halo appears around the colony where this positive reaction occurs. Digestion of lipids by bacterial lipase is studied by streaking a plate of spirit blue agar. This medium contains a source of fat and spirit blue that acts as a pH indicator. This compound becomes a deep blue in the presence of acid. If fats are hydrolyzed to fatty acids and glycerol, a dark blue halo appears around the colony. This lipolytic activity is common in the genera *Bacillus* and *Clostridium*.

Gelatin is an animal protein derived from collagen. Gelatin is solid in the refrigerator and liquid at 25°C (room temperature). For these studies, nutrient gelatin is used. This medium contains 12% gelatin and nutrient broth and must be kept under refrigeration until used. In this test a heavy inoculum of a broth culture of the organism is stabbed into an agar deep of nutrient gelatin and incubated at 35°C for 48 hours. After incubation the tubes are placed in a refrigerator for at least 30 minutes and then examined for evidence of liquefaction. Any degree of liquefaction after refrigeration shows positive gelatinase activity due to digestion of the protein into water-soluble amino acids. No liquefaction means a negative reaction. Bacteria that show positive gelatinase activity include *Bacillus subtilis*, *Slaphylococcus aureus*, *Proteus vulgaris* and *Pseudomonas aeruginosa*. *Escherichia coli* lacks gelatinase activity.

Litmus milk broth contains skim milk and the indicator litmus. The skim milk is a source of the milk protein casein and the sugar lactose. The litmus is a pH indicator and is pink in acid and purple in alkali. The litmus also accepts electrons and hydrogens released during bacterial metabolism and is reduced so that it turns white. A number of other reactions are observed when bacteria are inoculated into litmus milk and this medium is incubated. If fermentation of lactose to acids occurs, then the litmus changes to a pink color. The protein in the tube may also form an acid curd in the bottom of the tube. *Escherichia coli* and *Enterobacter aerogenes* produce an acid reaction in litmus milk. If amino acids in the milk are digested to release alkaline products, the litmus will change to a purple color. This alkaline reaction is found for *Proteus vulgaris*, *Moraxella (Branhamella) catarrhalis* and sometimes for *Pseudomonas aeruginosa*. An alkaline or rennet curd may also appear in the bottom of the tube. If the proteins of the milk are digested, the milk medium clears and becomes somewhat golden-colored. This proteolysis, or **peptonization**, reaction is typical of *Bacillus subtilis* and sometimes *Pseudomonas aeruginosa*. Reduction of the litmus is found with *Staphylcoccus aureus* and *Enterococcus faecalis*. The bottom half of the litmus broth medium appears white, and the top half shows a pink acid reaction with both of these organisms.

The optional test media mannitol-salt agar and bile-esculin agar should be used where gram-positive cocci are suspected as the clinical unknown. If *Staphylococcus aureus* is suspected, the student should streak a plate of mannitol-salt agar with the unknown. The appearance of yellow halos around the colonies after incubation confirms the presence of this organism. If *Enterococcus faecalis* is suspected, then a slant of bile-esculin medium should be streaked. The appearance of a brown black color in the agar of the slant confirms that the unknown is this enterococcus.

Materials

20-hour trypticase soy broth cultures of *Bacillus subtilis*, *Escherichia coli*, *Proteus vulgaris*, *Pseudomonas aeruginosa*, *Staphylococcus aureus* and *Enterococcus faecalis* and the unknown.

plates of starch agar

plates of milk protein (casein) agar

plates of spirit blue (lipid) agar

nutrient gelatin agar deep tubes (these must be refrigerated prior to use)

tubes of litmus milk broth

Optional media:

plates of mannitol-salt agar

slants of bile-esculin agar

Procedures

First Period (See Figure 38-1)

1. *Starch Agar, Milk Protein Agar and Spirit Blue Agar Tests:*
   a. Select plates of starch agar, milk protein agar and spirit blue agar. Label each plate with the name of the medium as it is taken.

   b. Divide each plate into three sections with a wax marking pencil. Label the first section *"Escherichia coli,"* the second section *"Bacillus subtilis"* and the third section "unknown."

   c. Streak each labeled section with the proper organism.

   d. Incubate the plates at 35°C for 48 hours.

2. *Nutrient Gelatin Agar Test:*
   a. Select four cold nutrient gelatin agar deeps.

   b. Label the first tube *"Escherichia coli"* the second *"Bacillus subtilis,"* the third *"Staphylococcus aureus,"* and the fourth "unknown."

   c. Stab each nutrient gelatin agar deep with the proper bacterial culture.

   d. Incubate all the tubes at 35°C for 48 hours.

3. *Litmus Milk Broth Test:*
   a. Select six tubes of litmus milk broth.

   b. Label the first tube *"Escherichia coli,"* the second *"Proteus vulgaris,"* the third *"Bacillus subtilis,"* the fourth *"Enterococcus faecalis,"* the fifth *"Pseudomonas aeruginosa"* and the last "unknown."

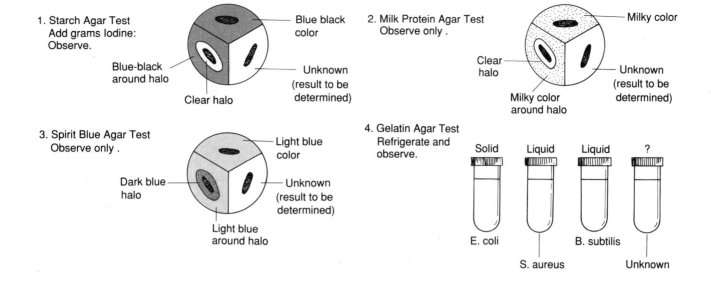

1. Starch Agar Test
   Add grams Iodine:
   Observe.

   Blue black color
   Blue-black around halo
   Clear halo
   Unknown (result to be determined)

2. Milk Protein Agar Test
   Observe only .

   Milky color
   Clear halo
   Milky color around halo
   Unknown (result to be determined)

3. Spirit Blue Agar Test
   Observe only .

   Light blue color
   Dark blue halo
   Unknown (result to be determined)
   Light blue around halo

4. Gelatin Agar Test
   Refrigerate and observe.

   Solid   Liquid   Liquid   ?
   E. coli   S. aureus   B. subtilis   Unknown

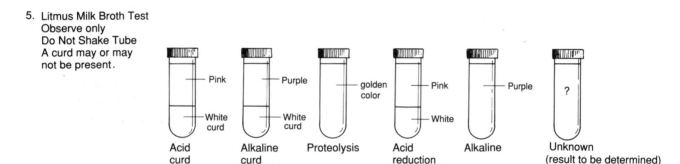

5. Litmus Milk Broth Test
   Observe only
   Do Not Shake Tube
   A curd may or may not be present.

   Pink / White curd — Acid curd
   Purple / White curd — Alkaline curd
   golden color — Proteolysis
   Pink / White — Acid reduction
   Purple — Alkaline
   ? — Unknown (result to be determined)

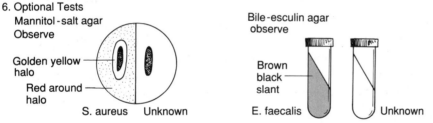

6. Optional Tests
   Mannitol-salt agar
   Observe

   Golden yellow halo
   Red around halo
   S. aureus   Unknown

   Bile-esculin agar observe
   Brown black slant
   E. faecalis   Unknown

Compare unknown results to these test results and identify type of reaction present

Figure 38-1
Macromolecule and
Specialty Tests

c. Inoculate a loopful of the proper bacterial culture into each labeled tube.

d. Incubate all the tubes at 35°C for 48 hours.

Optional Tests

4. *Mannitol-Salt Agar Plates and Bile-Esculin Agar Slants:*
   a. Select a plate of mannitol-salt agar. Divide the plate into two sections with a wax marking pencil.

   b. Label the first section *"Staphylococcus aureus"* and the second section "unknown."

   c. Streak each section with the proper organism.

   d. Select two bile-esculin slants. Label the first slant *"Enterococcus faecalis"* and the second slant "unknown."

e. Streak each slant with the proper organism.

f. Incubate the mannitol-salt agar plates and bile-esculin slants at 35°C for 48 hours.

Second Period: Evaluation

In all tests, compare the unknown to the positive test organisms to determine its reaction.)

1. *Starch Agar Test:*
   a. Pour Gram's iodine onto the agar surface of the starch agar plate. Observe the plate for a clear halo around the growth for each organism. This is a positive test and indicates starch hydrolysis. The presence of a blue black color around the growth indicates the presence of starch and no hydrolysis. This is a negative test.

2. *Milk Protein Agar Test:*
   a. Observe the milk protein agar plates for clearing around the growth of each organism. Any clearing indicates digestion of casein to amino acids and is a positive test. The presence of cloudy and milky-looking agar at the margin of the growth means no digestion of casein occurred. This is a negative test.

3. *Spirit Blue Agar Test:*
   a. Observe the spirit blue plate for a dark blue halo around the growth of each organism. This indicates digestion of the fats to fatty acids and glycerol and is a positive test. If no change is seen, then no digestion of fats occurred. This is a negative test.

4. *Nutrient Gelatin Agar Test:*
   a. Place the nutrient gelatin agar deeps in the refrigerator for 30 minutes.

   b. After refrigeration, examine the agar deeps for any evidence of liquefaction. Liquefaction after refrigeration indicates digestion of the protein gelatin to water-soluble amino acids by the bacterial enzyme gelatinase. This is a positive test. If the gelatin is hard after refrigeration, then no digestion of the protein occurred. This is a negative test.

5. *Litmus Milk Broth Test:*
   a. Observe the litmus milk broth for evidence of an acid reaction, an alkaline reaction, proteolysis or reduction in the known control standard organisms.

   b. *Escherichia coli* produces an acid reaction in litmus milk. The indicator changes to pink. A curd may also be present. *Proteus vulgaris* produces an alkaline reaction in litmus milk. The indicator changes to purple. An alkaline or rennet curd may be present. *Bacillus subtilis* produces proteolysis (peptonization) in litmus milk. This peptonization is seen as a clearing of the litmus milk broth. An alkaline zone is also visible at the top of the tube. *Enterococcus faecalis* produces an acid reaction at the top of the broth and a reduction reaction in the bottom of the litmus milk broth. The broth in the top of the tube is pink, and the remainder of the litmus milk broth is white. *Pseudomonas aeruginosa* produces an alkaline to proteolytic reaction in litmus milk.

   c. Compare the unknown culture of litmus milk to these control standard tests and determine its litmus milk reaction.

Optional Tests

6. *Mannitol-Salt Agar Plates and Bile-Esculin Agar Slants:*
   a. Observe the yellow halo around the growth of *Staphylococcus aureus*. This is a positive test and indicates mannitol fermentation. Compare the unknown results to those for *Staphylococcus aureus*. A red color in the agar at the margin of the growth of the unknown indicates that this unknown is not *Staphylococcus aureus*. It may indicate *Staphylococcus epidermidis*, which grows on mannitol-salt agar but does not ferment mannitol.

   b. Observe the brown black color in the bile-esculin slant of *Enterococcus faecalis*. This result indicates hydrolysis of the esculin compound and is specific for *Enterococcus faecalis*. Compare the unknown slant to this result. Any absence of this brown black color in the unknown slant means this unknown is not *Enterococcus faecalis*.

7. Record your results in the appropriate tables in the Results section.

8. Answer the questions for the exercise.

9. See Summary Tables 1, 2, 3.

Summary Table 1

| | Macromolecule and Specialty Tests | | |
| | Hydrolysis of | | |
Bacteria	Starch	Milk Protein (Casein)	Spirit Blue Lipid
Escherichia coli	–	–	–
Bacillus subtilis	+	+	+

Summary Table 2

Bacteria	Hydrolysis of Gelatin in Nutrient Gelatin
Bacillus subtilis	–
Staphylococcus aureus	+

Summary Table 3

Bacteria	Litmus Milk Reactions
Escherichia coli	acid reaction
Proteus vulgaris	alkaline reaction
Bacillus subtilis	alkaline reaction to proteolysis
Enterococcus faecalis	acid reaction + reduction
Pseudomonas aeruginosa	alkaline reaction to proteolysis

Guidelines for the Identification of a Clinical Unknown

Medical personnel must frequently order laboratory tests to identify pathogens responsible for infections in the human body. They rule out (R/O) a number of possible microbial causes of infection by these laboratory data. In the process of ruling out, they are eliminating all those organisms that are not the source of the problem until they are left with the particular cause of the medical problem. In this clinical unknown study, the process of ruling out will be followed to make a differential identification of an unknown culture.

The first step of this process is to perform a Gram stain of the unknown. This will provide the student with the shape and arrangements of the cells and the Gram-reaction of the bacteria. For example, this would allow the student to distinguish between short gram-negative bacilli in pairs such as *Escherichia coli* and gram-positive cocci in chains such as *Streptococcus pyogenes*. This stain immediately narrows the number of choices of available organisms.

In the next step the metabolic tests are used to further reduce the number of choices. For example, streptococci do not show positive-catalase activity. *Pseudomonas aeruginosa* shows positive-oxidase activity, while all members of the *Enterobacteriaceae* lack this activity. By using these tests to sequentially eliminate the number of choices, the process of ruling out can be used to make a differential identification of a clinical unknown. The steps and valuable suggestions for identification of a clinical unknown by ruling out are listed here.

Initial Procedures

1. Make a Gram stain from the unknown culture to determine the Gram-reaction, shape and arrangement of the cells.

2. Make a confirmation Gram stain to check the original result.

3. Assemble all the test results for the unknown.

Gram-Positive Findings

1. If gram-positive bacilli are seen, check the catalase test for positive results and expect positive results on the macromolecule test media.

2. If gram-positive cocci are seen, check the catalase test. Recall that staphylococci show positive-catalase activity, while streptococci lack this activity.

3. Use the mannitol-salt agar or bile-esculin agar if necessary to confirm the presence, respectively, of *Staphylococcus aureus* or *Enterococcus faecalis*.

4. Follow the steps in the differential identification chart (Figure 38-2) to complete the differential decision.

Gram-Negative Findings

1. If gram-negative bacilli are seen, check the oxidase test results and fermentation behavior on Kligler's iron agar and in Durham tube sugar broth medium. Recall that members of the *Enterobacteriaceae* are oxidase-

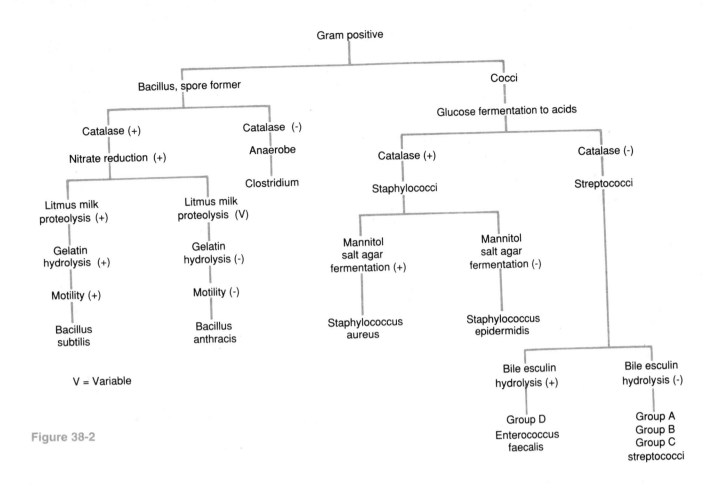

Figure 38-2

V = Variable

negative and ferment sugars. Other gram-negative bacilli that are oxidase-positive and do not ferment sugars are members of the aerobic nonfermentative group of bacilli. An example is *Pseudomonas*. Recall that *Moraxella (Branbamella) catarrhalis*, a diplococcus, is also oxidase-positive and a nonfermenter.

2. Some helpful reminders are:
   a. *Klebsiella pneumoniae* is nonmotile and shows urease activity, while *Enterobacter aerogenes* is motile and lacks urease activity.
   b. Only *Proteus* shows phenylalanine deaminase activity. *Proteus* also shows urease activity and a positive hydrogen sulfide reaction on Kligler's iron agar.
   c. *Shigella* is nonmotile and generally non-reactive in many tests.
   d. *Salmonella* is motile, lacks urease activity, shows lysine decarboxylase activity and usually produces hydrogen sulfide on Kligler's iron agar.
   e. *Escherichia coli* shows a + + − − series of reactions in the IMViC test, and *Enterobacter aerogenes* shows a − − + + response in this reaction sequence.

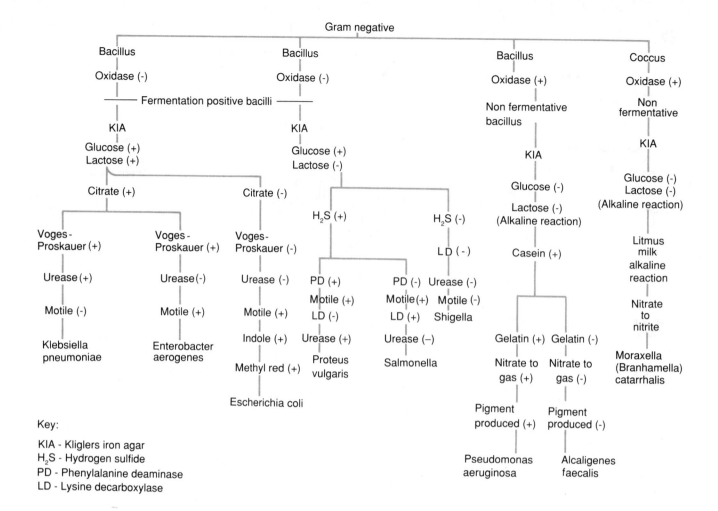

Key:

KIA - Kliglers iron agar
H₂S - Hydrogen sulfide
PD - Phenylalanine deaminase
LD - Lysine decarboxylase

Figure 38-3
Gram-Negative
Identification Chart.

3. Follow the steps in the proper differential identification chart (Figure 38-3) to make the differential decision.

4. A chart for recording the results of the procedures for identifying a clinical unknown appears in the Results section.

5. Answer the questions for the exercise.

Rapid Multimedia Test: Enterotube II®

Objectives

1. Inoculate a rapid multimedia test Enterotube II® to identify selected members of the family *Enterobacteriaceae*.

2. Use the results, Enterotube II® Results Pad and Color Reaction Chart, and Enterotube II® Interpretation Guide to identify specific members of the *Enterobacteriaceae*.

Background

In the clinical unknown exercises a variety of liquid and solid media were inoculated for the purpose of making a differential identification of an unknown organism. These unknowns included several members of the fimily *Enterobacteriaceae*. The traditional unknown methodology presents some problems for clinical and commercial microbiology laboratories. It requires use of much culture media and glassware. It is laborious to perform and is time-consuming. Many of today's nosocomial, urinary tract, postsurgical, abdominal and wound infections, as well as community-acquired pneumonias and cases of food poisoning, are caused by members of the *Enterobacteriaceae*. These are gram-negative facultative anaerobic, non–spore-forming bacilli that ferment glucose. The clinical diagnostic laboratory, the food microbiology laboratory in industry and laboratories in health agencies that deal with water, food and dairy microbiology problems need a system that permits the accurate and rapid identification of these microorganisms with a minimum of labor and effort.

The **Enterotube II system** offers a convenient and accurate solution to this problem. The Enterotube II® is a self-contained sterile plastic tube that has 12 compartments. These compartments contain distinct conventional media that permit different biochemical tests to be performed. The Enterotube II® contains its own enclosed inoculating wire that allows simultaneous inoculation and completion of 15 standard biochemical tests for the identification of enteric unknowns. After incubation, the specific chambers show color changes for positive tests. These positive test results are summarized on the coding pads, and the identification of the unknown is made using the Enterotube II® Computer Coding and Identification System interpretation guide booklet- This system does not require knowledge of sophisticated mathematics nor does it require a computer. The Enterotube II® Coding Identification System is able to identify distinct members in the *Enterobacteriaceae*. These organisms are all oxidase negative. Each organism is identified by a five-digit number based on the positive and negative test reactions in the Enterotube II®.

Entcrotube II is a trademark of Becton Dickinson and Company

The Enterotube II® system offers a number of distinct advantages for the student of microbiology. It is a safe and self-contained system that can perform 15 tests in one tube from a single colony growing on a plate of agar. The results are obtained after overnight incubation. The media has a definite shelf life and expiration date. This system saves on media preparation, sterilization time, storage and incubation space for experimental results. It has an accurate coding system built into the interpretation guide that makes identification of an organism safe, easy and reliable to do. This system provides students in the health sciences an opportunity to work with a rapid identification system that is widely used in clinical and commercial settings.

An illustration of the identification of an unknown organism follows: A colony of an unknown organism is isolated on agar medium. It shows positive reactions for glucose, gas, lysine, adonitol, lactose, arabinose, sorbitol, urea. and citrate. The results pad and color reaction chart show the following summary numbers for the chambers with positive results. They are 34363. Examination of the Enterotube II Interpretation Guide shows that this number corresponds to *Klebsiella pneumoniae.*

Rapid Multimedia Test: Enterotube II®: An Overview

Single cultures of bacteria in the family *Enterobacteriaceae* are streaked on separate plates of trypticase soy agar to isolate pure colonies. The organisms used for this study are *Escherichia coli, Enterobacter aerogenes, Proteus vulgaris* and *Klebsiella pneumoniae.* These organisms are identified by number only for this experiment. The Enterotube II® compartments are inoculated in the prescribed fashion and incubated. The results are recorded and the identification is made with the aid of the results pad and interpretation booklet.

Materials

Escherichia coli

Enterobacter aerogenes

Proteus vulgaris

Klebsiella pneumoniae

(All of these cultures are identified by a number only.)

Enterotube II® tubes (These should be stored at 2°C–8°C when not in use.)

Enterotube II® Results Pad and Color Reaction Chart°

Enterotube II® Interpretation Guide°

Technical information about these items may be obtained from:

Becton Dickinson Microbiology Systems
Becton Dickinson and Company
250 Schilling Circle
Cockeysville, Maryland 21030 USA
Customer Support Services 1-(800)-638-8663

Kovac's reagent

Barritt's A reagent (5% alpha naphthol solution)

Barritt's B reagent (20% potassium hydroxide solution)

Sterile Pasteur pipettes

inoculating loop

Procedures

First Period (See Figure 39-1)

1. Obtain an Enterotube II® and a trypticase soy agar plate of an unknown organism.

2. Remove the caps from both ends of the Enterotube II®. Notice that one end is a straight wire for inoculation, while the other end has a short loop handle. Do not flame wire.

3. Pick a well-isolated colony from the agar surface with the straight wire end of the Enterotube II®. Do not puncture the agar.

4. Be sure some inoculum is visible at the tip and the side of the wire.

5. Hold the loop handle. Twist the wire. Pull the wire through all 12 compartments with a turning motion.

6. Reinsert wire, without sterilizing, into the Enterotube II®. Push the wire through all 12 compartments with a twisting motion. The tip of the wire is lined up with the citrate chamber and the notch is lined up with the

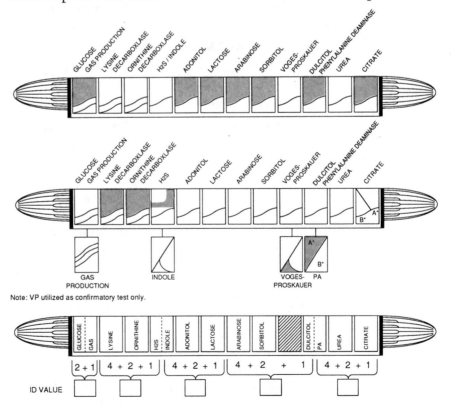

Figure 39-1
Enterotube II®

opening of the tube. Break wire at the notch and discard in a jar of disinfectant. The portion of the wire remaining in the tube maintains anaerobic conditions necessary for true fermentation of glucose, production of gas and decarboxylation of lysine and ornithine.

7. Use a flamed loop to punch holes through plastic foil covering the air inlet of the last eight chambers. (Adonitol, lactose, arabinose, sorbitol, Voges-Proskauer, dulcitol/PA, urea and citrate). This allows aerobic growth in these chambers.

8. Incubate the Entcrotube II® at 35° to 37°C for 18–24 hours on its flat surface. Separate the tubes from each other to provide for some circulation of air.

9. Interpret and record all results except for indole and Voges-Proskauer tests. These must be done last.

Second Period

Interpretation: The positive results are summarized in the table below. (A complete database table for the Enterotube II® Interpretation Guide follows this Procedure section.)

Test	Negative to Positive Change and Reaction
COMPARTMENT 1	
Glucose	Red to yellow due to acid production by fermentation (note c)
Gas	Separation of wax overlay from glucose medium means gas produced (note d)
COMPARTMENT 2	
Lysine	Yellow to purple due to decarboxylation of lysine to alkaline cadaverine
COMPARTMENT 3	
Ornithine	Yellow to purple due to decarboxylation of ornithine to putrescine
COMPARTMENT 4	
H_2S Production	Beige to black color in medium due to reaction of H_2S produced from sulfur compounds in medium with iron salts to form a black precipitate of iron sulfide
Indole	Colorless to pink or red color due to indole formed from tryptophan hydrolysis. This product is detected by development of a pink to red color after addition of Kovac's reagent, which is added to the compartment after incubation (note a)
COMPARTMENT 5	
Adonitol	Red to yellow due to acid production by fermentation of adonitol

Test	Negative to Positive Change and Reaction
COMPARTMENT 6 Lactose	Red to yellow due to acid production by fermentation of lactose
COMPARTMENT 7 Arabinose	Red to yellow due to acid production by fermentation of arabinose
COMPARTMENT 8 Sorbitol	Red to yellow due to acid production by fermentation of sorbitol (note f)
COMPARTMENT 9 Voges-Proskauer	Colorless to pink color due to acetoin production. from glucose by fermentation (note b)
COMPARTMENT 10 Dulcitol	Green to yellow due to acid production by fermentation (note e)
Phenylalanine tion of Deaminase	Green to black to smoky gray color due to deamina-phenylalanine to yield pyruvic acid, which reacts with iron salts to yield characteristic colors.
COMPARTMENT 11 Urea	Beige to red-purple color due to hydrolysis of urea to release alkaline ammonia
COMPARTMENT 12 Citrate	Green to blue color due to metabolism of citrate to release alkaline products

Note: A red or orange color in a carbohydrate chamber is a negative test. Only yellow is positive.

Additional Notes:

a. To perform the indole test, sterilize a loop and puncture the bottom of the plastic covering on the indole chamber. Add 2 drops of Kovac's reagent into this chamber with a Pasteur pipette. Any pink color within 10 seconds in the chamber is a positive test.

b. The Voges-Proskauer test is only done as a confirmatory test where indicated by the Enterotube II® Interpretation Guide. Puncture a hole in the VP chamber as described above, and add 2 drops of Barritt's A and 2 drops of Barritt's B reagent. Look for a pink color within 10 to 20 minutes.

c. *Proteus vulgaris* may give a weak positive reaction in the glucose compartment. This is acceptable.

d. The amount of gas produced by *Proteus vulgaris* and *Escherichia coli* may be weak or a negative reaction may be seen. This is acceptable.

e. The dulcitol reaction for *Escherichia coli* and *Klebsiella pneumoniae* may be weak or negative after 24 hours. This is acceptable.

f. The sorbitol reaction for *Escherichia coli* may be weak or at times negative. This is acceptable.

1. Observe all positive and negative results. Use the table on pages 184-185 as a guide for the results.

2. Obtain a coding pad and circle the ID numbers in each group for positive test results. Add the numbers in each group and place in the proper rectangle for the ID number. (A sample pad is provided in the Results section.)

3. Find the ID value in the Enterotube II® Computer Coding and Identification System interpretation guide. Write the name of the organism identified.

4. Write the culture number on the petri dish and your name on the coding pad and submit the results to the instructor for verification.

5. Answer the questions for this exercise.

Database Table for Enterotube II® Interpretation Guide—*Enterobacteriaceae* Reaction Chart†

	GLU	GAS	LYS	ORN	H₂S	IND	ADO	LAC	ARA	SOR	DUL	PAD	URE	CIT
Buttiauxella														
* *B. agrestis*	100	100	0	100	0	0	0	100	100	0	0	0	0	100
Cedecea														
* *C. davisae*	100	70	0	95	0	0	0	19	0	0	0	0	0	95
* *C. lapagei*	100	100	0	0	0	0	0	60	0	0	0	0	0	99
* *C. neteri*	100	100	0	0	0	0	0	35	0	100	0	0	0	100
* *Cedecea species 3*	100	100	0	0	0	0	0	0	0	0	0	0	0	100
* *Cedecea species 5*	100	100	0	50	0	0	0	0	0	100	0	0	100	100
Citrobacter														
C. freundii	100	95	0	20	80	5	0	50	99	98	55	0	70	95
C. diversus	100	98	0	99	0	100	98	35	98	99	50	0	75	99
* *C. amalonaticus*	100	97	0	95	0	100	0	50	99	97	0	0	80	85
* *C. amalonaticus biogroup 1*	100	93	0	100	0	100	0	19	100	100	4	0	45	1
Edwardsiella														
* *E. tarda*	100	100	100	100	100	99	0	0	9	0	0	0	0	1
* *E. tarda biogroup 1*	100	50	100	100	0	100	0	0	100	0	0	0	0	0
* *E. hoshinae*	100	35	100	95	0	13	0	0	15	0	0	0	0	0
* *E. ictaluri*	100	50	100	65	0	0	0	0	0	0	0	0	0	0
Enterobacter														
E. aerogenes	100	100	98	98	0	0	98	95	100	99	5	0	2	95
E. agglomerans	100	20	0	0	0	20	7	40	95	30	15	20	20	50
E. cloacae	100	100	0	96	0	0	25	93	99	95	15	0	65	98
* *E. gergoviae*	100	98	90	100	0	0	0	55	99	0	0	0	93	99
* *E. sakazakii*	100	98	0	91	0	11	0	99	100	0	5	50	1	99
* *E. taylorae*	100	100	0	99	0	0	0	10	100	1	0	0	1	100
* *E. amnigenus biogroup 1*	100	100	0	55	0	0	0	70	100	9	0	0	0	70
* *E. amnigenus biogroup 2*	100	35	0	100	0	0	0	35	100	100	0	0	0	100
Escherichia														
E. coli	100	95	90	65	1	98	5	95	99	94	60	1	1	1
E. coli (AD), inactive	100	5	40	20	1	80	3	25	85	75	40	0	1	1
* *E. fergusonii*	100	95	95	100	0	98	98	0	98	0	60	0	0	0
* *E. hermanii*	100	97	6	100	0	99	0	45	100	0	19	0	0	1
* *E. vulneris*	100	97	85	0	0	0	0	15	100	1	0	0	0	0
* *E. blattae*	100	100	100	100	0	0	0	0	100	0	0	0	0	50
Ewingella														
* *E. americana*	100	0	0	0	0	0	0	70	0	0	0	0	0	95
Hafnia														
H. alvei	100	98	100	98	0	0	0	5	95	0	2	0	4	10
* *H. alvei biogroup 1*	100	0	100	45	0	0	0	0	0	0	0	0	0	0
Klebsiella														
K. pneumoniae	100	97	98	0	0	0	90	98	99	99	30	0	95	98
K. oxytoca	100	97	99	1	0	99	99	100	98	99	55	1	90	95
* *Klebsiella group 47*	100	100	100	100	0	100	100	100	100	100	10	0	100	100
K. ozaenae	100	50	40	3	0	0	97	30	98	65	2	0	10	30
* *K. rhinoscleromatis*	100	0	0	0	0	0	99	1	99	99	0	0	0	0
Kluyvera														
* *K. ascorbata*	100	93	97	100	0	92	0	98	100	40	25	0	0	96
* *K. cryocrescens*	100	95	23	100	0	90	0	95	100	45	0	0	0	80
Leminorella														
* *Leminorella species*	100	0	0	0	100	0	0	0	100	0	50	0	0	0
Moellerella														
* *M. wisconsensis*	100	0	0	0	0	0	100	100	0	0	0	0	0	80
Morganella														
M. morganii	100	90	0	98	5	98	0	1	0	0	0	95	98	1
* *M. morganii biogroup 1*	100	91	100	95	41	100	0	0	0	0	0	100	100	0

Database Table for Enterotube II® Interpretation Guide—*Enterobacteriaceae* Reaction Chart† *(Continued)*

	GLU	GAS	LYS	ORN	H₂S	IND	ADO	LAC	ARA	SOR	DUL	PAD	URE	CIT
Obesumbacterium														
* O. proteus biogroup 2	100	0	100	100	0	0	0	0	0	0	0	0	0	0
Proteus														
P. mirabilis	100	96	0	99	98	2	0	2	0	0	0	98	98	65
P. vulgaris	100	85	0	0	95	98	0	2	0	0	0	99	95	15
* P. penneri	100	45	0	0	30	0	0	1	0	0	0	99	100	0
* P. myxofaciens	100	100	0	0	0	0	0	0	0	0	0	100	100	50
Providencia														
P. rettgeri	100	10	0	0	0	99	100	5	0	1	0	98	98	95
P. stuartii	100	0	0	0	0	98	5	2	1	1	0	95	30	93
P. alcalifaciens	100	85	0	1	0	99	98	0	1	1	0	98	0	98
* P. rustigianii	100	35	0	0	0	98	0	0	0	0	0	100	0	15
Rhanella														
* R. aquatilis	100	98	0	0	0	0	0	100	100	94	88	95	0	94
Salmonella														
* Salmonella species	100	96	94	96	93	1	0	1	99	94	96	0	1	88
* S. typhi	100	0	98	0	97	0	0	1	2	99	0	0	0	0
* S. cholera-suis	100	95	95	100	50	0	0	0	0	90	5	0	0	25
* S. paratyphi A	100	99	0	95	10	0	0	0	99	95	90	0	0	0
* S. gallinarum	100	0	90	1	100	0	0	0	80	1	90	0	0	0
* S. pullorum	100	90	100	95	90	0	0	0	100	10	0	0	0	0
* Salmonella (ARIZ) 3A	100	99	99	99	99	1	0	15	99	99	1	0	0	99
* Salmonella (ARIZ) 3B	100	99	99	99	99	2	0	85	99	99	1	0	0	99
Serratia														
S. marcescens	100	55	99	99	0	1	40	2	0	99	0	0	29	98
* S. marcescens biogroup 1	100	0	55	65	0	0	30	4	0	92	0	0	0	30
S. liquefaciens	100	75	95	95	0	1	5	10	98	95	0	0	3	90
* S. rubidea	100	30	55	0	0	0	99	100	100	1	0	0	2	95
* S. odorifera biogroup 1	100	0	100	100	0	60	50	70	100	100	0	0	5	100
* S. odorifera biogroup 2	100	13	94	0	0	50	50	97	100	100	0	0	0	97
* S. plymuthica	100	40	0	0	0	0	0	80	100	65	0	0	0	75
* S. ficaria	100	0	0	0	0	0	0	15	100	100	0	0	0	100
* S. fonticola	100	79	100	97	0	0	100	97	100	100	91	0	13	91
Shigella														
* Shigella serogps A,B,C	100	1	0	1	0	50	0	0	60	30	2	0	0	0
* S. sonnei	100	0	0	98	0	0	0	2	95	2	0	0	0	0
Tatumella														
* T. ptyseos	100	0	0	0	0	0	0	0	0	0	0	90	0	2
Yersinia														
* Y. enterocolitica	100	5	0	95	0	50	0	5	98	99	0	0	75	0
* Y. frederiksenii	100	40	0	95	0	100	0	40	100	100	0	0	70	15
* Y. intermedia	100	18	0	100	0	100	0	35	100	100	0	0	80	5
* Y. kristensenii	100	23	0	92	0	30	0	8	77	10	0	0	77	0
* Y. pestis	100	0	0	0	0	0	10	0	99	50	0	0	5	0
* Y. pseudotuberculosis	100	0	0	0	0	0	0	0	50	0	0	0	95	1
* Y. ruckeri	100	5	50	100	0	0	0	0	5	50	0	0	0	0
Enteric Groups														
* Enteric Group 17	100	95	0	95	0	0	0	75	100	100	0	0	65	100
* Enteric Group 41	100	100	0	0	0	100	100	100	100	0	100	0	50	0
* Enteric Group 45	100	89	100	100	0	0	0	0	100	0	0	0	0	100
* Enteric Group 58	100	85	100	85	0	0	0	30	100	100	85	0	70	85
* Enteric Group 59	100	100	0	0	0	10	0	80	100	0	0	30	0	100
* Enteric Group 60	100	100	0	100	0	0	0	0	25	0	0	0	50	0

*Rarely encountered organisms.

Numbers represent percent positive reactions on conventional media incubated at 36° C for 48 hours.

†J.J. Farmer III, BR Davis, FW Hickman-Brenner, et al., Biochemical Identification of New Species and Biogroups of *Enterobacteriaceae* Isolated from Clinical Specimens, *Journal of Clinical Microbiology* 1985;21:46-76.

Case Study 6

After repeated respiratory therapy treatments, a hospitalized patient develops a nosocomial respiratory infection. One of the common gram-negative nosocomial infectious organisms in his hospital is *Acinetobacter*. Sputum cultures are taken for laboratory analysis. The laboratory isolates gram-negative bacteria that are catalase positive, nonfermentative, and oxidase-negative. The report sheet lists *Pseudomonas* as the cause of infection. Antibiotic therapy is instituted. The patient does not recover and eventually dies.

Answer the following.

1. Explain why *Pseudomonas* could not be the cause of the problem.

_____

_____

2. Explain how this problem could have been prevented.

_____

_____

_____

_____

_____

_____

_____

_____

_____

_____

_____

_____

Control of Microorganisms

40 **Chemical Control of Microorganisms** **227**

evaluates effectiveness of antimicrobial agents used to control bacteria
on environmental surfaces or body surfaces.

41 **Antibiotic Sensitivity Testing: A Differential Decision** **231**

evaluates the differential sensitivity to antibiotics of simulated clinical
isolates and mimics the differential decision making process involved
in antibiotic selection for the patient.

42 **Effects of Antiseptic Agents on Transmission of Oral Flora
or Nasal Flora** **237**

evaluates the effects of antiseptic agents on the transmission of oral flora
or nasal flora.

43 **Beta-Lactamase Activity in Gram-Positive Cocci** **241**

evaluates the beta-lactamase activity in selected gram-positive cocci

44 **Oligodynamic Action Against Bacteria** **245**

evaluates the sensitivity of gram-positive and gram-negative bacteria
to heavy metals.

45 **Ultraviolet Lethality and Photoreactivation** **249**

evaluates the sensitivity of gram-positive and gram-negative bacteria
to ultraviolet light and the use of photoreactivating light to reverse
the radiation damage.

Case Study 7 **253**

Chemical Control
of Microorganisms

Objectives

1. Define **chemical control**.

2. Distinguish between bactericidal and bacteriostatic action of chemical agents.

3. Name three categories of chemical agents and indicate their mode of action.

Background

One of the major problems in microbiology is to control the increase in the numbers of microorganisms on body surfaces and on environmental surfaces. This control involves either killing microorganisms or blocking their growth. In the first case a **cidal** agent is used. In the second case a **static** agent is used. For example, a **bactericidal agent** kills bacteria, while a **bacteriostatic agent** stops the multiplication of bacteria but does not necessarily kill them.

Disinfectants are commonly used in microbiology laboratories to kill microorganisms on nonliving environmental surfaces such as work areas, countertops and sterile areas. They are also used to kill microorganisms present in spills. In contrast, antiseptics are used on the body. They are less toxic than disinfectants and tend to be inhibitory to microorganisms.

The antimicrobial agents discussed in this exercise can be divided into distinct categories. These include phenols, halogens, alcohols, and quaternary ammonium compounds (quats). **Phenols** include phenol, cresols, orthophenylphenol, hexachlorophene and Lysol®. These agents denature proteins and break down the cell membranes of the bacterial cells so that nutrients leak out of the cells and the cells die. **Halogens** are potent oxidizing agents. For example, povidone iodine is used to kill microorganisms on the skin prior to surgery. Iodine combines with the amino acid tyrosine and inactivates and denatures the proteins containing it. Chlorine is used in drinking water supplies and swimming pools as a disinfecting agent. Chlorine combines with water to form hypochlorous acid, which is a strong oxidizing agent. **Alcohols** disinfect by dissolving the lipids in cell membranes and by denaturing proteins. Absolute alcohol is not effective as an antimicrobial agent since the presence of water is required for denaturation of proteins. The most effective concentrations are 70% to 80%. Alcohols with a higher molecular weight are more effective than those of lower molecular weight. **Quaternary ammonium compounds (quats)** contain long-chain organic hydrophobic chains attached to a positively or negatively charged group. The positively charged quats are cationic compounds, while the negatively charged quats are anionic compounds. The cationic compounds are more effective against bacteria than are the anionic compounds. The cationic compounds are also more effective against gram-positive than gram-negative bacteria. The positively charged cationic compound combines with the negatively charged phospholipids of the cell membranes. They break down the cell membranes and also denature the proteins of the cells. Commonly used quaternary ammonium compounds include alkyldimethylbenzylammonium chloride (benzalkonium chloride), which is used in some microbiology laboratories to disinfect environmental surfaces, and cetyl pyridinium chloride, which is used in mouthwash.

Chemical Control of Microorganisms: An Overview

In this exercise, sample antimicrobial agents are tested for their action against gram-positive and gram-negative bacteria. Petri dishes are labeled on the underside with the names of the antimicrobial agents tested. The bacteria are inoculated into tubes of molten trypticase soy agar, mixed and poured into the labeled petri dishes. The agar is allowed to harden. Sterile filter paper disks are dipped into antimicrobial solutions and then placed on the agar over the proper labels. The plates are incubated overnight and then examined for the presence of a clear halo or zone of inhibition around any treated disk. The chemical agent diffuses from the disk into the surrounding agar. If the agent is effective against the microbe and is present in a sufficient concentration, a zone of inhibition will appear. The size of the inhibition zone is not a direct measure of the effectiveness of any antimicrobial agent, since some effective chemicals may diffuse only very slowly in agar. These agents would produce very narrow zones of inhibition. The zone of inhibition does not distinguish between bactericidal (cell death) activity or bacteriostatic (lack of cell multiplication) activity of an antimicrobial agent. Either mode of action produces a zone of inhibition on an agar plate.

Materials

20-hour trypticase soy broth cultures of *Staphylococcus aureus*, *Escherichia coli*, *Enterococcus faecalis*, *Pseudomonas aeruginosa* or unknown. If so instructed, the 20-hour trypticase soy broth culture of the clinical unknown may be substituted for the organisms listed above.

sterile petri plates

tubes of molten trypticase soy agar stored in a 50°C water bath

individual coplin jars with the following single antimicrobial agents: 70% ethyl alcohol, benzalkonium chloride (quat) 1:750 solution, povidone iodine solution and mouthwash containing the quat cetylpyridinium chloride as the effective ingredient

sterile filter paper disks stored in a sterile glass petri dish

Procedures

First Period (See Figure 37-1)

If the clinical unknown is used, on this exercise, follow these procedures for your identified organism.

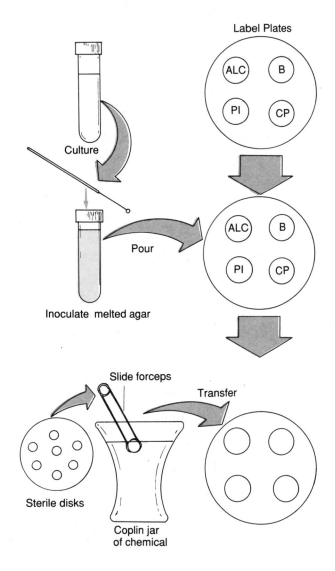

Label Plates

Culture

Pour

Inoculate melted agar

ALC B

PI CP

ALC B

PI CP

Slide forceps

Transfer

Sterile disks

Coplin jar
of chemical

Figure 40-1
Chemical Control of
Microorganisms

Incubate and examine for zones of inhibition

1. *Inoculating the Agar and Pouring of the Plates:*
   a. Select four sterile petri dishes and label the underside of the bottom portion of each dish with four circles in the corners. Label the first circle "ALC" for 70% alcohol, the second circle "B" for the quat benzalkonium chloride solution, the third "PI" for povidone iodine solution and the fourth "CP" for mouthwash containing cetyl pyridinium chloride as the active ingredient.

   b. Label the first dish *"Staphylococcus aureus,"* the second *"Escherichia coli,"* the third *"Enterococcus faecalis"* and the fourth *"Pseudomonas aeruginosa."*

   c. Select four tubes of melted trypticase soy agar and label the first *"Staphylococcus aureus,"* the second *"Escherichia coli,"* the third *"Enterococcus faecalis"* and the fourth *"Pseudomonas aeruginosa."* Be sure the tubes of agar are warm, not hot, to touch before inoculating with bacteria.

   d. Transfer a loopful of the proper bacterial culture into the labeled tubes of melted agar.

e. Roll each tube between the palms of the hands to mix the contents. Pour the inoculated agars into the properly labeled plates. Allow the agar to harden.

2. *Preparation of Antimicrobial Treated Disks and Plates:*
   a. Select the *Staphylococcus aureus* plate.

   b. Sterilize a slide forceps by passing it through a flame.

   c. Pick up a sterile filter paper disk and gently immerse two-thirds of it in the 70% alcohol solution. Place this disk on the agar over the circle with the label "ALC."

   d. Sterilize the slide forceps again and pick up a sterile disk and gently immerse two-thirds of it in the solution of the quat benzalkonium chloride (1:750). Place this disk on the agar over the circle with the label "B."

   e. Sterilize the slide forceps again and pick up a sterile disk and gently immerse two-thirds of it in the povidone iodine solution. Place this disk on the agar over the circle with the label "PI."

   f. Sterilize the slide forceps again and pick up a sterile disk and gently immerse two-thirds of it in the cetylpyridinium chloride mouthwash solution. Place this disk on the agar over the circle with the label "CP."

   g. Repeat this procedure for the remaining seeded bacterial culture plates.

   h. Incubate all plates at 35°C for 24 hours.

Second Period

1. *Evaluation:*

   a. Observe each of the plates for the presence or absence of a zone of inhibition. A zone of inhibition is indicated by the presence of a clear halo around the disk.

   b. Record the findings in the table in the Results section.

2. Answer the questions for the exercise.

Antibiotic Sensitivity Testing: A Differential Decision

Warning: The organisms used in this exercise are pathogenic. Extreme care must be used to avoid accidents and contamination. All accidents must be promptly reported to the instructor. Spills must be promptly disinfected.

Objectives

1. Define the term **antibiotic**.

2. Describe three distinct modes of action of antibiotics.

3. Distinguish between a broad spectrum and narrow spectrum antibiotic.

4. Define **zone of inhibition**.

5. Describe how sensitivity testing can be used to make a differential decision for the use of a specific antibiotic.

Background

Many microorganisms produce antimicrobial substances that either kill or inhibit other microbes. These antimicrobial agents that are produced by living organisms are called **antibiotics**. In 1929, Fleming discovered that the mold *Penicillium*, which was a contaminant on a plate produced a substance that inhibited *Staphylococcus aureus*. In 1940, Waksman discovered that the actinomycete *Streptomyces griseus* produced an antimicrobial compound, which was named streptomycin. This antibiotic was successfully used against the tuberculosis bacillus and gram-negative organisms. Today antibiotic resistance to this antibiotic is fairly common. Currently a number of species of *Bacillus, Penicillium, Streptomyces* and *Acremonium* are antibiotic producers.

Modes of Action of Antibiotics

Antibiotics show a number of different mechanisms of action against microorganisms. They include inhibition of cell wall formation during division, inhibition of protein synthesis, inhibition of nucleic acid synthesis, breakdown of the cell membrane permeability mechanisms, and efflux mechanisms which chase the antibiotic out of the cell after entry..

Antibiotic Survey

Some of the common antibiotics include the penicillins, the cephalosporins, the tetracyclines, the macrolide antibiotic erythromycin the aminoglycosides, the quinolones and the polymyxins. **Penicillins** interfere with the crosslinking of one strand of peptidoglycan to another during the formation of the cell wall. These antibiotics are bactericidal since they block formation of the cell wall.

They are only effective against actively reproducing bacteria. Bacteria in an abscess that might not be reproducing would be resistant to penicillin. Since members of the genus *Mycoplasma* lack a cell wall, they also are resistant to penicillins. This family of antibiotics is the drug of choice for staphylococcal and streptococcal infections. However, resistance to these antibiotics is becoming more common. For example, penicillinase producing *Neisseria gonorrhoeae* (PPNG) produce a beta-lactamase enzyme that opens the beta-lactam ring and destroys the effectiveness of the antibiotic. In another example, methicillin-resistant *Staphylococcus aureus* (MRSA) destroys this antibiotic and related antibiotics. Patients infected with MRSA organisms are treated with the antibiotic vancomycin.

Cephalosporins are related to the penicillins. Some of these show activity against gram-positive and gram-negative bacteria. These are **broad spectrum** antibiotics. An example is cephalexin. Some cephalosporins are more resistant than penicillins to the action of beta-lactamases.

Tetracyclines are broad spectrum bacteriostatic antibiotics. They are effective against gram-positive and gram-negative bacteria, rickettsias, chlamydiae, and mycoplasmas. Some examples of tetracyclines are doxycycline, minocycline and oxytetracycline.

An example of a **macrolide** antibiotic is erythromycin. It inhibits protein synthesis. This antibiotic is used to treat respiratory infections, whooping cough, Legionnaires disease and mycoplasma infections. This antibiotic is prescribed for patients who are allergic to penicillin or cephalosporins. Other examples include biaxin and azithromycin.

Aminoglycoside antibiotics are effective against a variety of gram-negative microorganisms. These organisms are responsible for hospital-acquired infections, postsurgical infections, sepsis and puncture infections. Examples of these antibiotics include tobramycin, streptomycin, amikacin, gentamycin and netilimycin. These antibiotics do show serious side effects. They are nephrotoxic, neurotoxic and ototoxic. Patients taking these antibiotics for an extended time should be evaluated for liver functions, neurological functioning and hearing acuity. The organism *Pseudomonas aeruginosa*, which is resistant to penicillins, is sensitive to some aminoglycosides.

Quinolones are a new category of antibiotic. They interfere with DNA replications. They are effective in treating urinary tract infections and lower respiratory tract infections. An example is ciprofloxacin. This antibiotic is bactericidal and is effective against some gram-positive and most gram-negative enteric bacteria. Other examples include ofloxacin, norfloxacin and levofloxacin.

Polymyxins are antibiotics that are commonly used in topically applied ointments. They are effective against gram-negative bacteria. They damage the cell membrane of bacteria and interfere with its selective permeability.

A Differential Decision–Case History

Patient X visits a physician for treatment of a urinary tract infection. The patient's complaints include difficulty in urination, pelvic pain, low back pain and frequent urination. The physician prescribes an antibiotic based on prior experience with this problem in this patient and other patients. This decision, based on prior experience, is called an **empiric decision**. The patient returns a week later, with complaints of the same problem. In this case the physician orders a urine culture and a culture-antibiotic sensitivity test. The laboratory finds a single microbe that is causing the problem. The antibiotic sensitivity results are then reported to the physician as R, I or S: for those microbes that show resistance or no effect of the antibiotic on the microorganism (R), or a moderate effect of the antibiotic on the microbe (I) or are effective antibiotic against the microbe (S). When the clinician receives the report, an evaluation shows that the prescription should be changed to a different antibiotic, since the microorganism is resistant to the original antibiotic prescribed. The new prescription resolves the urinary tract infection. This antibiotic sensitivity test allowed the clinician to make a **differential decision** about the choice of antibiotic to treat a medical problem. The general approaches to this decision-making process are described in the next section.

Antibiotic Sensitivity Testing: An Overview

In this exercise the pure cultures of bacteria are assumed to represent clinical specimens obtained from patients. The gram-positive and gram-negative bacterial cultures chosen for this exercise represent a spectrum of organisms responsible for respiratory, genitourinary, sepsis, nosocomial and postsurgical infections. These include some of the same bacteria found in the exercises covering the clinical unknown. The present exercise represents the next step after the identification of the clinical unknown specimen. (If so instructed, the identified clinical unknown organism may be used for antibiotic testing.) These specimens are sent to the laboratory for antimicrobic susceptibility studies to determine the most suitable antibiotic for prescription by the clinician for the patient. The student assumes the role of laboratory technician and completes the Kirby-Bauer test on these bacterial culture specimens and reports on which are the most effective antibiotics. This exercise should also help the student entering a career in health sciences understand why a decision on a proper differential treatment plan for patients takes time.

Kirby-Bauer Disk Agar Diffusion Method. Mueller-Hinton agar is used in this method. The pH of this agar is between 7.2–7.4 and this medium is poured to a depth of 4 mm. Normally a clinical laboratory adjusts the turbidity of the bacterial culture to that of a MacFarland No. 0.5 turbidity standard, or 1.5×10^8 colony forming units per ml. In this exercise, for simplicity, 18-hour broth cultures of the bacteria are used. The bacterial culture is swabbed onto the surface of the agar. Sterile antibiotic disks are placed on the agar with the aid of a mechanical plunger type of antibiotic dispenser obtained from Difco Laboratories or BBL. This dispenser contains cartridges of different antibiotics. When the plunger is depressed, single different antibiotic disks are dispensed onto the agar surface at the same time. The plates are then incubated at 35°C for 18 hours. During incubation the antibiotics diffuse outward from the disk into the agar.

If the bacteria are susceptible to an antibiotic, then a clear halo appears around the disk. In this case the antibiotic has killed or inhibited the bacteria. This clear halo is called a **zone of inhibition**. In the absence of a zone of inhibition, growth of bacteria is seen instead of the clear halo. The size of the zone of inhibition depends in part on the rate of diffusion of the antibiotic through the agar. A large zone of inhibition is not always an indication of the effectiveness of an antibiotic. Some antibiotics that are effective diffuse slowly and produce small zones of inhibition. Instead, the size of the zone of inhibition is compared to a standard table that evaluates the antibiotic effectiveness in zone diameter as resistant, intermediate or sensitive to the antibiotic. **Resistant** means that the microbe is resistant to the antibiotic. **Intermediate** means that the microbe is somewhat sensitive to the antibiotic. **Sensitive** means that the microbe is sensitive to the antibiotic. Generally these results are reported to the clinicians in culture sensitivity tests as R, I or S so that the clinician can make a differential decision regarding the best antibiotic to use for a specific medical problem. The student on completing the Kirby-Bauer procedure must complete the culture sensitivity report in the Results section that would represent the information sent to the clinician.

Materials

18-hour trypticase soy broth cultures of *Enterococcus faecalis, Staphylococcus aureus, Streptococcus pyogenes, Escherichia coli, Klebsiella pneumoniae* and *Pseudomonas aeruginosa*

If desired, the 18-hour trypticase soy broth culture of the clinical unknown may be substituted for the organisms listed above.

plates of Mueller-Hinton agar

packets of sterile cotton tipped swabs

plunger type antibiotic disk dispenser available from Difco Laboratories or BBL

suggested antibiotic cartridges include: amikacin, ampicillin, bacitracin, erythromycin, gentamycin, neomycin, nitrofurantoin, tetracycline and vancomycin

metric ruler

slide forceps

beakers of 95% alcohol

Procedures

First Period (See Figure 41-1)

If the clinical unknown is used, follow these procedures for only the organism identified.

1. Select separate plates of Mueller-Hinton agar and label them "unknown" or "*Enterococcus faecalis*," "*Staphylococcus aureus*," "*Streptococcus pyogenes*," "*Escherichia coli*," "*Klebsiella pneumoniae*" and "*Pseudomonas aeruginosa*."

2. Use a separate sterile cotton-tipped applicator to swab each plate of Mueller-Hinton agar. Dispose of each swab in the pipette discard filled with disinfectant. (Swab the surface of each plate completely.)

3. Allow each plate to dry for 5 minutes before applying the antibiotics.

4. Remove the petri dish cover. Place the antibiotic dispenser over the petri dish. Depress the plunger handle once to apply the selected antibiotic disks to the agar surface of each swabbed dish.

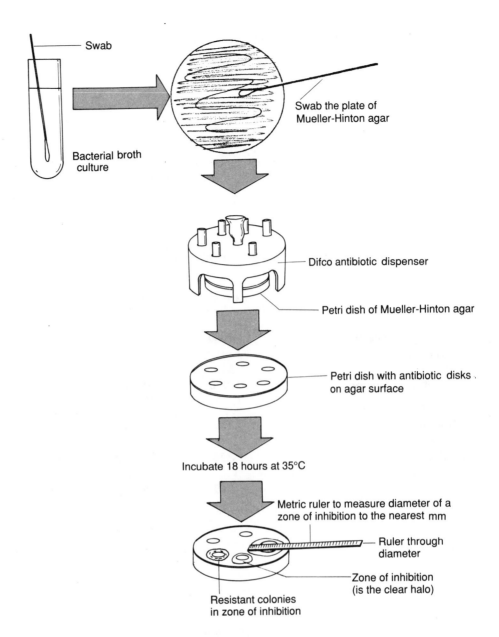

Swab

Bacterial broth culture

Swab the plate of Mueller-Hinton agar

Difco antibiotic dispenser

Petri dish of Mueller-Hinton agar

Petri dish with antibiotic disks on agar surface

Incubate 18 hours at 35°C

Metric ruler to measure diameter of a zone of inhibition to the nearest mm

Ruler through diameter

Zone of inhibition (is the clear halo)

Resistant colonies in zone of inhibition

Figure 41-1
Antibiotic Sensitivity Testing—A Differential Decision

5. Sterilize the slide forceps by dipping in alcohol followed by flaming, and gently tap each antibiotic disk onto the surface of the agar.

6. Replace the cover on the petri dish.

7. Invert and incubate each dish at 35°C for 18 hours. Refrigerate the dishes until the next laboratory period.

Second Period

1. Examine each of the incubated Mueller-Hinton plates for zones of inhibition. Some zones of inhibition may show small colonies. These represent bacteria that are resistant to the particular antibiotic.

2. Measure the diameter of each zone of inhibition to the nearest mm. Record any evidence of resistant bacteria.

3. Record these findings in the Results section. Compare your results to those in the standardized table of zone diameters in mm to determine whether the microbe is resistant (R), intermediate (I) or sensitive (S) to the given antibiotic.

4. Record the R, I or S finding in the Results section for each clinical microorganism specimen studied.

5. Review your findings to determine whether there is any relationship between Gram reaction of a microorganism and antibiotic sensitivity.

6. Answer the questions for the exercise.

Antibiotic Zone Size Interpretive Chart (BBL Sensidisc Data)

Antibiotic	Code	Conc.	Resistant	Zone dia., mm Intermediate	Sensitive
			<		>
Ampicillin, gram-neg & enterococ.	AM10	10 mcg	11	12–13	14
Ampicillin, staph & highly sensitive	AM10	10 mcg	20	21–28	29
Bacitracin	B10	10 U	8	9–12	13
Carbenicillin, *Pseudomonas* spp.	CB50	50 mcg	12	13–14	15
Cephaloglycin	CG30	30 mcg	16	17–26	27
Cephaloridine	CD30	30 mcg	11	12–15	16
Cephalothin	CF30	30 mcg	14	15–17	18
Chloramphenicol	C30	30 mcg	12	13–17	18
Clindamycin	CC2	2 mcg	11	12–15	16
Erythromycin	E15	15 mcg	13	14–17	18
Gentamycin	GM10	10 mcg	12		13
Kanamycin	K30	30 mcg	13	14–17	18
Lincomycin	L2	2 mcg	9	10–14	15
Methicillin	DP5	5 mcg	9	10–13	14
Nafcillin, Oxacillin	NF1, Ox1	1 mcg	10	11–12	13
Nalidixic acid	NA30	30 mcg	13	14–18	19
Neomycin	N30	30 mcg	12	13–16	17
Nitrofurantoin	F/M300	300 mcg	14	15–16	17
Novobiocin	NB30	30 mcg	17	18–21	22
Oleandomycin	OL15	15 mcg	11	12–16	17
Penicillin G, staphylococci	P10	10 U	20	21–28	29
Penicillin G, other organisms	P10	10 U	11	12–21	22
Polymyxin B	PB300	300 U	8	9–11	12
Rifampin	RA5	5 mcg	24		
Streptomycin	S10	10 mcg	11	12–14	15
Triple sulfa	SSS.25	250 mcg	12	13–16	17
Tetracycline	Te30	30 mcg	14	15–18	19
Vancomycin	Va30	30 mcg	9	10–11	12

Source: Kelley, Susan G. and Post, Frederick J. 1989. Basic Microbiology Techniques Third Edition. Published by Star Publishing Company, Belmont, CA. Reprinted with permission of the publisher.

Effects of Antiseptic Agents on Transmission of Oral Flora or Nasal Flora

Warning: This exercise uses human oral and nasal flora. Some of these may be opportunistic pathogens or pathogenic. Use care to avoid spills, coughing or sneezing and prevent transmission of these organisms to others.

Objectives

1. Define infection.
2. Distinguish between direct and indirect transmission.
3. Define communicable disease.
4. Name a pathogenic yeast and the medical problems produced in humans.

Background

Infection is the presence and multiplication of microorganisms in or on the surface of a host to produce damage to that host. These microbes can produce damage directly to the host tissues, can produce toxins which cause tissue damage or can cause immune reactions which are injurious to the host. Communicable infections include those that can be spread or transmitted from one host to another. In direct transmission, infected persons can transfer their organisms by intimate person to person contact with a body surface. These include kissing, handshaking, sexual intercourse, bacteria crossing the placenta or entering into a nursing mother's milk and contact with open sores. Hands contaminated with pus from wounds or boils or other bodily infections can readily spread disease producing organisms to others. Indirect methods of transmission of infection lack the intimate contact with a bodily surface. They require a contaminated intermediate agent or fomite. Examples include contact with contaminated dressings, clothing, bedpans, drinking cups and eating utensils. These items can become contaminated with a patient's secretions and then serve as a bridge to spread infections to others who contact them. Fecal-oral transmission of gastrointestinal pathogens is another example of indirect transmission.

In the microbiology laboratory and medical facilities asepsis practices are used to prevent direct and indirect transmission of infectious microorganisms. Applications in medical facilities include medical and surgical asepsis. Medical asepsis which include handwashing and good sanitation or disinfection serves to reduce the chances of transmission of disease organisms. These practices are included in the safety rules and practices in all microbiology laboratories.

Medical practitioners such as nurses, doctors, physician assistants and nurse practitioners practice the accepted medical practice of rigorous handwashing with antiseptic soap solutions to prevent the spread of microbes from one patient to another. Surgical asepsis includes swabbing the area of a patient's skin with antiseptic scrubs prior to incision to prevent the entry of microbes and use of sterile drapes around the area of surgery to create a sterile field as well as rigorous scrubbing of hands and forearms followed by wearing gloves, gown, mask and caps by the surgical team to prevent transfer of microorganisms to the field of a surgical procedure. All dressings, instruments and sutures are sterilized prior to use in surgery. Surgical sepsis is also practiced in the obstetrical delivery room to protect the newborn and mother from infection.

Effects of Antiseptic Agents on Transmission of Oral or Nasal Flora: An Overview

This exercise evaluates the bacteriostatic and bactericidal effects of selected antiseptic mouthwashes and antiseptic handwashing solutions. You will also be presented with a model to illustrate ability of the products to interfere with the transmission of upper respiratory tract flora found in the oral cavity or nasal cavity. The infectious microorganisms found in the respiratory tract include *Staphylococcus aureus*, *Hemophilus influenzae*, *pneumococci*, and *streptococci*.

Swab either the oral cavity or the nasal cavity four times with different sterile swabs. These swabs are then separately placed in sterile tubes containing Cepacol®, Betadine® solution, Hibiclens® solution and trypticase soy broth for 15 minutes. These tubes are designated as the **first infected host**. The first three solutions contain antimicrobial solutions that have potentially bacteriostatic or bactericidal activity against bacteria. These swab tubes contain agents that can also block the transmission of infectious bacteria. The trypticase soy broth tube simulates a control individual who is infected with microorganisms. After storage incubation, the students then swab separate prelabeled antiseptic and control plates of trypticase soy agar plates lacking any test chemical with the incubated swabs. The swabbed plates represent the consequences of different treatments on the attempt to transmit bacteria to another individual, allow them to reproduce and create an infection. Therefore, the swabbed plates simulate a **second infected host** and are used as a culture model to demonstrate (a) transmission of infectious bacteria, (b) bacteriostasis and bactericidal effects of antimicrobial agents and (c) blocking transmission of infectious bacteria. The tubes containing their swabs and the plates are incubated at 35°C for 48 hours and evaluated. The control broth tube and the control swabbed plate show heavy growth. This plate shows that microorganisms can be transmitted from one individual to another and grow. The mouthwash tube is compared to the plates. Usually the mouthwash tube lacks growth while the plate shows almost as much growth as the control. This suggests that the mouthwash is only bacteriostatic to bacteria. In bacteriostasis, no growth is found in the presence of the test chemical. Typically, growth is observed when the bacteria are transferred to medium free of the test chemical. Bacteriostatic agents do not prevent the transmission and growth of the bacteria in an individual free of the test chemical. The tubes of Betadine® and Hibiclens® are too dark to permit observation of any growth. However, the plates swabbed from the Betadine® and Hibiclens® tubes lack any growth. This indicates that Betadine® and Hibiclens® solutions killed the bacteria during incubation of the swabs in the tubes. These two antiseptics therefore are bactericidal to them. Bactericidal agents typically show no growth when the bacteria are transferred to medium lacking the test agent. This exercise also demonstrates that bactericidal agents can block the transmission of harmful bacteria from one individual to another, while bacteriostatic agents afford protection only in the presence of the agent. This exercise demonstrates the importance of using germicidal scrubs for pre-surgical scrubbing by surgical teams and for prepping of patients prior to surgery as well as handwashing to prevent transmission of infectious bacteria to patients in the operating room as well as from patient to caregiver to patient.

Materials

sterile swabs

tubes of sterile distilled water

separate sterile tubes containing 5 ml of mouthwash (Cepacol®), and the antiseptic scrub solutions Betadine® and Hibiclens®.

tubes of trypticase soy broth

plates of trypticase soy agar

Procedures

First Period

1. Obtain a sterile swab and sterile tubes containing Cepacol®, Betadine®, Hibiclens® and trypticase soy broth (see Figure 42-1).

2. Moisten the swab by dipping it into a tube of sterile distilled water. Use good aseptic technique.

3. Swab the oral cavity thoroughly. Be sure to touch the mucous membranes of the cheeks, gums and tongue. Alternatively, roll the swab just inside the nostrils.

4. Place this swab in the tube of Cepacol®.

5. Use 3 separate swabs to repeat this swabbing procedure three more times. Place these swabs individually into the tubes of Betadine®, Hibiclens® and trypticase soy broth.

6. Incubate these swab containing tubes for 15 minutes at room temperature.

7. While the tubes are incubating, select 4 trypticase soy agar plates and label them Cepacol®, Betadine®, Hibiclens® and trypticase soy agar control. Also, label the plates oral cavity or nasal cavity.

8. After incubation, completely swab the agar surfaces of the labeled plates with the matching swabs.

9. Incubate all the plates at 35°C for 48 hours and then evaluate for the presence of growth or no growth.

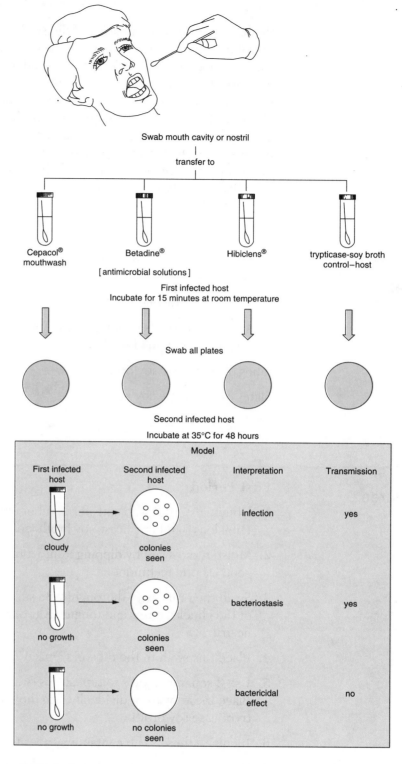

Swab mouth cavity or nostril

|

transfer to

Cepacol®
mouthwash

Betadine®

Hibiclens®

trypticase-soy broth
control−host

[antimicrobial solutions]

First infected host
Incubate for 15 minutes at room temperature

Swab all plates

Second infected host

Incubate at 35°C for 48 hours

Model

First infected host	Second infected host	Interpretation	Transmission
cloudy	colonies seen	infection	yes
no growth	colonies seen	bacteriostasis	yes
no growth	no colonies seen	bactericidal effect	no

Figure 42-1
Effects of Antiseptic Agents on Transmission of Oral Flora or Nasal Flora

Second Period

1. The presence of heavy growth means the agent does not block transmission of respiratory flora. Reduced growth means partial blocking of transmission of respiratory flora and no growth means blocking or inhibition of transmission of respiratory microbial flora.

2. Record the observations in the Results section.

3. Answer the questions for the exercise.

Exercise 43

Beta-Lactamase Activity in Gram-Positive Cocci

Caution: Nitrocefin can cause mutations in the Ames test. It may also cause hypersensitive reactions and must not be ingested, inhaled, or contact the skin. Use aseptic techniques in handling these disks.

Objectives

1. Describe the cell wall structure of gram-positive bacteria.
2. Name some beta-lactam category antibiotics.
3. Describe the action of beta-lactamase enzymes.

Background

The cell wall of bacteria contains peptidoglycan which is composed of alternating molecules of N-acetylglucosamine and N-acetyl muramic acid which are linked by a β 1,4 glycosidic (sugar) bond to form glycan chains. In addition, each muramic acid molecule contains a tetrapeptide sidechain extending from it. The third amino acid of one tetrapeptide chain is crosslinked to the alanine end amino acid of another glycan chain by a process called transpeptidation. These crosslinks anchor one chain to another. The combination of the glycan chains and the crosslinked tetrapeptides form the peptidoglycan layer of the cell wall in bacteria. The crosslinks give the peptidoglycan layers a three dimensional shape and strengthen the cell wall. When the gram-positive bacteria are treated with beta-lactam antibiotics, the crosslinks are cut and the adjacent layers of the glycan chains peel apart. Destruction of the peptidoglycan make the cells susceptible to osmotic lysis. Water flows into the hypertonic cytoplasm and the cell swells and bursts.

In effect, this class of antibiotics interfere with the process of transpeptidation. Beta-lactam antibiotics include the penicillins, cephalosporins, carbapenems and monobactams. These antibiotics are highly bactericidal to bacteria. Bacteria that lack cell walls such as *Mycoplasma* are resistant to beta-lactam antibiotics. Also, stationary phase cells that are not actively multiplying are not killed by these antibiotics. Gram-negative bacteria which routinely have a thin peptidoglycan layer are resistant to beta-lactam antibiotics because they have an outer lipolysaccharide layer around the peptidoglycan which resists the entry of these antibiotics.

Some bacteria can produce a beta-lactamase enzyme that can cut the carbon-nitrogen bond of the beta-lactam ring, opening this ring and inactivating the antibiotic. This change in structure makes these bacteria resistant to these antibiotics. This exercise considers a significant aspect of the problem of antibiotic resistance that is common today. Beta-lactamase producing bacteria include *Staphylococcus aureus*, *Neisseria gonorrheae*, *Moraxella (Branhamella) catarrhalis* and ampicillin resistant *Hemophilus influenzae*. This exercise focusses on the beta-lactamase activity of *Staphylococcus aureus* ATCC 29213.

Beta-Lactamase Activity in Gram-Positive Cocci: An Overview

In this exercise, a Cefinase® disk is used. Cefinase® contains the color producing cephalosporin nitrocefin. When the beta-lactam ring of this antibiotic is split, the yellow disk changes color to red. A single disk can be used to test one bacterial culture for the presence of a beta-lactamase. The Cefinase® disks are only used to detect beta-lactamase in *Neisseria gonorrheae*, *Moraxella (Bramhamella) catarrhalis*, *Staphylococcus aureus*, *Hemophilus influenzae*, enterococci and anaerobic bacteria.

Materials

24 hour streak plate of *Staphylococcus aureus* ATCC 29213 grown on blood agar

If desired, 24 hour streak plate of *Enterococcus faecalis* grown on blood agar

Cefinase® disks: Store unopened package in a refrigerator or freezer. After using, store the cartridge of Cefinase® disks in an air tight glass jar containing dessicating agent at refrigerator or freezer temperature. Do not use the disks if they appear orange or red in color.

slide forceps

tubes of sterile distilled water

1 ml pipettes

pipette pumps

sterile petri dishes

Procedures

1. Obtain a blood agar culture plate of *Staphylococcus aureus* ATCC 29213 and if desired a blood agar culture plate of *Enterococcus faecalis*. (See Figure 43-1.)

2. Obtain a cartridge of Cefinase® disks, a tube of sterile distilled water, a slide forceps, inoculating loop or needle, sterile petri dish, 1 ml pipette and pipette pump.

3. Pass the tip of a slide forceps through the flame. Grasp the cartridge of Cefinase® disks and gently push one disk part way through the cartridge. Grasp the free end of the protruding disk by the tip of the forceps and transfer it to a sterile petri dish.

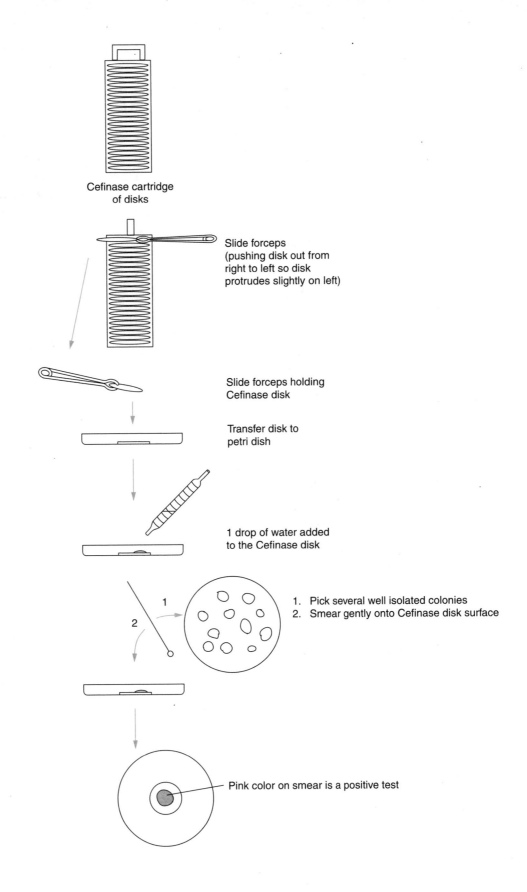

Cefinase cartridge
of disks

Slide forceps
(pushing disk out from
right to left so disk
protrudes slightly on left)

Slide forceps holding
Cefinase disk

Transfer disk to
petri dish

1 drop of water added
to the Cefinase disk

1. Pick several well isolated colonies
2. Smear gently onto Cefinase disk surface

Pink color on smear is a positive test

Figure 43-1
Beta-Lactamase Activity in
Gram-Positive Cocci

4. Draw up 0.1 ml of sterile distilled water into the pipette and transfer exactly one drop of water to the disk surface. Do not flood the disk.

5. Grasp the inoculating loop or needle, flame sterilize it and pick several well isolated colonies and gently smear them on to the disk surface.

6. Repeat these procedures in a separate petri dish for the culture of *E. faecalis*, if desired.

7. Observe the disk or disks for any color changes. The appearance of a red color in the region of a bacterial smear is a positive test for beta-lactamase activity. The positive color test reaction can appear in 5 minutes to one hour after completion of the test procedure. No color change indicates lack of any beta-lactamase activity.

8. Dispose of the petri dishes containing the disks in a metal discard for autoclaving.

Oligodynamic Action Against Bacteria

Objectives

1. Define the term **oligodynamic action**.
2. Describe two illustrations of this process on bacteria.
3. Describe the mechanism for the action of mercury compounds.

Background

The lethal action of heavy metals on microorganisms is known as **oligodynamic action**. The heavy metals that are commonly used to control microorganisms are mercury, silver and copper. Mercury is incorporated into an organic compound to form the antiseptic thimerosal (Merthiolate). Mercury combines with the sulfhydryl (–SH) groups of proteins and forms a S–Hg–S bridge. This bridge denatures the protein. A silver salt compound (silver sulfadiazine) is used in an ointment to place on infected burns. This ointment is lethal to *Pseudomonas aeruginosa*, which is frequently found in tissue burns. Copper sulfate at 1 ppm is used to control and kill algae in lakes and other bodies of water.

Oligodynamic Action Against Bacteria: An Overview

This exercise examines the lethal effect of heavy metals on gram-positive and gram-negative bacterial cultures that are swabbed on separate plates of nutrient agar. The heavy metals aluminum, copper and zinc are used. These are aseptically placed on the swabbed agar surfaces and the plates are incubated. The culture plates are then examined for zones of inhibition. Any correlation between sensitivity to heavy metals and Gram reaction should be made on evaluation of the results.

Materials

20-hour nutrient broth cultures of *Escherichia coli* and *Staphylococcus aureus* plates of nutrient agar

packages of sterile swabs

sterile glass petri dishes containing sterile thin, short copper rods and sterile small disks of aluminum foil

bottle of reagent-grade zinc powder

slide forceps

small beaker of 95% alcohol

Procedures

First Period (See Figure 44-1)

1. Select two plates of nutrient agar. Label the bottom of each dish with three circles. Mark the first circle "Al" for aluminum, mark the second circle "Cu" for copper and mark the third circle "Zn" for zinc.

2. Mark the first plate *"Escherichia coli"* and the second plate *"Staphylococcus aureus."*

3. Select the *"Escherichia coli"* labeled plate. Select a sterile cotton swab and swab *Escherichia coli* on the surface of the agar of this plate. Dispose of the swab in the appropriate discard container.

4. Select the *"Staphylococcus aureus"* labeled plate. Select another cotton swab and swab *Staphylococcus aureus* on the surface of the agar of this plate. Dispose of this swab in the appropriate discard container.

5. Select the swabbed plate of *Escherichia coli.* Dip the tip of the slide forceps in the beaker of 95% alcohol and then pass it through a flame. Allow

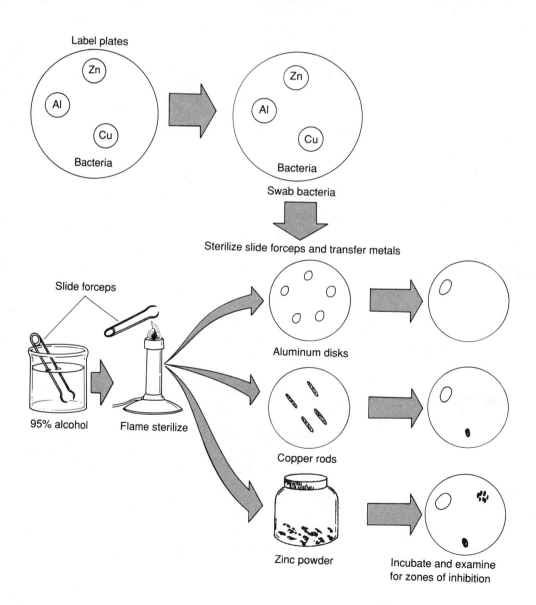

Label plates

Bacteria

Swab bacteria

Bacteria

Sterilize slide forceps and transfer metals

Slide forceps

95% alcohol   Flame sterilize

Aluminum disks

Copper rods

Zinc powder

Incubate and examine for zones of inhibition

Figure 44-1
Oligodynamic Action
Against Bacteria

the alcohol to burn off. This sterilizes the forceps. Pickup and transfer an aluminum disk to the surface of the agar over the circle marked "Al."

6. Flame sterilize the forceps again and transfer a copper rod to the surface of the agar over the circle marked "Cu."

7. Flame sterilize the forceps again and transfer several crystals of zinc powder to the surface of the agar over the circle marked "Zn."

8. Repeat this series of transfers for the swabbed plate of *Staphylococcus aureus*.

9. Incubate both plates at 35°C for 48 hours.

Second Period

1. Examine both plates for the presence of zones of inhibition.

2. Write a brief statement to indicate any correlation between oligodynamic action and Gram reaction.

3. Answer the questions for the exercise.

Ultraviolet Light Lethality and Photoreactivation

Warning: Ultraviolet light can cause skin burns, blindness and cancer. Do not under any circumstances look at the ultraviolet light source when it is operating. Do not permit your hands to come into contact with any reflected light from this apparatus when it is operating. Turn off the appliance when inserting plates for irradiation or removing plates.

Objectives

1. Indicate the wavelength spectrum for ultraviolet light.
2. Describe the formation. of a pyrimidine dimer.
3. Describe the events that occur in photoreactivation.
4. Describe an experiment to show that ultraviolet light is primarily a surface-acting agent.

Background

Ultraviolet light radiation is frequently used in microbiology to sterilize surfaces. The ultraviolet light spectrum ranges from 100 nm to 400 nm. A nanometer (nm) is 10^{-9} meter. The most effective ultraviolet radiation is in a range near 260 nm. Germicidal lamps emit ultraviolet light radiation in a range near 260 nm. They are frequently used in clean rooms and hospital operating rooms to sterilize surfaces. The radiation at 260 nm is strongly absorbed by purine and pyrimidine bases in DNA. Thymine and cytosine are the pyrimidine bases in DNA, and adenine and guanine are the purine bases. The sequence of these bases is responsible for the triplet genetic code in the DNA. When two pyrimidines located next to each other on the same chain in DNA absorb ultraviolet light, they form an unusual cyclobutane (four-carbon) bond between their adjacent carbons. This bond links the two pyrimidines in the same chain tightly together. This structure is called **pyrimidine dimer**. The dimer does not properly pair with the complementary bases in the opposite chain. The dimer also interferes with the replication of DNA. The wrong bases are inserted into DNA during replication, thus creating a **mutation**. The most common dimer is the thymine dimer. Accumulation of these dimers in the cells create mutations that are lethal to the organism.

Many microorganisms have repair systems that can eliminate the damage produced by ultraviolet light. One of these is the **photoreactivation pho-**

tolyase enzyme, which restores the dimerized bases to their original shape. In the presence of longer wavelength light, the photoreactivation enzyme splits the cyclobutane type bonds in the dimer and restores the adjacent pyrimidines to their original condition.

Ultraviolet Light Lethality and Photoreactivation: An Overview

In this exercise, duplicate sets of gram-positive and gram-negative bacterial cultures are swabbed on separate plates of trypticase soy agar. These are irradiated without the covers with a germicidal lamp at graded doses of ultraviolet light. One set is wrapped with aluminum foil immediately after irradiation to prevent any light-induced repair of the radiation damage; the other set is exposed to photoreactivating light from a 75-watt, 130-volt reflector bulb flood lamp to demonstrate a reversal of the dimer damage to the normal state. A third set is irradiated at the maximum exposure with the covers on to measure the influence of shielding in preventing the damage produced by ultraviolet light. All the plates are incubated at 30°C for a week and evaluated either for the immediate lethal damage effect of ultraviolet light or for the restorative effect of photoreactivating light or for the effect of shielding in preventing ultraviolet light damage in cells.

Materials

18-hour trypticase soy broth cultures of *Escherichia coli* and *Staphylococcus aureus*

trypticase soy agar (TSA) plates

packets of sterile cotton swabs

wooden box containing an ultraviolet light source, which is a 15-watt 15T8 germicidal lamp. The height of the lamp from the floor of the box is 20 cm, or 8 inches.

aluminum foil

75-watt, 130-volt reflector bulb flood lamp

Procedures

First Period (See Figure 45-1)

1. *Preparation Prior to Irradiation:*

   a. Select 14 TSA plates. Label 7 of the plates *"Escherichia coli"* and 7 of the plates *"Staphylococcus aureus."*

   b. Label 3 of the *Escherichia coli* plates "UV only" and "0 minutes," "1 minute," and "2 minutes." Label the other 3 *Escherichia coli* plates "UV + PHR" and "0 minutes," "1 minute" and "2 minutes." Label the last *Escherichia coli* plate: "UV only—cover on—2 minutes."

   c. Label 3 of the *Staphylococcus aureus* plates "UV only" and "0 minutes," "1 minute," and "2 minutes." Label the other 3 *Staphylococcus aureus*

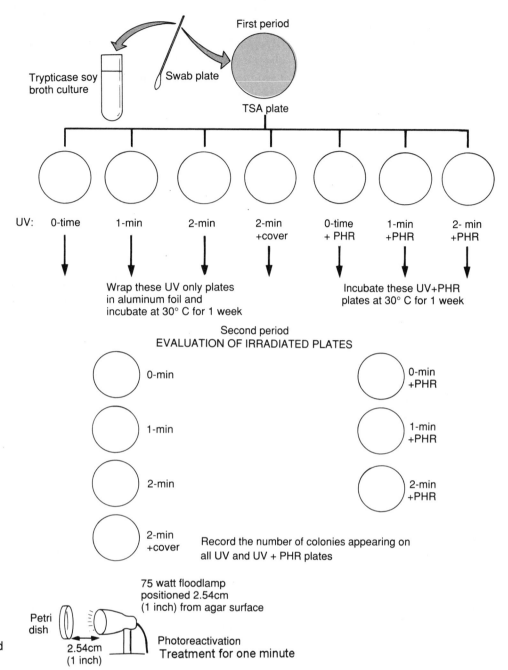

Trypticase soy
broth culture

Swab plate

First period

TSA plate

UV: 0-time   1-min   2-min   2-min   0-time   1-min   2- min
                                 +cover   + PHR   +PHR   +PHR

Wrap these UV only plates
in aluminum foil and
incubate at 30° C for 1 week

Incubate these UV+PHR
plates at 30° C for 1 week

Second period
EVALUATION OF IRRADIATED PLATES

0-min

1-min

2-min

2-min
+cover

0-min
+PHR

1-min
+PHR

2-min
+PHR

Record the number of colonies appearing on
all UV and UV + PHR plates

75 watt floodlamp
positioned 2.54cm
(1 inch) from agar surface

Petri
dish

2.54cm
(1 inch)

Photoreactivation
Treatment for one minute

Figure 45-1
Ultraviolet Light Lethality and
Photoreactivation (PHR)

plates "UV + PHR" and "0 minutes," "1 minute," and "2 minutes." Label
the last *Staphylococcus aureus* plate "UV only—cover on—2 minutes."

d. Swab all the *"Escherichia coli"* labeled plates with *Escherichia coli*. Use
separate swabs for each plate. Dispose of each swab in the pipette discard filled with disinfectant.

e. Swab all the *"Staphylococcus aureus"* labeled plates with *Staphylococcus aureus*. Use separate swabs for each plate. Dispose of each swab
in the pipette discard filled with disinfectant.

f. Assemble all the plates on the table near the ultraviolet lamp source.
Wrap the UV only plates labeled "0 minutes" in aluminum foil.

2. *Irradiation:*
   a. Remove the covers of the 1-minute UV only and UV + PHR plates and place the swabbed dishes in the box under the ultraviolet light source. Turn on the lamp. **Do not look at the lamp when it is on and keep all hands clear of the lamp.** After irradiation, turn off the ultraviolet light source and remove the plates. Replace the covers. Wrap the UV only plates in aluminum foil.

   b. Repeat Step 2a for the plates labeled "2 minutes" UV only and UV + PHR. At the same time, place the plates labeled "UV only—cover on—2 minutes" under the ultraviolet lamp. **Do not remove the covers from these plates.** Be sure to irradiate all these plates for 2 minutes.

3. *Photoreactivation:*
   a. Remove the cover from a UV + PHR plate and hold it 1 inch from the 75-watt flood lamp for photoreactivation. Expose the plate for 1 minute. Replace the cover. Repeat this photoreactivation treatment for each "UV + PHR"-labeled plate. After photoreactivation, replace the cover.

   b. Incubate all the UV only and the UV + PHR plates at 30°C for 1 week.

Second Period

1. *Evaluation:*
   a. Assemble the UV only, UV + PHR and UV only—cover on—2 minutes plates by organism into two stacks.

   b. Examine the UV only plates for 0 minutes, 1 minute, and 2 minutes exposure. Note the decrease in number of colonies with increasing ultraviolet light exposure.

   c. Examine the UV + PHR plates for 1 minute and 2 minutes exposure. Note whether long wavelength light-induced restoration occurred after photoreactivation treatment. This is noted as an increase in survival and a greater number of colonies on the UV + PHR plates than on the UV only plates.

   d. Examine the UV only—cover on—2 minutes plates for any effect of the cover on survival during irradiation. Determine whether the thin petri dish cover protects the cells from the damage produced by ultraviolet light.

   e. Record all findings in the Results section.

2. Answer the questions for the exercise.

Case Study 7

A patient visits a physician for severe chest pain, fever and coughing. Blood and mucus are found in the sputum. The physician prescribes erythromycin. The patient takes the medicine as prescribed. The symptoms are only partly resolved. The patient returns to the physician. A sputum sample is sent to the laboratory for analysis. The laboratory report shows sensitivity of the isolated organism to ciprofloxacin. The physician changes the antibiotic. After taking the ciprofloxacin as prescribed, the patient recovers fully.

Answer the following:

1. Devise an explanation for the failure of the first antibiotic.

_____

_____

_____

2. Explain why the second antibiotic was effective.

_____

_____

_____

_____

46 **A Model for Soft Tissue Infection** **257**

describes the procedures and development of a soft tissue infection using bacterially inoculated and incubated apples as the model host.

47 **A Lethal Action of Lysozyme on Bacteria** **263**

characterizes the lethal action of lysozyme on a selected gram-positive and gram-negative bacterial culture.

48 **Staphylococci on Skin** **267**

describes procedures to isolate and characterize staphylococci found on the skin.

49 **Upper Respiratory Tract Culture** **271**

uses blood agar and selective media to isolate and identify staphylococci and other microbes in the upper respiratory tract.

50 **Gastrointestinal Infections** **281**

uses a variety of specialized media to identify the cause of simulated gastrointestinal disease in patients caused by gram-negative enteropathogens.

51 **Urinary Tract Infections** **289**

uses specialized media to identity common gram-positive and gram-negative causes of this problem.

51 **Optional: Uricult System for Urinary Tract Infection** **297**

52 **Snyder Test for Dental Caries Susceptibility** **299**

determines the sensitivity towards developing dental caries.

53   **Salmonella Serology: Slide Agglutination Test**   **303**

uses this procedure as an alternative approach to identify this grain-negative pathogen.

54   **Mutagens and Carcinogens: The Ames Test**   **307**

evaluates a variety of commonly used agents for their mutagenic and carcinogenic ability.

Case Study 8   **311**

A Model for Soft Tissue Infection

Objectives

1. Define infection.

2. Describes observed features in two different soft tissue infections.

3. Devise a non-human model to demonstrate soft tissue infection.

Background

Infection is the presence and multiplication of microorganisms on the surface of or in the tissues of the host organism that produce damage or pathology. Common well-known infections include yeast infections (frequently found after extended use of antibiotics), Hepatitis B infection, AIDS infection, streptococcal sore throat, chickenpox, and the sexually transmitted diseases such as syphilis, gonorrhea, and chlamydiae. Each of the pathogens that causes these infections multiplies in the host and produces pathological changes to the tissues of the host.

This exercise focuses on soft tissue infection, many of which involve anaerobes as well as staphylococci, and gram-negative bacilli. Examples include: (a) *Anaerobic cellulitis*, caused by *Bacteroides, Clostridium* species, coliforms and streptococci. These infections are characterized by little change in skin color, abundant gas, foul odor, and no change in muscle. Treatment involves removing infected tissue (debridement), draining of abscesses and antibiotics, (b) *Progressive bacterial synergistic gangrene*, a necrotic spreading skin infection, which can be found in diabetics, in immunosuppressed hosts, and as a complication of abdominal surgery and thoracic surgery. The cause of this infection is polymicrobic in nature and includes anaerobic streptococci, *Staphylococcus aureus* and gram-negative bacilli. The lesions are characterized by a central zone of necrotic tissue, a middle zone of purplish discoloration and an outer red edge. The treatment used is to surgically excise or remove the infected tissues together with high dose of antibiotics such as metronidazole, ticarcillin/clavulanate and ampicillin/sulbactam. (c) *Synergistic nonclostridial anaerobic myonecrosis* is very common in diabetic patients. The skin shows scattered regions of blue-gray necrosis in a background of normal tissue.

There may be much necrosis of the underlying dermis, subcutaneous tissue and muscle. There is a foul odor and gas may be present in 25% of the patients. These last two infections frequently involve a synergistic cooperation between anaerobes such as *Bacteroides* as well as aerobic or facultative gram-negative bacilli and produce extensive tissue destruction. Surgical removal of infected tissue together with antibiotics are the accepted treatments. (Refer to Exercise 27—Synergism for additional information.)

A Model for Soft Tissue Infection: An Overview

The purpose of this exercise is to simulate a soft tissue infection. The hosts, which substitute for human beings, are apples. The skin of the apple corresponds to the human epidermis and the meat of the apple corresponds to the dermis, subcutaneous and muscle layers in a human host. The surface of the apple is swabbed with 70% alcohol. A puncture wound is created in the apple. This wound is deliberately contaminated with *Escherichia coli* or *Staphylococcus aureus*. The apple is then incubated overnight to permit multiplication of the microbes and development of an infection. The critical period which determines whether contamination of a surgical wound leads to infection lies within the first three hours after the contamination. The overnight incubation period allows this infection to occur. After incubation, redness, discoloration and soft rots are seen in the skin around the puncture wound area. The meat of the apple may also be discolored. The selective media mannitol-salt agar and MacConkey agar are used to demonstrate the presence of bacteria in streaks made from the puncture wound. Gram stains are prepared to confirm the identification of the microorganisms.

Materials

20 hour nutrient broth culture of *Staphylococcus aureus*

20 hour nutrient broth culture of *Escherichia coli*

petri plates of mannitol-salt agar

petri plates of MacConkey agar

sterile surgical gloves

medium size Macintosh apples

sterilized straight dissecting needles

400 ml sterile beakers covered with sterile 6 inch by 6 inch squares of aluminum foil

coplin jars containing 70% alcohol

packets of sterile swabs

sterile 1 ml pipettes

pipette pumps

Procedures

First Period

1. Carefully open the package of sterile gloves.

2. Place the gloves on your hands.

3. Select 2 apples and swab each apple with 70% alcohol.

4. Remove the foil covers from the beakers and place the apples in separate beakers so that the stem faces up. Label the outside of one beaker *Staphylococcus aureus*. Label the other beaker *Escherichia coli* (see Figure 46-1).

5. Separately stab an apple with the sterile dissecting needle. Wiggle the needle back and forth to widen the opening slightly. The opening made should be cone shaped so that the tip of a 1 ml pipette can fit into the opening.

6. Repeat this stab wound on the second apple with a second sterile dissecting needle.

7. Pipette 0.1 ml of the *Staphylococcus aureus* culture into the wound opening of the apple contained in the beaker labeled *Staphylococcus aureus*. Do not remove the apple from the beaker during this procedure.

8. Pipette 0.1 ml of the *Escherichia coli* culture into the wound opening of the apple contained in the beaker labeled *Escherichia coli*. Do not remove the apple from the beaker during this procedure.

9. Cover both beakers with the sterile foils and fold the corners lightly to secure the foils.

10. Incubate both beakers containing the bacterially inoculated apples at 35°C for 24 hours.

11. Remove the surgical gloves and discard them in a metal microbiological discard container for autoclaving.

Second Period

1. Remove the beakers containing the apples from the incubator. Remove the foil covers.

2. Observe the apples for any discoloration around the wound opening and any unusual odors. Discoloration around the wound opening is indicative of tissue damage found in a soft tissue infection. Any discoloration or rot inside the wound area suggests tissue damage. Any strong odors may suggest fermentation of sugars found in the apples.

3. Record your observations in the Results section.

4. Flame an inoculating loop and insert it into the opening of the apple inoculated with *Staphylococcus aureus*. Rub the loop against the flesh of the apple and use this loop to streak a plate of mannitol-salt agar to isolate single colonies.

5. Flame an inoculating and insert it into the opening of the apple inoculated with *Escherichia coli*. Rub the loop against the flesh of the apple and use this loop to streak a plate of MacConkey agar to isolate single colonies.

6. Incubate both of these plates at 35°C for 72 hours.

1.

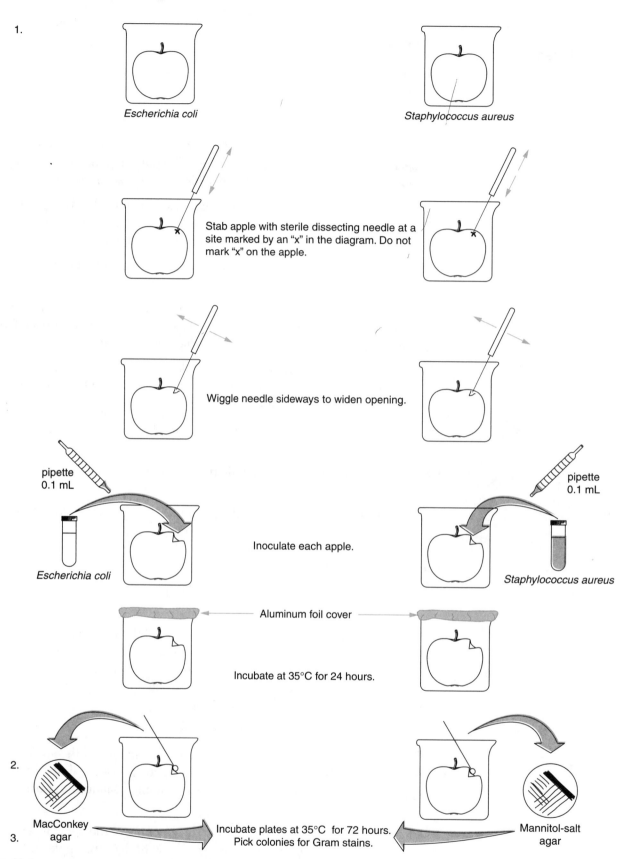

Escherichia coli

Staphylococcus aureus

Stab apple with sterile dissecting needle at a site marked by an "x" in the diagram. Do not mark "x" on the apple.

Wiggle needle sideways to widen opening.

pipette 0.1 mL

pipette 0.1 mL

Inoculate each apple.

Escherichia coli

Staphylococcus aureus

Aluminum foil cover

Incubate at 35°C for 24 hours.

2.

MacConkey agar

3.

Incubate plates at 35°C for 72 hours. Pick colonies for Gram stains.

Mannitol-salt agar

Figure 46-1

A Model for Soft Tissue Infection

7. Discard the beakers containing the apples and their foil covers in the microbiological discard container.

Third Period

1. Examine the plates for the presence of growth, the color of the agar and the appearance of the colonies.

2. Recall that *Staphylococcus aureus* ferments mannitol in mannitol-salt agar. The pH drops and the phenol red indicator changes from red to yellow. Yellow halos are observed around the colonies.

3. Recall that *Escherichia coli* ferments lactose contained in MacConkey agar. The pH drops and the neutral red indicator changes to a pink color. This pink color is absorbed by the colonies so that pink colonies surrounded by clear zones are seen.

4. Pick selected well isolated colonies from each plate for Gram staining.

5. Gram stains of *Staphylococcus aureus* show gram-positive staphylococci. Gram stains of *Escherichia coli* show gram-negative short bacilli.

6. Record all observations in the Results section.

7. Answer the questions for the exercise.

Reference

Finegold, S. M., Baron, E. J. and Wexler, H. M. (1992). *A Clinical Guide to Anaerobic Infections*. Belmont, CA: Star Publishing Company.

A Lethal Action of Lysozyme on Bacteria

Objectives

1. Indicate sources of lysozyme in the human body.
2. Describe the lethal action of lysozyme on the bacterial cell wall.
3. Describe the role of lysozyme in the viral infection cycle.

Background

Lysozyme, an enzyme found in mammalian cells, is an example of innate immunity in human beings. This immunity is always present. Lysozyme synthesis does not require induction by the prior presence of foreign antigens such as microorganisms. Lysozyme is commonly found in tears, body fluids and tissues. It splits the 1,4 glycoside bond between the glucosamine and muramic acid components of the bacterial cell wall peptidoglycan and breaks the backbone of this peptidoglycan. In this way, the bacterial cell wall is disrupted and the cell then undergoes osmotic lysis. Water flows into the cell and the cell membrane bursts resulting in the death of the cell.

Lysozyme is also a late enzyme produced during the bacterial virus infection cycle. It produces destruction of the host cell wall so the viruses escape and then invade new host cells to start a new infection cycle.

A Lethal Action of Lysozyme on Bacteria: An Overview

In this exercise, trypticase soy agar swab plate cultures of the gram-positive *Micrococcus luteus* and the gram-negative *Escherichia coli* are separately treated with disks wetted with lysozyme solution. These plates are incubated at 35°C for 48 hours and are then examined for the presence of a zone of inhibition. The presence of a zone of inhibition means sensitivity to lysozyme and its absence means resistance to lysozyme.

Materials

Sigma lysozyme from chicken egg white, lot 2879, containing 57,000 units/mg solid and 65,000 units per mg protein. Lysozyme powder must be stored in a freezer at –20°C.

20 hour trypticase soy broth cultures of *Micrococcus luteus* and *Escherichia coli*

sterile swabs

empty sterile petri dishes

trypticase soy agar plates

beakers of 95% ethyl alcohol

slide forceps

petri dishes containing sterile disks

Procedures

First Period

Preparation of Lysozyme Solution

1 gram of lysozyme powder added to a final volume of 100 ml in distilled water, must be filter sterilized. A Nalgene disposable filter (cellulose nitrate filter pad with a 0.45 nm pore size) can be used. (Nalge Nunc International) Filter available from Carolina Biological Supply Co. The filtrate is decanted into a sterile flask and 0.5 ml samples are pipetted into sterile small tubes for use by the students. The lysozyme solution can be stably stored in the refrigerator for 4 weeks.

Preparation of Lysozyme Test Plates. (See Figure 47-1.)

1. Select two trypticase soy agar plates. Label the first *Micrococcus luteus* and the second *Escherichia coli*.

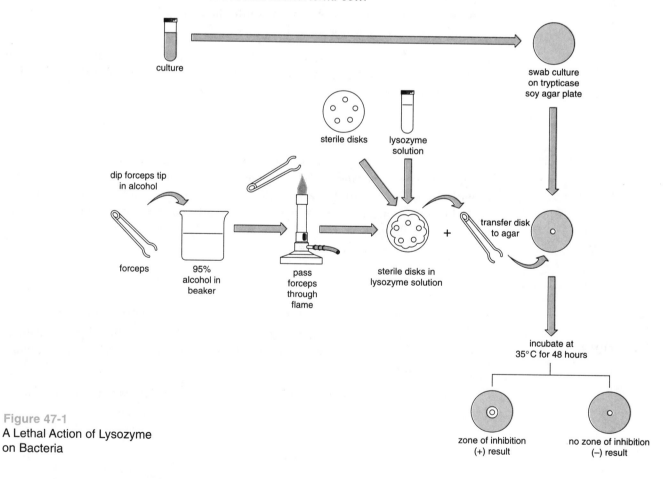

Figure 47-1
A Lethal Action of Lysozyme on Bacteria

2. Swab the first plate with *Micrococcus luteus* and the second with *Escherichia coli*.

3. Pour 0.5 ml of lysozyme solution into a sterile petri dish.

4. Dip a slide forceps into the alcohol and remove it and pass the alcohol wetted portion through a flame. Allow the flame to burn out and sterilize the forceps.

5. Transfer a sterile disk into the lysozyme solution and wet the disk with enzyme solution. Place the lysozyme soaked disk on the agar surface of the dish labeled *Micrococcus luteus*. Tap the disk down gently. Repeat this procedure for *Escherichia coli*.

6. Incubate both plates at 35°C for 48 hours.

Second Period

1. Examine both plates for the presence of zones of inhibition. The presence of a zone of inhibition indicates sensitivity to lysozyme and the absence means lack of sensitivity to the enzyme.

2. Record the findings in the Results section.

3. Answer the questions for the exercise.

Staphylococci on Skin

Objectives

1. Name resident flora common to skin.

2. Describe two reasons why skin is an effective barrier to many microorganisms.

3. Explain the reason for the pH of 5 found on skin.

Background

The intact outer skin is an effective barrier to the entry of many microorganisms, but does allow for the survival of select microorganisms. The resident bacteria that survive on skin for extended time periods include *Staphylococcus epidermidis* and *Propionibacterium* species and other staphylococci. The transient organisms that appear on skin survive for shorter periods of time. There are a number of reasons for this: (1) The outer epidermis is made up of a number of layers of flattened and dead cells containing the hardened protein keratin. This presents a physical barrier to entrance of microbes. In addition, many bacteria cannot digest the keratin protein in skin cells. (2) These outer cell layers are periodically shed and lost as new layers are formed from the germinative layer underneath. Thus, many bacteria attached to these shed cells are lost also. (3) The sweat released from the sweat glands of the skin contains a high concentration of sodium chloride which is inhibitory to many microorganisms. The staphylococci on skin are somewhat osmotolerant. (4) The sebaceous glands release sebum which contain complex lipids that can be broken down by lipase enzymes from *Propionibacterium* to fatty acids. These fatty acids lower the pH of skin to 5 which is inhibitory to many other gram-negative transient organisms. (5) The normal skin resident microorganisms tend to compete with many other bacteria by occupying sites for attachment to skin and compete for available nutrients. (6) The outer skin is somewhat dry. This slows the growth of many transients.

The gram-positive *Staphylococcus aureus* is a major cause of skin infections. These include boils, carbuncles, impetigo and scalded skin syndrome. Staphylococci carried by asymptomatic carriers or infected persons can be readily spread to others where they can produce disease in virtually any organ or tissue of the body. *Staphylococcus epidermidis* can cause wound infections and infections of implanted devices. This organism can produce a biofilm of slime that adheres to living and nonliving surfaces that is not readily penetrated by antimicrobial agents.

Staphylococci on Skin: An Overview

In this exercise, swabbings of outer skin are made to isolate types of staphylococci that are present. Streak plates are made on selective media to identify the staphylococci present. The media used are staphylococcus medium 110, mannitol-salt agar and tellurite-glycine agar.

On staphylococcus medium 110, *Staphylococcus aureus* forms yellow to golden colonies while *Staphylococcus epidermidis* forms white to creamy colonies. On mannitol-salt agar, *Staphylococcus aureus* ferments mannitol to acids. The phenol red indicator in this medium turns yellow and a yellow halo appears around the colony. *Staphylococcus epidermidis* does not ferment mannitol so the agar remains red around the colony. The lithium chloride and potassium tellurite in tellurite-glycine agar are inhibitory to many bacteria and partly inhibitory to the coagulase-negative *Staphylococcus epidermidis*. *Staphylococcus aureus* reduces the tellurite to tellurium and forms black colonies. *Staphylococcus epidermidis* shows no growth or grows poorly on this medium and forms small gray colonies. Each student should evaluate the results seen for streak plates on these media for single colonies and determine the types of staphylococci present on the skin.

Materials

packets of sterile swabs

tubes of sterile distilled water

plates of staphylococcus medium 110

plates of mannitol-salt agar

plates of tellurite-glycine agar

Procedures

First Period

1. Select 3 packets of sterile swabs and single plates of staphylococcus medium 110, mannitol-salt agar and tellurite-glycine agar. (See Figure 48-1.)

2. Dip the cotton bulb of a sterile swab in sterile distilled water. Use good aseptic technique.

3. Select a specific area of the external skin to swab. Suggested areas to sample include the skin of the palm, the fingers, the nose near the nostrils, the outer ear, the cheek, the skin above the upper lip and the chin. Swab this area thoroughly and then transfer this swabbing to the entire surface of a plate of Staphylococcus medium 110. Dispose of this swab in a container of disinfectant.

4. Select the remaining 2 sterile swabs. Remove one at a time from its sterile envelope and repeat this swab and streak procedure for the *same* area of the skin and transfer the isolates to mannitol-salt agar and tellurite-glycine agar. Dispose of these swabs in a container of disinfectant. Be sure to use separate sterile swabs for each of these transfers.

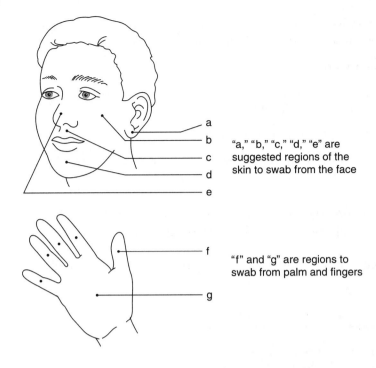

"a," "b," "c," "d," "e" are
suggested regions of the
skin to swab from the face

"f" and "g" are regions to
swab from palm and fingers

PICK ONE AREA TO SWAB
and transfer to selective media

SM 110
staphylococcal
medium 110

MSA
mannitol–salt
agar

TG
tellurite–glycine
agar

INCUBATE AT 35°C for 24 to 48 HOURS
and evaluate

Table of Results

	SM 110	MSA	TG
S. aureus	yellow to golden colonies	yellow halo around colony	black colonies
S. epidermidis	white to creamy colonies	agar remains red around colony	scattered few gray colonies or no colonies

Figure 48-1
Staphylococci on Skin

5. Incubate these 3 plates at 35°C for 24 to 48 hours. Examine after 24 and 48 hours for the selective growth patterns.

Second Period

1. Determine whether *Staphylococcus aureus* or *Staphylococcus epidermidis* is present on the skin.

2. Record the findings in the Results section.

3. Answer the questions for the exercise.

Optional Demonstration

Question: Why swab skin with an antimicrobial agent before drawing blood, before injections and before inserting intravenous lines?

Goal: Demonstration of the degerming action of alcohol on skin.

Materials

nutrient agar petri plates
bottle of sterile distilled water
packets of sterile cotton swabs
coplin jar containing 70% alcohol

Procedures

1. Select a nutrient agar plate. Label one half of the plate "no alcohol" and the other half "alcohol treatment."

2. Select a sterile swab and dip it into sterile distilled water. Swab a portion of skin used as an injection site. Transfer the swabbing to the "no alcohol half of the dish.

3. Select a second sterile cotton swab. Dip it in 70% alcohol and swab the same portion of the skin with alcohol. Transfer this swabbing to the "alcohol treatment" side of the plate. Be sure to dispose of the swabs properly in a container of disinfectant.

4. Incubate the plate at 37°C for 48 hours.

5. Examine for the presence of colonies on both sides of the plate.

6. Notice the dramatic reduction or absence of colonies on the alcohol treatment side.

Explanation

The degerming action of alcohol treatment removes skin oils, dirt, bacteria and kills some transient microorganisms. 70% alcohol damages the structure of the bacterial cell membrane by dissolving lipids in the membrane. Alcohol that enters into a bacterial cell coagulates and denatures proteins in the cell.

Upper Respiratory Tract Culture

Warning: This exercise poses some risk. The students must be very careful in all transfers and inoculations. The oral cavity in humans contains a variety of opportunistic and pathogenic organisms.

Objectives

1. Name three organisms commonly found in the upper respiratory tract and the medical problems they produce.

2. Describe the problem posed by methicillin-resistant *Staphylococcus aureus*

3. Describe three tests that distinguish between *Staphylococcus aureus* and *Staphylococcus epidermidis*.

4. Describe the three types of reactions observed on growth of microorganisms on blood agar.

5. Indicate the medical importance of the coagulase test.

Background

The flora of the upper respiratory tract includes a variety of bacteria. For example, the mucous membranes of the nose and the oropharynx contain sizable numbers of staphylococci. These include *Staphylococcus aureus* and *Staphylococcus epidermidis*. The nose also contains diphtheroids, species of *Haemophilus*, *Moraxella (Branhamella) catarrhalis* and occasionally *Streptococcus pneumoniae*. In addition to the staphylococci, the oropharynx also contains a variety of streptococci that produce an alpha-hemolytic reaction when grown on sheep blood agar. In the **alpha-hemolytic reaction** these streptococci release an enzyme called an alpha hemolysin that partly destroys the red blood cell membrane and the hemoglobin so that a green halo appears in the blood agar around the colony. Examples of these alpha-hemolytic gram-positive cocci include *Streptococcus mitis* and *Streptococcus mutans*. The last organism is important in initiating the development of dental caries. The oropharynx also contains aerobic diphtheroids, a variety of anaerobes that are members of the genus *Bacteroides*, species of *Haemophilus* and *Moraxella (Branhamella) catarrhalis*.

Respiratory tract infections are a common medical problem in human beings. In general most upper respiratory infections in humans are caused by viruses. These include the rhinoviruses, adenoviruses, coxsackie viruses, respiratory syncytial viruses (RSV) and influenza viruses. These are not treatable with antibiotics. In contrast, severe sore throats that require antibiotic therapy are caused by the Group A beta-hemolytic gram-positive coccus *Streptococcus pyogenes*. Throat swabbings cultured on sheep blood agar show very small white colonies surrounded by clear zones called **beta-hemolysis**. This beta-hemolytic reaction is due to release of a beta-hemolysin enzyme into the sheep blood agar, which lyses the red blood cell membrane and completely reduces the hemoglobin to a colorless compound, thus a clear halo appears around the colony. Group A beta-hemolytic streptococci commonly are responsible for streptococcal sore throat, scarlatina, necrotizing fasciitis and myositis, and sepsis after a surgical wound or after penetration of the skin by a sharp instrument. Gram-negative bacteria such as *Pseudomonas aeruginosa* also produce infections after puncture wounds.

In preschool-age children, ages 4 to 5, and older children, ages 12 to 15, streptococcal sore throats are very common. These bacteria are easily spread by sneezing, coughing and contact with droplet-contaminated nonliving surfaces or **fomites**. The increased susceptibility of preschool-age children reflects their generally immature immune systems and limited resistance to Group A streptococci coupled with increased exposure due to crowding at home and the presence of siblings who carry this microorganism. The increased susceptibility at ages 12 to 15 may reflect exposure to different serological types of these streptococci. As individuals enter adolescence, their immunity to this organism increases and their susceptibility decreases. Typically in streptococcal sore throat, redness and swelling are seen in the pharynx and on the tonsils. Frequently patches of yellowish pus are seen on the tonsils. A fever of 102°F (39°C) is commonly present.

The throat culture is an important tool to identify the presence of Group A beta-hemolytic streptococci. To confirm their presence a presumptive streptococcal colony should be restreaked to fresh sheep blood agar. A Taxo®-A disk containing 0.04 units of bacitracin is placed on the streak line and the plate is incubated at 35°C for 18–24 hours in a carbon dioxide enriched environment in a GasPak jar. The presence of a clear zone of no growth around the colony known as a zone of inhibition is presumptive evidence that the organisms isolated on the blood agar are group A beta-hemolytic streptococci.

The target microorganism in this group is *Streptococcus pyogenes*. The group A beta-hemolytic streptococci are also responsible for impetigo in children and for erysipelas. These patients must be protected against these Group A streptococci by taking penicillin (or erythromycin in the case of allergy to penicillin) to eliminate these bacteria from the oropharynx. Another reason for taking an antibiotic for Group A streptococcal sore throats is to prevent pus-produced infections of the mastoid, tonsils, and middle ear as well as other major complications. Complications of the streptococcal infections include rheumatic fever and glomerulonephritis. Symptoms of rheumatic fever include inflammation of the heart valves and arthritis. In patients with a history of rheumatic fever, this disease tends to reappear and cause increased heart valve damage with repeated streptococcal infections. Glomerulonephritis causes an inflammation of the kidneys. This results in protein and blood in the urine. Penicillin or erythromycin therapy is prescribed for an acute attack of glomerulonephritis to eliminate the streptococci and to prevent the spread of these organisms to others. Use of these antibiotics can also prevent repeat kidney infections during periods of recurring streptococcal infections. Pneumonia caused by these Group A streptococci is a possible complication of viral infections such as influenza or measles (Rubeola) virus.

Lower respiratory tract infections commonly are cause by the gram-positive and hemolytic diplococcus *Streptococcus pneumoniae*. A Gram stain prepared from a sputum sample presents a useful clue for identifying this cause of the pneumonia and for selecting appropriate antibiotic therapy. The presence of a capsule on this organism makes it very resistant to phagocytosis by white blood cells and in turn enhances its virulence.

Other bacteria that can produce pneumonia include *Haemophilus influenzae* and *Klebsiella pneumoniae*. These two bacteria are examples of nonhemolytic organisms. Growth of these organisms on sheep blood agar does not result in any change in color of the agar around the colonies. In a nonhemolytic reaction, formerly called gamma hemolysis, the organisms do not produce any change to the red blood cell membranes or to the hemoglobin, so that no change appears in the color of the blood agar around the colonies. *Klebsiella pneumoniae*, a gram-negative short bacillus, produces about 3% of pneumonias. It produces a highly fatal form of necrotizing pneumonia. *Haemophilus influenzae* is a gram-negative oval-shaped bacillus that commonly produces secondary pneumonia after a respiratory viral infection. This organism causes meningitis, pneumonia, otitis media and severe epiglottitis in young children. In this last medical problem, the epiglottis becomes very swollen and blocks the airway so breathing is not possible. Death can occur without medical intervention. *Haemophilus influenzae* produces pneumonia primarily in the very young and the elderly. Currently young children are immunized with Hemophilus influenzae b (Hib) vaccine to protect them against this organism. In HIV infected patients Haemophilus influenzae produces meningitis or pneumonia. The antibiotic ciprofloxacin, a quinolone antibiotic, is effective against this organism.

Another respiratory pathogen, *Moraxella (Branhamella) catarrhalis*, a gram-negative diplococcus, has penicillinase activity and causes sinusitis, otitis media and occasionally pneumonia. These can be treated with amoxicillin + clavulanate or some cephalosporin antibiotics.

Anaerobes such as the gram-negative bacillus *Bacteroides* are also found in the oral cavity. These are involved in gum disease and pyogenic infections in the body. The anaerobes are not considered further since they do not grow under the conditions of this exercise.

The yeast *Candida albicans* produces oral mucocandidiasis (thrush), in which plaques of white growth are found on the gums, hard palate, tongue and throat mucosa. This is treated with oral clotrimazole troches, which are dissolved slowly in the mouth.

Staphylococcus aureus rarely causes pneumonia. This organism and *Staphylococcus epidermidis* are common inhabitants of the skin. They are arranged as irregular groups of cocci and stain gram-positive. Staphylococci, in contrast to streptococci, produce a positive **catalase test**. This is a rapid and easily performed test to distinguish between these two organisms. The staphylococci have an enzyme called catalase that splits the hydrogen peroxide produced in respiration into water and oxygen. All streptococci lack catalase activity. In practice, the growth is flooded with hydrogen peroxide and immediate and profuse bubbling of oxygen is seen in a positive test.

Pathogenic *Staphylococcus aureus* are identified by their ability to ferment mannitol, reduce tellurite to tellurium, hydrolyse DNA and produce coagulase, which clots plasma. *Staphylococcus epidermidis* is coagulase negative. Staphylococcal coagulase converts the fibrinogen protein in plasma into insoluble fibrin threads. This results in the formation of a clot in the tube. Any degree of clot formation in the coagulase plasma tube is a positive result. This test is a definitive test for the identification of beta-hemolytic pathogenic *Staphylococcus aureus*. Usually clinical isolates form large white or yellow colonies that show beta-hemolytic reactions on blood agar. Many of the staphylococci have penicillinase (beta lactamase) activity and are resistant to penicillin. Many staphylococci also show resistance to methicillin. This resistance is in addition to penicillinase activity. An example is MRSA, or methicillin-resistant *Staphylococcus aureus*. Generally these patients are treated with vancomycin. *Staphylococcus epidermidis* causes urinary tract infections, wound infections and infections of artificial heart valves. *Staphylococcus aureus* commonly produces skin infections. The organism can spread to other areas of the body because of surgical incisions, severe abrasions, burns, introduction of foreign bodies such as catheters, use of contaminated needles, tampons or artificial heart valves or deficiencies in the cellular or humoral immune response. For example, these bacteria can spread from the skin to the blood and then spread to the bones and joints or to the lungs to produce a secondary *Staphylococcus aureus* pneumonia. Other possibilities include kidney abscess, endocarditis, brain abscess and toxic shock syndrome. Illnesses such as diabetes mellitis, tumors and alcoholism that affect host resistance to infection increase the chances of infection with *Staphylococcus aureus*.

Upper Respiratory Tract Culture: An Overview

The aims of this exercise are to isolate and characterize by Gram stain reactions some of the organisms commonly found in the upper respiratory tract and cultured on blood agar and to identify the presence of pathogenic *Staphylococcus aureus*. Pathogenic *Staphylococcus aureus* is commonly found as a transient organism in the throats of health care workers. A throat or nostril swabbing is made and transferred to blood agar. The blood agar differentiates between organisms showing alpha- or beta-hemolysis and no hemolysis. These organisms are further characterized by the Gram stain reaction. The Gram reaction and morphology of the bacteria are then described. A plate of staphylococcus medium 110 is also swabbed to isolate staphylococci. After incubation, yellow colonies are *Staphylococcus aureus* and white to creamy colonies are *Staphylococcus epidermidis*. A portion of selected different cononies are then streaked on mannitol salt agar, tellurite agar and DNase Test agar. The results of these tests are used to distinguish between *Staphylococcus aureus* and *Staphylococcus epidermidis*. *Staphylococcus aureus* ferments mannitol. The indicator phenol red in the agar changes from red to yellow in the presence of acids produced by fermentation. A yellow halo then appears in the agar around the colonies. This medium is highly selective for staphylococci since it contains 7.5% salt. *Staphylococcus epidermidis* grows on this medium but does not ferment mannitol, and the medium around the colonies remains red or turns a deeper shade of red than before inoculation. This suggests that proteolytic reactions have occurred to release alkaline by-products. On tellurite glycine agar, coagulase-positive *Staphylococcus aureus* reduce tellurite to form tellurium and form black colonies. Coagulase-negative staphylococci such as *Staphylococcus epidermidis* generally are inhibited on this medium but sometimes form very small gray colonies after incubation at 35°C for 24 hours. These two organisms are readily distinguished by their reactions on this medium. Gram-negative bacteria are generally inhibited by the lithium chloride and potassium tellurite in this medium. Only *Staphylococcus aureus* shows DNase activity. Some of the growth from the mannitol-salt agar plate is first transferred to a tube of BHI broth incubated overnight then transferred to a tube of rehydrated rabbit plasma to test for coagulase activity. These tubes are incubated in a rack placed in a water bath set at 37°C for 1–4 hours or if needed overnight to permit the clotting of the plasma. After incubation, the coagulase test tubes can be refrigerated till the next laboratory session. This procedure is used since it reduces the chances of destruction of the clot by fibrinolytic enzyme reactions produced by the staphylococci. The coagulase test is the definitive test for the identification of pathogenic *Staphylococcus aureus*.

Materials

bottles of sterile distilled water

blood agar T-streak plate culture of *S. pyogenes*

plates of blood agar

plates of staphylococcus medium 110

plates of mannitol-salt agar

plates of tellurite-glycine agar

plates of DNase test agar

tubes containing 1 ml of brain heart infusion (BHI) broth

packets of sterile swabs

bottles of 1N hydrochloric acid (HCl)

tubes of rehydrated rabbit plasma

metal rack for incubating inoculated coagulase plasma tubes

temperature controlled water bath set at 37°C

GasPak jar and carbon dioxide generating envelopes

beaker of distilled water

10 ml pipettes

10 ml pipette pumps

Taxo® A discs (0.04 units bacitracin per disc)

beaker of 95% alcohol

Rehydrate coagulase plasma with sterile distilled water to give a 1:1 solution. Mix gently and refrigerate before use. Do not refrigerate beyond 5 days.

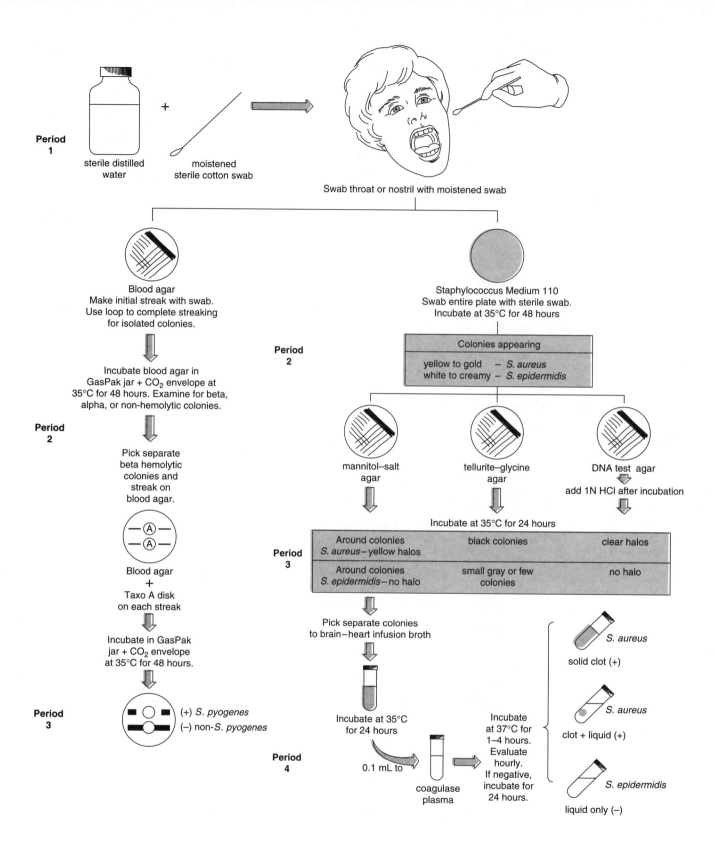

Figure 49-1
Upper Respiratory Tract
Culture Procedures

Procedures

First Period (See Figure 49-1)

Isolation of Upper Respiratory Tract Cultures

1. Select a plate of blood agar and a plate of Staphylococcus medium 110 and a sterile swab. Label the plate and tube "throat or nostril culture."

2. Wash your hands thoroughly before starting this experiment. Select a sterile swab and moisten the cotton bulb by dipping it into a bottle of sterile distilled water. Swab the nostril or throat in the region of the tonsils. Avoid the uvula to prevent gagging.

3. Streak one line of the swabbings by rolling the swab on one comer of the blood agar surface. Flame the loop and complete the streaking of the blood agar to obtain single colonies. Swab the entire agar surface of the Staphylococcus Medium 110 with this swab.

4. Invert and place all the blood agar plates in the GasPak jar. Place the carbon dioxide generator envelope in the GasPak jar. Tear the corner of the carbon dioxide generator envelope and pipette 10 ml of distilled water into the envelope. Place the lid on the jar and hand tighten snugly. Incubate the sealed GasPak jar at 35°C for 48 hours.

5. Invert and incubate all the streaked Staphylococcus Medium 110 plates at 35°C for 48 hours.

6. Scrub your hands after incubating these plates.

Second Period

Identification of Beta-Hemolytic Streptococci and Streaking to Selective Media for Staphylococcal Identification

1. Obtain the incubated blood agar and Staphylococcus Medium 110 plates.

2. Examine the blood agar plate for well-isolated colonies that show alpha, beta or no hemolysis. Circle the bottom of the petri dish for each of these selected colonies.

3. Note those colonies which are very tiny and show beta-hemolysis. These are presumptive Streptococcus *pyogenes*. Compare these with the control culture of Streptococcus *pyogenes* grown on blood agar.

4. Singly pick and streak these on the surface of a blood agar plate to form a row of streaks.

5. Label one streak "control" and pick one colony from the *Streptococcus pyogenes* plate and streak it to this blood agar plate.

6. Obtain a vial of Taxo® A bacitracin discs and aseptically transfer a single disc to each streak line on the blood agar.

7. Incubate these blood agar plates in a GasPak jar with a properly prepared carbon dioxide generator envelope. (See step 4 above for the First Period.)

8. Prepare Gram stains from the other colonies circled on the blood agar plate. Record your findings in the Results section.

9. Examine the streaked Staphylococcus Medium 110 plate. The presence of yellow to gold colored colonies on this medium indicates presumptive *Staphylococcus aureus* which is coagulase-positive. White to creamy colonies indicate the presence of *Staphylococcus epidermidis* which are coagulase-negative. In some cases, both types of colonies are present on this agar medium.

10. Select a plate of mannitol-salt agar, tellurite-glycine agar and DNase test agar. Select an additional plate of each medium if both types of colonies are present.

11. Label the medium properly and write white or yellow for the type of staphylococcal colony observed. Label an additional set of plates if both types of colonies are found.

12. Pick a portion of a large white colony from Staphylococcus Medium 110 agar and make a single streak on a plate of mannitol-salt agar. Flame the loop and streak this plate to isolate single colonies. Flame the loop and pick a second small portion of this white colony and make a single streak to tellurite-glycine agar. Flame the loop and pick the remaining portion of the white colony to DNase test and prepare a single streak on this medium.

13. Flame the loop and complete the streaks for isolated colonies on both of these media.

14. If yellow colonies are found, repeat the procedures from steps 12 and 13.

15. If yellow and white colonies are found, pick and streak a separate set of plates for the white and yellow colonies.

16. Incubate these plates at 35°C for 24 hours.

17. If necessary, the tellurite-glycine agar plates should be refrigerated after incubation until the next laboratory class session. This prevents any blackening of the coagulase-negative colonies that may appear.

Third Period

Identification of Staphylococci

1. Obtain the Taxo® A disk blood agar plates and examine the unknown streaks and that of *Streptococcus pyogenes* for the presence of a zone of inhibition. Sensitivity to 0.04 units of bacitracin is commonly found for *Streptococcus pyogenes* and is observed as a zone of inhibition of growth near the disc. This test is presumptive evidence for the presence of *Streptococcus pyogenes*. Determine whether any of the unknown streaks are *Streptococcus pyogenes*.

2. Obtain the plates of mannitol-salt agar, tellurite-glycine agar and DNase test agar. Observe the mannitol-salt agar for fermentation of the mannitol sugar to acids and the production of a yellow halo around the colonies. This result is found for *Staphylococcus aureus*. Colony formation with no color change to the agar indicates the presence of the nonfermenter *Staphylococcus epidermidis*.

3. Observe the tellurite-glycine agar plate for presence of black colonies formed by the reduction of tellurite to tellurium. These are formed by

coagulase-positive *Staphylococcus aureus*. Coagulase-negative staphylococci such as *Staphylococcus epidermidis* are inhibited or partly inhibited by the lithium chloride in this medium and form small grey colonies on this medium.

4. Pour a small quantity of 1 N hydrochloric acid on the surface of the DNase test agar plate. Gently rotate the dish to spread the acid over the agar surface. Wait 2 to 3 minutes and observe the plate for clearing around the colonies. Clearing indicates hydrolysis of the DNA by staphylococcal DNase and is a positive test . Cloudiness around the growth means no DNA hydrolysis and is a negative result. In this case, the DNA is precipitated in the agar as a white cloud. DNA hydrolysis is found for *Staphylococcus aureus* and not for *Staphylococcus epidermidis*.

5. Flame the loop and transfer a well isolated colony from the mannitol-salt agar plate to a tube of brain heart infusion broth. Incubate this tube at 35°C for 24 hours. Transfer a separate colony to a separate tube of brain heart infusion broth if more than one type of colony is observed on the mannitol-salt agar plate. Label each tube with the name of the proper organism. Recall that the presence of yellow halos on mannitol-salt agar indicates the presence of *Staphylococcus aureus* and the absence of any color change in this medium indicates *Staphylococcus epidermidis*.

Fourth Period

Coagulase Test Confirmation

1. Obtain a tube or tubes of coagulase plasma. Label the tube *Staphylococcus aureus* or *Staphylococcus epidermidis* or if necessary label separate tubes for each organism.

2. Obtain the turbid brain heart infusion broth tube and pipette 0.1 ml of the broth culture into the properly labeled coagulase plasma tube. Repeat this procedure for any additional cultures.

3. Incubate the coagulase plasma tubes in a water bath at 37°C for 1 to 4 hours. Check the tubes hourly for any evidence of clot formation. The entire contents of any tube can clot or clots can be suspended in some of the liquid in the tube. Either of these results is considered positive. If no clotting is found after 4 hours, continue to incubate up to 24 hours and examine again.

4. Clotting of coagulase plasma is a positive test for the presence of *Staphylococcus aureus*. *Staphylococcus epidermidis* does not clot coagulase plasma. These results should be correlated with the reactions on mannitol-salt agar, tellurite-glycine agar and DNase test agar. Generally, *Staphylococcus aureus* ferments mannitol, reduces tellurite and hydrolyses DNA, while *Staphylococcus epidermidis* lacks these reactions.

5. Record all findings in the Results section.

6. Answer the questions for the exercise.

A Health Care Alert

Glycopeptide Intermediate *Staphylococcus aureus* (GISA) and Vancomycin Intermediate *Staphylococcus aureus* (VISA)

Recently, *Staphylococcus aureus* has become highly resistant to antibiotics. Methicillin resistant *S. aureus* (MRSA) has already been described and isolated. Normally, vancomycin is used as therapy for this strain. Now, new reports in the health care field of *S. aureus* strains that show reduced sensitivity to vancomycin have appeared. These are the VISA and GISA strains of *S. aureus*. GISA strains show reduced susceptibility to 8 ug/ml of vancomycin. Vancomycin is not suitable for use against these strains and there are very limited antibiotic therapies available for use against these strains. An example of a drug used against VISA is Synercid, a drug developed in France. Patients at risk of developing these infections include those who are severely ill and receiving extended antibiotic therapy particularly with vancomycin. This microorganism is easily spread by direct contact. It can be spread by health care workers' hands in going from one patient to another or from one body site to another. For example, it can be spread from a wound site on a patient to the respiratory tract of the same patient. Anterior nares may also be a site colonized by this microorganism. Hence, the importance of keeping the hands away from the face.

Control measures include:

a. Gloves must be worn when entering the patient's room.

b. Gown and mask must be worn if close contact with the patient is necessary.

c. Equipment used on this patient must stay in the room with the patient. Any equipment removed from this room must be disinfected with a disinfectant approved by the medical center.

d. The number of staff, residents and physicians having contact with this patient must be limited to prevent spread of this infection.

e. Scrupulous handwashing with an antimicrobial soap solution after removal of gloves and before leaving this patient's room must be rigorously practiced.

f. Patients, on discharge, must be informed of the absolute importance of handwashing before food preparation and eating and after contact with any wound care area. Household towels and linen heavily soiled with body fluids must be laundered separately in detergent and bleach.

g. Patients with these infections must inform any doctor or hospital at the time of making an appointment that they have a GISA/VISA infection so that precautions can be taken to avoid and prevent the spread of these organisms to others.

h. Doctors may obtain surveillance cultures to determine if the GISA/VISA organisms still persist in the patients.

Gastrointestinal Infections

Warning: The organisms used in this exercise are pathogenic. Great care must be used during any manipulations of cultures containing *Salmonella*. All spills must be promptly disinfected. Any accidents must be promptly reported to the instructor.

Objectives

1. Describe the symptoms of a gastrointestinal infection.

2. List characteristics that clearly distinguish between infections produced by *Salmonella* and *Shigella*.

3. Explain the need for selective media to identify the source of gastrointestinal infections.

Background

Infections of the gastrointestinal tract are commonly caused by viruses, by bacteria in the family *Enterobacteriaceae* and by members of the genus *Campylobacter*. The viruses commonly involved include the hepatitis A virus, the Norwalk agent and the Rotavirus. The hepatitis A virus is transmitted by a fecal-oral route. This virus most frequently enters the body by ingestion of contaminated raw shellfish or by drinking contaminated water. Furthermore, food handlers infected with this virus can contaminate food products they are processing. Patients with hepatitis A may suffer from nausea, vomiting and excrete virus particles in the feces. Jaundice is not always present. While a fecal-oral route of transmission is common, a sexual route of transmission is also possible. Sudden, very severe cases of hepatitis A are frequently found in intravenous drug abusers. This virus is resistant to many disinfectants. The Norwalk agent is also transmitted by a fecal-oral route, by contaminated fingers and by ingestion of contaminated food or water. This virus is responsible for epidemics of gastrointestinal infections, particularly in large communal gatherings or in nursing homes and mental institutions where the patients may not be able to practice good hygiene. The symptoms of this gastroenteritis include vomiting, diarrhea, fever and muscle aches. These symptoms usually resolve in a few days. The Rotavirus produces the symptoms of diarrhea and vomiting in children between 6 months and 2 years of age. This virus is responsible for outbreaks of gastrointestinal infection in pediatric nurseries in hospitals. This virus is also transmitted by a fecal-oral route.

The enteric bacteria that produce gastrointestinal infections include *Escherichia*, *Salmonella* and *Shigella*. In addition, bacteria in the genus of *Campylobacter* are significant sources of infection. All the enteric bacilli give a negative oxidase test, ferment glucose and reduce nitrates anaerobically. In contrast, the *Campylobacter* pathogenic to humans show positive oxidase activity and do not ferment sugars. These organisms are microaerophiles. The typical organism is *Campylobacter jejuni*.

Many of these microorganisms are transmitted through contaminated food and water. Collectively, these bacteria produce gastrointestinal infection by invading and multiplying in the tissues of the intestinal wall. They then secrete enterotoxins which are examples of exotoxins. These enterotoxins are responsible for serious symptoms, as described below. An example of this mode of action is *Salmonella*. These organisms produce enteric fever and gastroenteritis. An example of an enteric fever is typhoid fever. This is caused by *Salmonella typhi*. During typhoid fever the bacteria multiply in the epithelial lining of the small intestine. They can spread into the bloodstream and produce bacteremia. The bacteria then spread into the liver to produce abscesses, or they invade the lymph nodes of the intestines known as Peyer's patches. They also invade the spleen and kidneys and damage these organs. High fever is common. This disease organism is sometimes found in fecally contaminated food and water. Typhoid fever is treated with ampicillin. Other *Salmonella* produce gastroenteritis. Frequently this results from ingestion of foods containing large numbers of these organisms. Eggs and poultry products are foods that can have large numbers *Salmonella*. These infections are characterized by weakness, diarrhea and nausea.

Shigellosis or bacillary dysentery is a diarrhea disease in which mucus and blood are found in the feces. Severe diarrhea is possible. This disease is caused by *Shigella sonnei*, *Shigella flexneri* and *Shigella dysenteriae* in the United States. The disease organism is transmitted by a fecal-oral route, by contaminated food handlers and by flies. Humans are the major host for this organism. Ingestion of very few *Shigella* can produce a severe gastrointestinal infection. During an infection, *Shigella* invade the mucosa and submucosa of the intestines. They cause some ulceration of the mucosa followed by profuse diarrhea. This damage is due to an enterotoxin made by these bacteria. The subsequent invasion of the large intestine by these bacteria results in dysentery, with blood and pus in the feces. Treatment involves chloramphenicol, ampicillin or trimethoprim-sulfamethoxsazole. The *Shigella* organism, in contrast to *Salmonella*, does not penetrate beyond the intestinal wall into the bloodstream. Also, few members of the genus *Shigella* are necessary for infection, in contrast to *Salmonella* infections where a large number of organisms must be ingested to produce infection.

Certain strains of enterotoxigenic *Escherichia coli* produce an excessive diarrhea and nausea known as traveler's diarrhea. This is due to a heat-labile toxin called LT or a heat-stable toxin called ST. These toxins promote secretion of water and lead to severe diarrhea that lasts for several days. Treatment involves trimethoprim-sulfamethoxazole or doxycycline. Recently some strains of *Escherichia coli* have been isolated that produce a verotoxin. These strains of *Escherichia coli* are responsible for hemorrhagic colitis and hemolytic-uremic syndrome. Severe diarrhea is found in the former case, while severe kidney damage is found in the latter syndrome. *Escherichia coli* strain 0157:H7 is an example of a verotoxin-producing strain of this organism. This strain can be found in poorly cooked chopped meat products.

Campylobacter jejuni invades the mucosa of the small intestine and produces an inflammation. Diarrhea with blood in the stool is a common observation. Other symptoms include fever, cramps and weakness. Erythromycin is helpful in resolving the symptoms.

Gastrointestinal Infections: An Overview

A simulation of gastrointestinal infections involving some of the bacteria described in the previous section is presented in this exercise to illustrate the problems and time necessary to make a differential diagnostic identification of enteropathogens in the digestive tract. If desired, those completing this exercise can view themselves as members of an infection control committee in a medical facility that must identify both the source of serious gastrointestinal infections in patients and the microorganism causing the infection so that proper treatment can be instituted. One patient represents an infection with *Escherichia coli* and *Salmonella typhimurium*, the second patient represents an infection with *Enterobacter aerogenes* and *Salmonella typhimurium* and the third patient represents an infection with *Proteus vulgaris* and *Salmonella typhimurium*. *Escherichia coli*, *Enterobacter aerogenes* and *Proteus vulgaris* are found in the intestinal tract as normal flora, and *Salmonella typhimurium* is an enteropathogen. These mixed culture broth tubes simulate stool cultures from the infected individuals and are marked with the numbers 1, 2, and 3 to represent their medical chart numbers. These should be treated as unknowns. The designation of the numbers is strictly arbitrary. The student is given a refrigerated unknown broth mixed culture and must use a variety of selective media to isolate each of the organisms. Then specialized media are used to identify the specific organisms involved.

One goal of the exercise is to illustrate procedures to isolate and identify the pathogenic *Salmonella* and to clearly distinguish it from the normal flora *Escherichia coli*, *Enterobacter aerogenes* or *Proteus vulgaris*. A second goal is to indicate that delay and incorrect diagnostic decisions could enhance the risks of more severe or of nosocomial or community-acquired infections for an already sick individual. To test this premise this exercise also employs methods to differentiate between the two gram-negative, noncoliform, non-lactose fermenting intestinal bacilli *Salmonella typhimurium* and *Proteus vulgaris* that produce the same results in several biochemical tests used to identify an unknown. A differential decision between these two organisms depends on the results of few specific biochemical reactions. There is no room for error. The differential and selective media used are MacConkey agar and *Salmonella-Shigella* agar (SS agar).

MacConkey agar contains bile salts and crystal violet, which inhibit gram-positive bacteria, and this medium distinguishes between those gram-negative bacteria that ferment lactose and those that do not. This is a good medium to isolate enteric gram-negative organisms from a mixed flora culture. Lactose is the only sugar present. *Escherichia coli* ferments the sugar and produces red colonies that may or may not be surrounded by a halo of precipitated bile. *Enterobacter aerogenes* ferments the lactose and forms pink to red mucoid glistening colonies. Non-lactose-fermenting organisms such as *Salmonella* and *Proteus* produce translucent to colorless colonies.

Salmonella-Shigella agar medium is designed for the isolation of the enteropathogens in the genera of *Salmonella* and *Shigella*. It contains almost six times more bile salts than MacConkey agar and is selective against growth of gram-positive bacteria and is very inhibitory to growth of coliforms. This medium also contains lactose, sodium thiosulfate and the iron salt ferric citrate. The few small *Escherichia coli* and *Enterobacter aerogenes* colonies that appear are pink to red or cream-pink to red, respectively, due to lactose fermentation. *Salmonella typhimurium* and *Proteus vulgaris* form colorless colonies with or without a black center. The black area is due to release of hydrogen sulfide from thiosulfate with the subsequent formation of the black iron sulfide product in the colony. Each of these mixed cultures should be streaked on these differential and selective media to isolate single colonies.

After incubation a presumptive identification is made of *Escherichia coli*, *Enterobacter aerogenes*, *Salmonella typhimurium* and *Proteus vulgaris*. The pink to red colonies appearing on MacConkey agar or *Salmonella-Shigella* agar are strong presumptive evidence for the presence of the coliforms *Escherichia coli* and *Enterobacter aerogenes*. The differential identification of *Escherichia coli* and *Enterobacter aerogenes* can be made by the IMViC test. Refer to Exercise 34 for the procedures to complete this test. Recall that the results on the IMViC test for *Escherichia coli* are + + − − and for *Enterobacter aerogenes* are − − + +.

Samples from non-lactose-fermenting colonies on MacConkey agar or *Salmonella-Shigella* agar are then inoculated into Kligler's iron agar to confirm the presence of the noncoliform enteropathogen *Salmonella typhimurium* and the normal flora organism *Proteus vulgaris*. Both of these organisms produce an alkaline slant and acid deep due to only glucose fermentation. They also release hydrogen sulfide, which on subsequent reaction with the ferric salts blackens this medium. This blackening may mask any acid reaction seen in the deep portion of this medium, so that the yellow color is not readily seen.

Additional confirmatory tests are then made to complete the identification. These tests include urea hydrolysis and phenylalanine deaminase activity. Bacteria that have the enzyme urease can split the substrate urea into ammonia and carbon dioxide. In the presence of the alkaline ammonia, the phenol red indicator in this medium changes color from yellow to a cerise (red-purple) color. Bacteria that have phenylalanine deaminase will deaminate phenylalanine to phenylpyruvic acid. This product is detected on the addition of 10% ferric chloride solution to this growth medium. In a positive test a green color develops in the liquid and in the agar medium. The nonlactose-fermenting *Salmonella typhimurium* does not hydrolyse urea, does not deaminate phenylalanine and produces hydrogen sulfide. In contrast, the gram-negative, noncoliform, non-lactose-fermenting, intestinal tract normal flora organism *Proteus vulgaris* has urease activity, deaminates phenylalanine and produces hydrogen sulfide. These results are summarized in the following table:

Organism	Lactose Fermented	H2S Produced	Urea Hydrolyzed	Phenylalanine Deaminated
Salmonella	−	+	−	−
Proteus	−	+	+	+

The table shows that the results of the urea hydrolysis test and phenylalanine deaminase reactions are crucial in the differential identification of these two organisms. These tests will be completed in this exercise to demonstrate the importance of accuracy in any differential identification of bacteria causing any medical problem.

Optional Method: If desired, the Enterotube II® can be substituted for the traditional methods of differential identification of unknown organisms. Cultures should be picked from well-isolated colonies growing on MacConkey agar and Salmonella-Shigella agar, and the procedures for inoculating, incubating and evaluating the Enterotube II® should be completed. Consult Exercise 36 for the details of this procedure and evaluation.

Materials

trypticase soy broth mixed culture of *Escherichia coli* and *Salmonella typhimurium*

trypticase soy broth mixed culture of *Enterobacter aerogenes* and *Salmonella typhimurium*

trypticase soy broth mixed culture of *Proteus vulgaris* and *Salmonella typhimurium*

(The mixed cultures should be prepared in the following fashion by the instructor or the laboratory technician before the class meets. Prepare an overnight trypticase soy broth culture of each organism. 0.1 ml from overnight trypticase soy broth cultures of the proper organisms should be pipetted into a tube of sterile trypticase soy broth to make up the unknown mixed cultures 1, 2 and 3. The mixed cultures are gently swirled and refrigerated until use. The cultures must be refrigerated to prevent overgrowth of the *Escherichia coli, Enterobacter aerogenes* or *Proteus vulgaris*.)

tubes of sterile trypticase soy broth

plates of MacConkey agar

plates of *Salmonella-Shigella* agar

Kligler's iron agar slants

slants of phenylalanine agar

bottle of 10% ferric chloride

1-ml pipettes

pipette pumps

Optional Tests:

Media and reagents for the IMViC Test (see Exercise 37)

Materials for use of Enterotube II® (see Exercise 39)

First Period (See Figure 50-1)

1. *Inoculation of unknown mixed culture to selective/differential media.*
   a. Select a chilled tube of unknown mixed culture number 1, 2 or 3. These hypothetical chart numbers simulate patients with gastrointestinal infections.

   b. Select three plates of MacConkey agar and SS agar. Label each plate with the name of the proper media. Separate them into three sets. Each set must contain both media. Label one set with the chart number 1 and the other set with the chart number 2 and the last with the chart number 3.

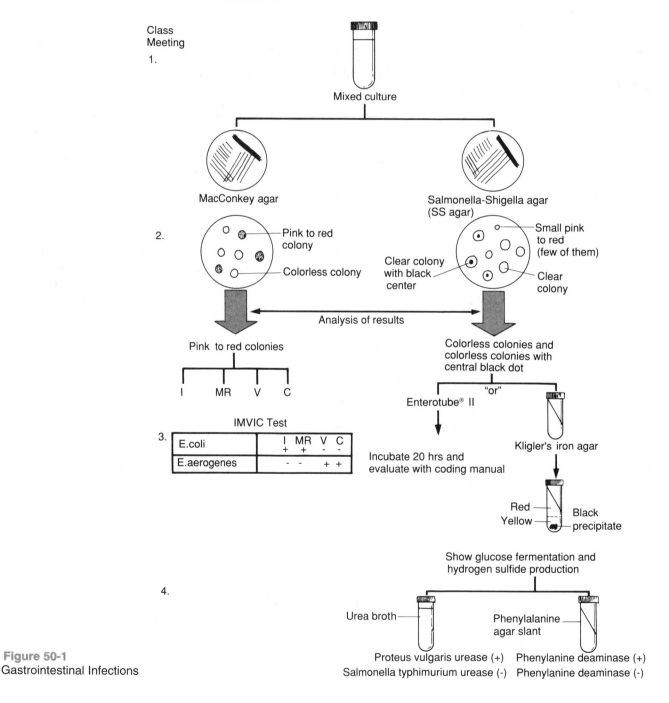

Figure 50-1
Gastrointestinal Infections

c. Streak each plate of a given set with the proper mixed culture to isolate colonies of a single organism. Be sure to streak the proper mixed culture on the plates of differential and selective media.

d. Incubate all the plates at 35°C for 48 hours.

Second Period

1. *Evaluation: (Presumptive Identification):*
   a. Examine these plates for the color of the colonies. Recall that red colonies indicate *Escherichia coli*. Pink to red somewhat mucoid colonies on MacConkey agar indicate *Enterobacter aerogenes*. On *Salmonella-Shigella* agar these organisms form pink colonies. Colorless to translucent colonies on MacConkey agar indicate either *Salmonella* or *Proteus*. Colonies with black centers on *Salmonella-Shigella* agar indicate *Salmonella* or *Proteus*. Both of these organisms do not ferment lactose. The lack of fermentation on these two media is presumptive evidence for the presence of these two organisms.

   b. If desired, the differential identification of *Escherichia coli* and *Enterobacter aerogenes* can be made by completing the IMViC test. Consult Exercise 37 for the procedures for this test. Recall that *Escherichia coli* gives a + + − − reaction in this test and *Enterobacter aerogenes* gives a − − + + reaction.

2. *Culturing the Presumptive Organisms.*
   (*The remainder of this exercise is concerned with the differential identification of* Proteus vulgaris *and* Salmonella typhimurium.)

   a. Select the MacConkey agar and *Salmonella-Shigella* agar streak plates. Draw circles on the bottom of the petri dishes around well-isolated colorless colonies and colorless colonies with dark centers.

   b. Stab the butt and streak the slant portions of separate Kligler's iron agar slants for the individual isolated colonies circled on the plate media of the unknown mixed culture studied. Be sure to label these slants with the proper number of the plate media and the type of colony sampled.

   c. Incubate the Kligler's iron agar slants at 35°C for 18 hours. These slants must be read after overnight incubation to avoid any oxidative or proteolytic reactions that raise the pH and mask any fermentation reaction. This phenomenon is called alkali reversion.

3. *Enterotube II® Option*
   (*This option many be started at the Second Period and completed at the Third Period.*)

   a. Select several Enterotubes®. Label each with the sample of presumptive *Salmonella typhimurium* or *Proteus vulgaris* colonies. Use only clear colonies or those with black centers.

   b. Inoculate each Enterotube® with a single culture taken from MacConkey agar or *Salmonella-Shigella* agar. Use the procedures described in Exercise 39.

   c. Incubate these Enterotubes® at 35°C for 24 hours.

Third Period

1. *Evaluation of Kligler's Iron Agar Slants:*
   a. Obtain the Kligler's iron agar slants. Examine them for the following reactions: A red slant/yellow deep (alkaline slant/acid deep) indicating glucose fermentation coupled with a black color in the deep portion indicates hydrogen sulfide production. Recall that *Salmonella* and *Proteus* show an alkaline slant/acid deep reaction. *Salmonella* and *Proteus* also show a positive reaction for hydrogen sulfide production. The acid reaction in the deep portion of the tube may be masked by the presence of the black color.

   b. List these findings in the Results section.

2. *Confirmatory Reactions for Differential Identification:*
   (The problem remaining is to distinguish between Proteus and Salmonella.)

   a. *Reactions Studied.*
      Obtain tubes of urea broth and phenylalanine agar. Label them 1, 2 or 3 to correspond to the chart numbers on the Kligler's iron agar slants.

   b. Transfer an inoculum from the presumptive *Proteus* and *Salmonella* Kligler's iron agar slants to separate tubes of urea broth.

   c. Streak separate slants of phenylalanine agar for each of the presumptive organisms selected.

   d. Incubate the urea broth tubes and phenylalanine agar slants at 35°C for 48 hours.

3. *Enterotube II® Evaluation:*
   a. Obtain the report sheets and coding manual for the Enterotube II®. Use the procedures in Exercise 39 to identify the unknown cultures sampled.

   b. Save these results to compare with those obtained by culturing in urea broth and on phenylalanine agar.

Fourth Period

1. *Final Confirmation:*
   a. Observe the urea broth for a cerise color, which indicates urea hydrolysis to ammonia and carbon dioxide. Urease activity is found in *Proteus vulgaris* but is absent in *Salmonella typhimurium*.

   b. Pipette 0.5 ml of 10% ferric chloride solution into the phenylalanine agar slant tube. Gently tap the slant to flush the solution over the growth. Observe the slant and the solution for the appearance of a green color, which indicates deamination of this amino acid to phenylpyruvic acid. This reaction is highly specific for *Proteus vulgaris*.

   c. Record all findings for the differential identification of the microbes in these mixed gastrointestinal infections in the Results section.

   d. Compare these results with those found in the Enterotube II®.

2. Answer the questions for the exercise.

Urinary Tract Infections

Warning: This exercise uses pathogenic organisms. The students must exercise great care to avoid spills and accidents. All spills must be decontaminated with disinfectant. All accidents must be reported to the instructor.

Objectives

1. Define **lower urinary tract infection**.

2. Indicate a reason for the recommended change in bacterial standards for urinary tract infections.

3. List three desirable features that an antibiotic used in urinary tract infections should have.

4. Describe how gram-negative urinary tract pathogens are isolated and distinguished from each other.

Background

Lower urinary tract infections involve the urethra and the urinary bladder. These infections are a serious medical problem for one of five females in this country. The major symptoms of urinary tract infection are internal discomfort on urination, passing of small volumes of urine, a frequent number of times when patient has the urge to urinate, pain above the pubic bone, pus and sometimes blood in the urine.

The use of a diaphragm as a method of contraception is sometimes associated with an increase in urinary tract infection in women. The major causes of urinary tract infections are *Escherichia coli* and *Staphylococcus saphrophyticus* (Stamm 1988). Other causes are the enterococcus, *Klebsiella* and *Proteus* species (Schaeffer 1988). Currently a colony count of 100,000 bacteria per ml from cultures of midstream samples of urine in women is used to distinguish a urinary tract infection from contamination of urine. Many clinical laboratories use this standard. Unfortunately many women with confirmed symptoms of a urinary tract infection show negative midstream urine cultures when the 100,000 bacteria per ml of urine is used as the standard. These women would be regarded as false negatives and in many cases would be denied medical therapy. The supplement to the journal *Urology*: August 1988 vol. 32, no. 2, entitled *New Standards for UTI-1988*, recommends new standards for urinary tract infections. The new recommended standard is 100–10,000 bacteria per ml. This lower standard would include those women who show typical symptoms of urinary tract infections yet have low bacterial counts in the urine. Most physicians treat uncomplicated urinary tract infections empirically.

Recurrent urinary tract infections are commonly due to fecal flora that colonize the vagina and adhere to the mucous membrane epithelium of the urethra by their pili. These organisms then ascend to the bladder. These organisms are not readily washed out on urination. Women who have a history of repeated urinary tract infections have epithelial cells that more readily bind these urinary pathogens than the cells of women who only have an occasional infection. This type of infection may also reoccur after an inadequate antibiotic therapy against an original infection (Schaeffer 1988).

The indications for the use of a urine culture are: a recent history of urinary tract infection, symptoms for more than seven days and a recent hospitalization or the use of catheterization that could indicate an increased risk of hospital-acquired (nosocomial) urinary tract infection. Other reasons are pregnancy and diabetes (Stamm 1988).

The criteria for the selection of an antibiotic are that the drug should show a high concentration in the urine and a low serum concentration. It should not harm the bacteria flora in the gastrointestinal tract or the vagina. Lastly, it should not be expensive. Antibiotics that are poorly absorbed from the intestinal tract tend to kill intestinal flora and to predispose the patient to yeast infections. Examples of antibiotics that are used include nitrofurantoin, trimethoprim-sulfamethoxazole, cephalosporins, tetracyclines and quinolones. Nitrofurantoin becomes highly concentrated in the urine and has minimal effects on intestinal and vaginal flora. Trimethoprim-sulfamethoxazole and cephalosporins are effective against most urinary tract pathogens and have some effect on vaginal flora also. Tetracyclines are effective against urinary tract pathogens but tend to show a high concentration in the intestinal tract. Patients taking this antibiotic may show an increased risk of yeast infection. Norfloxacin, an example of a quinolone antibiotic, is frequently used to treat serious urinary tract infections caused by enteropathogens that are resistant to a variety of the commonly used antibiotics (Parsons 1988). Another quinolone antibiotic that is highly effective against the gram-negative enteropathogens and *Pseudomonas aeruginosa* that cause urinary tract infections is ciprofloxacin.

Urinary Tract Infection: An Overview

In this exercise, simulated urine samples made from trypticase soy broth are inoculated with those bacteria known to cause urinary tract infection. We will call these broth samples "urine." These samples simulate patients with urinary tract infection. The goal of this exercise is for the student to identify the microorganisms in each sample. The samples are coded with numbers to represent chart numbers of patients. Three methods are presented to demonstrate the presence of bacteria in a "urine" sample. The instructor should choose the method or combination of methods to be completed in the laboratory. In one method a drop of "urine" form a well-mixed uncentrifuged sample is placed on a slide, air dried and heat fixed. The slide sample is then stained by the Gram stain procedure and examined under the oil immersion lens. The presence of 1 microorganism and 1 or more white blood cells in a field suggests at least 100,000 bacteria are present in a urine sample. In the second method a 0.001 ml calibrated loop or a disposable sterile plastic 1 µl calibrated loop is used to completely streak a plate of CLED agar. One µl is the equivalent of a 1/1000 dilution of a ml. The number of colonies seen is multiplied by 1000 to obtain the number of cells per ml of urine. This streak plate method is the preferred approach for obtaining the number of cells per ml because it takes little time to perform and uses few media and supplies. If desired, the urine sample can be placed on the agar with a loop and streaked with a sterile bent glass rod.

In a third method a sample of the urine is diluted and pour plated with CLED agar. The number of bacteria per ml of urine is obtained by multiplying the number of colonies counted by the dilution factor. This third method is very accurate but is more difficult and time-consuming than the previous methods and therefore is not favored by many clinical laboratories.

CLED agar can be used for identification of specific organisms. However, some of the uropathogens used in this exercise produce similarly yellow-colored colonies on this medium. This could cause difficulty for some students. For example, enterococcus, *Enterobacter aerogenes* and *Escherichia coli* form yellow colonies, while *Proteus* forms clear colonies. In order to isolate the cause or causes of the urinary tract infection, the urine sample is streaked for single colony isolation on differential and selective media to identify gram-positive or gram-negative bacteria. The media used are PEAB or Columbia CNA agar with 5% sheep blood and EMB agar.

Selective and differential media such as phenylethyl alcohol agar with blood (PEAB) or Columbia CNA agar with blood and Levine's eosin methylene blue agar (EMB) agar can also be streaked for single colonies to isolate gram-positive and gram-negative bacteria, respectively. PEAB is highly selective for gram-positive cocci such as *Staphylococcus aureus* and *Enterococcus faecalis*. It inhibits most gram-negative bacteria. Those that grow form very small colonies. *Proteus* grows poorly on this medium but does not show a swarming reaction. If preferred, Columbia CNA agar with blood can be used. This medium promotes the growth of the gram-positive staphylococci, streptococci and enterococci. It inhibits *Escherichia coli*, *Proteus*, *Klebsiella Enterobacter* and *Pseudomonas*. *Proteus* and *Enterobacter* may show partial inhibition on PEAB and Columbia CNA agar with blood. EMB agar inhibits gram-positive bacteria. Lactose fermenters such as *Escherichia coli* produce colonies with a green metallic sheen in reflected light or show nucleated colonies with dark centers. *Enterobacter aerogenes* produces purplish-pink shiny colonies on EMB agar. *Klebsiella pneumoniae* produces mucoid purplish-pink colonies on EMB agar. Those that do not ferment lactose produce clear to translucent colonies. An example is *Proteus vulgaris*. *Enterococcus* may also show partial inhibition and green metallic sheen on EMB agar. *Pseudomonas aeruginosa* forms clear to translucent spreading colonies with irregular edges on EMB agar. Presumptive identification is made of the bacteria from their growth patterns on these media.

In both plating methods, in this exercise, the bacteria are then specifically identified by their reactions on specialized media such as Kligler's iron agar, urea broth, motility agar and SF broth. This exercise presents each method for examination of urine.

Materials

Five separate 20-ml trypticase soy broth samples in sterile bottles inoculated with: (a) *Escherichia coli*, (b) *Enterococcus faecalis*, (c) *Proteus vulgaris*,

(d) *Klebsiella pneumoniae*, (e) *Enterobacter aerogenes*, (f) *Pseudomonas aeruginosa*. (These urine cultures should be refrigerated and arbitrarily marked 1, 2, 3, 4, 5, and 6 to represent patient chart numbers.)

Gram stain reagents

0.001 ml platinum calibrated loops

sterile disposable plastic 1 μl calibrated loops in supplied container

bent glass rods for spreading bacteria

beakers containing 95% alcohol

sterile petri dishes

bottles containing 99 ml of sterile distilled water

sterile pasteur pipettes

sterile 1-ml pipettes

pipette pumps

Kligler's iron agar slants

urea broth tubes

motility agar deeps

Simmons citrate agar slants

SF broth tubes

plates of CLED agar

plates of EMB

plates of PEAB agar or plates of Columbia CNA agar with 5% sheep blood

bottles of CLED Agar held at 45°C in a water bath

nitrate broth with Durham tube

nitrite test reagent A (sulfanilic acid) in darkened dropper bottles

nitrite test reagent B (dimethyl alpha naphthylamine) in darkened dropper bottles

Optional demonstration: Uricult® (CLED/EMB) paddle in plastic screw cap containers, and Uricult® wall chart

Procedures

First Period (See Figure 51-1)

The student should use the same "urine" sample for all studies performed.

First Method:

1. *Gram Stain of Urine:*
   a. Mix the urine sample by swirling.

   b. Label a slide in the left corner with the number of the urine sample.

   c. Place a drop of urine on a slide with a sterile pasteur pipette or inoculating loop.

   d. Allow the drop to air dry. Then heat fix the smear.

   e. Gram stain the smear. Blot dry and observe under the microscope. Check for the presence of at least 1 or more bacteria and white blood cells per field. The presence of at least 1 organism and at least 1 or more white blood cells suggests at least 100,000 bacteria per ml of urine.

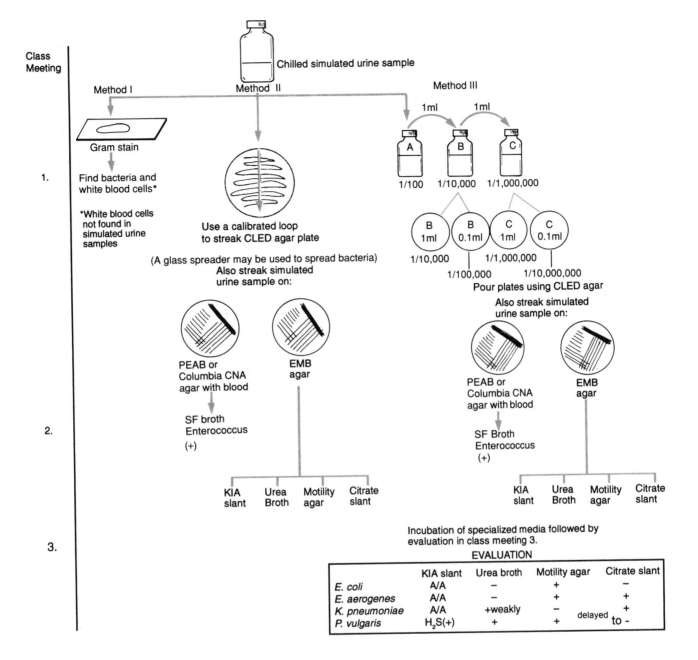

	KIA slant	Urea broth	Motility agar	Citrate slant
E. coli	A/A	−	+	−
E. aerogenes	A/A	−	+	+
K. pneumoniae	A/A	+weakly	−	+
P. vulgaris	H₂S(+)	+	+ delayed	+ to −

Figure 51-1
Urinary Tract Infection
Differential Procedures.

Second Method:

2. *Calibrated Loop Streaking of a Urine Sample/Use of the Calibrated Platinum Loop or Sterile Disposable 1 μl Plastic Calibrated Loop:*

a. Mix the urine sample by swirling.

b. Select a plate of CLED agar and label it with the number of the urine sample.

c. Gently flame the platinum loop or grasp the plastic loop by the middle of the handle and remove it from the container. Do not flame this loop.

d. Hold the loop vertically and immerse it just below the surface of the diluted urine.

e. Streak a loopful of the diluted urine sample down the center of the surface of the CLED agar plate. Then without flaming, streak closely spaced cross streaks from left to right across the original streak. Start from the top of the plate and continue to the bottom. Be sure to cover the entire plate.

    f. Dispose of this plastic calibrated loop in a container of disinfectant. (Clarridge, J.E. et al 1987)

3. *Glass Spreader Procedure for Spreading the Initial Streak Innoculum on the Plate:*

    a. If desired, the center streak can be spread with a bent glass rod as follows: Dip the glass spreader in a beaker of 95% alcohol. Pass the spreader through a flame to burn off the alcohol and then spread the urine on the surface of the CLED agar plate.

    b. Incubate the streaked or glass-spread CLED agar plates at 35°C for 24 to 48 hours.

Third Method:

4. *Quantitative Plate Count/Dilutions:*

    a. Select the urine sample. Dilute the urine sample 1:100, 1:10,000 and 1:1,000,000 in the following fashion into three prelabeled 99-ml sterile water dilution bottles.

    b. Mix the urine sample by swirling.

    c. Use a pipette to transfer 1 ml of the urine sample to a bottle containing 99 ml of sterile distilled water to make a 1:100 dilution.

    d. Place this pipette in the discard bin of disinfectant. Mix the dilution contents by swirling.

    e. Select a sterile pipette and transfer 1 ml from the 1:100 dilution to a bottle containing 99 ml of sterile distilled water to make a 1:10,000 dilution.

    f. Discard this pipette properly. Mix the dilution contents by swirling.

    g. Select a sterile pipette and transfer 1 ml from the 1:10,000 dilution to a bottle containing 99 ml of sterile distilled water to make a 1:1,000,000 dilution.

    h. Discard this pipette properly. Mix the dilution contents by swirling.

5. *Quantitative Plate Count/Plating:*

    a. Label four plates "1:10,000," "1:100,000," "1:1,000,000" and "1:10,000,000" and with the number of the urine sample.

    b. Select a pipette and transfer 0.1 ml from the 1:10,000 dilution bottle to the plate labeled "1:100,000." Use the same pipette to transfer 1 ml from this dilution to the plate labeled "1:10,000." Discard this pipette properly.

    c. Select a pipette and transfer 0.1 ml from the 1:1,000,000 dilution bottle to the plate labeled "1:10,000,000." Use the same pipette to transfer 1 ml from this dilution bottle to the plate labeled "1:1,000,000." Discard this pipette properly.

    d. Pour 15 ml of cooled melted CLED agar into each dish. Rotate each dish to distribute the agar and bacteria. Allow the agar to harden and then invert the dishes and incubate at 35°C for 24 to 48 hours.

6. *Streaking Selective Media:*
   a. Select a plate of PEAB agar or Columbia CNA agar and EMB agar.

   b. Streak these plates to isolate single colonies. Use the standard inoculating loop supplied to you.

   c. Incubate all CLED agar and selective media agar plates at 35°C for 24 to 48 hours.

Second Period

1. *Plate Count on CLED Agar after Streaking with a Calibrated Platinum Loop or the Sterile Disposable Calibrated Loop (method II):*
   a. Select those plates that show isolated colonies.

   b. Count the number of colonies on the CLED agar plate and multiply it by 1000 for the platinum 0.001 ml loops and for the 1 µl sterile plastic calibrated loop to give the number of bacteria per ml of urine sample.

2. *Plate Counts on CLED Agar (method III):*
   a. Count those plates showing between 30–300 colonies per plate. Multiply the colony count by the dilution factor to determine the number of cells per ml of urine sample.

3. Observe the growth patterns on CLED agar. *Escherichia coli* produces yellow-green dry flat colonies. *Enterobacter aerogenes* produces yellow convex, moist and glistening colonies. *Klebsiella pneumoniae* produces mucoid yellow colonies. *Enterococcus faecalis* produces very tiny yellow colonies. All these organisms ferment lactose. The medium turns yellow. *Proteus vulgaris* and *Pseudomonas aeruginosa* do not ferment lactose, produce clear colonies and the medium turns blue.

4. *Selective Agar Streak Plate Observation and Presumptive Identification:*
   a. Observe the PEAB agar plate for large colonies. The enterococcus forms large gray to off-white colonies on this media. Small colonies are probably *Proteus*.

   b. Observe the Columbia CNA agar. Enterococci produce small blue gray colonies. Staphylococci produce large white to gray or cream to yellow colonies. Small scattered white colonies may be *Proteus* or *Enterobacter*.

   c. Observe the EMB plate for colonies that show a green metallic sheen by reflected light or show nucleated colonies with a dark centers. These are *Escherichia coli.* Purplish-pink shiny colonies on EMB are *Enterobacter aerogenes*. *Klebsiella pneumoniae* colonies are very mucoid and purplish pink in color. These are lactose fermenters. White to transparent colonies on EMB are *Proteus vulgaris* and are non-lactose fermenters. Colorless to translucent spreading colonies with uneven edges are *Pseudomonas aeruginosa*. Very small scattered lactose fermenting colonies may be *Enterococcus faecalis*. A green metallic sheen may be seen. This microorganism is partially inhibited on this medium.

5. *Identification and Confirmation—Inoculations from PEAB/Columbia CNA Agar with Blood Evaluation:*
   a. Note the different types of colonies on PEAB or Columbia CNA agar. Be sure to transfer colonies of each type into separate tubes of SF broth to select for *Enterococcus faecalis*. Label these tubes with the source of media and color of the colony taken. This broth contains azide salts,

which inhibit coliforms and gram-negatives. This medium permits only the growth of the enterococcus, which ferments the sugar glucose to acids. The indicator bromcresol purple turns yellow/brown in the presence of acid.

6. *Use of EMB Colonies for Inoculation and Evaluation:*
   a. Streak some of the growth from colonies with a green metallic sheen, nucleated colonies, purplish pink colonies or clear colonies to separate Kligler's iron agar slants and stab the butt portion of the agar. After incubation, an acid slant and butt in this medium would indicate glucose and lactose fermentation. The color of the medium would become yellow throughout. Gas is indicated by splitting of the agar or displacement of the agar upwards. *Escherichia coli, Enterobacter aerogenes* and *Klebsiella pneumoniae* ferment both sugars to acids and gas. *Proteus vulgaris* produces hydrogen sulfide and a black color in the agar butt.

   b. Transfer the growth from EMB grown colonies to urea broth and nitrate broth with Durham tube; stab into a motility agar deep and streak a Simmons citrate agar slant. *Proteus* is motile and shows cloudiness in the motility agar. It also hydrolyses urea to ammonia and carbon dioxide. The indicator phenol red turns the broth cerise (pink). *Proteus* is negative or shows a delayed positive reaction on Simmons citrate agar. *Escherichia coli* is motile, does not hydrolyze urea and does not utilize citrate salts for growth. *Enterobacter aerogenes* is motile, does not hydrolyze urea and uses citrate for growth. *Klebsiella pneumoniae* is non-motile, hydrolyzes urea weakly and uses citrate for growth. *Pseudomonas aeruginosa* produces an alkaline slant and alkaline butt in Kligler's iron agar. The medium remains red throughout. It does not hydrolyse urea, is motile, uses citrate salts for growth, and produces nitrogen gas from nitrates (denitrification). All the other gram-negative uropathogens produce nitrites from nitrates.

   c. Incubate the SF broth, the nitrate broth, the urea broth, the motility agar deep, Simmons citrate slant and the Kligler's iron agar slant for 48 hours.

Third Period

1. *Identification and Confirmation—Reading of Results:*
   a. Observe the SF broth for a yellow/brown color, which indicates fermentation and the presence of *Enterococcus faecalis.*

   b. Examine all culture results for the gram-negative uropathogens. See 6b above. Add 3 drops of nitrite A solution followed by 3 drops of nitrite B solution to the nitrate broth tubes. Observe a color change to red for all uropathogens other than *Pseudomonas aeruginosa. Pseudomonas aeruginosa* produces a gas space in the Durham tube. This is nitrogen gas. This represents further reduction of nitrates to nitrous oxides and finally to nitrogen gas. This is called denitrification.

   c. Compare them to the summary chart.

   d. Record all your findings in the Results section and identify the cause or causes of the urinary tract infections in your patients.

2. Answer the questions for the exercise.

Uricult® System for Urinary Tract Infection

Testing—An Optional Exercise

The Uricult® System is commonly used in doctor's offices and hospitals for determination of the presence of urinary tract infection and presumptive identification of the uropathogens. This procedure is readily completed by nurses, physician assistants and physicians. It is highly cost effective and minimizes contact with a urine specimen.

Further information on Uricult® can be obtained from LifeSign Inc., P.O. Box 218, Somerset, New Jersey 08875-0218, tel: 1-800-526-2125, in New Jersey: 908-246-3366, Fax: 908-246-0570.

Materials

Four Uricult® dipslide culture paddles in their containers

Four "urine" samples to be singly inoculated with the organisms listed below: Each contains trypticase soy broth in a 500 ml beaker covered with aluminum foil. A 0.1 ml sample of a 20 hour trypticase soy broth culture of *Escherichia coli* or *Klebsiella pneumoniae* or *Proteus vulgaris* or *Enterococcus faecalis* is singly added to a specific beaker. The beakers are labeled 1 to 4 and are treated as patient unknowns.

Uricult® reference chart for identification of common urinary tract pathogens

Procedures

First Period

1. Obtain a "urine specimen" and a Uricult® dipslide paddle culture container. Mark the sample number on the Uricult® container.

2. Dip the Uricult® dipslide culture paddle into the "urine" specimen so that only both sides of the paddle medium are totally immersed in the liquid.

3. Remove the paddle. Allow any excess fluid to drain off into the beaker and replace the paddle in its plastic container. Screw the cap securely.

4. Repeat this procedure for the remaining "urine" cultures.

5. Incubate all Uricult® dipslide paddle culture containers at 35°C for 18 to 24 hours.

Second Period

1. Use the package insert or the Uricult® reference chart to identify the uropathogen present.

2. Compare the colony density on the agar paddles to the colony density chart to estimate the numbers of bacteria present in the sample.

3. Refer to the descriptions in Exercise 51 and the reference chart for further information on the patterns of growth of the uropathogens on the CLED and EMB agar.

4. Identify the uropathogen present in your sample and determine whether a urinary tract infection is indicated by your results.

References

Clarridge, J. E., M. Pezzlo and K. Vosti. 1987. *Laboratory diagnosis of urinary tract infections* (Cumitech 2A). Washington, DC: American Society for Microbiology.

Parsons, C. Lowell. 1988. *Protocol for treatment of typical urinary tract infection: Criteria for antimicrobial selection*, pp. 22–25. Supplement to *Urology*, 32(2) *New Standards for UTI 1988*. Published by Hospital Publications, Inc. Secaucus, N.J.

Schaeffer, A. 1988. *Pathogenesis of recurrent urinary tract infection: Use of understanding as therapy*, pp. 13–15. Supplement to *Urology*, 32(2) *New Standards for UTI 1988*. Published by Hospital Publications, Inc. Secaucus, N.J.

Stamm, W. 1988. *Protocol for diagnosis of urinary tract infection: Reconsidering the criterion for significant bacteriuria*, Supplement to *Urology*, 32(2) (*New Standards for UTI 1988*), 6–10. Published by Hospital Publications, Inc. Secaucus, N.J.

Snyder Test for Dental Caries Susceptibility

Warning

The student must use care in this exercise since the mouth contains a variety of opportunistic and pathogenic organisms. The beakers containing saliva must be discarded in the microbiological discard bin after use to prevent any possible spills and contamination of other individuals.

Objectives

1. Define **dental plaque**.

2. Explain how mouth microorganisms contribute to dental caries.

3. Name the important ingredients in Snyder Test agar.

Background

The mouth contains a variety of microorganisms. These include staphylococci, streptococci, actinomyces, lactobacilli and the enteric gram-negative bacteria. Some of the streptococci such as *Streptococcus mutans* are attached to tooth surfaces. *Streptococcus salivarius* organisms are attached to the gums and mucosa of the cheeks. Dental extractions or oral surgery can lead to bacteremia and sometimes to infective endocarditis, in which the heart valves are infected. The causes of these problems are the microbial flora in the mouth. Dentists frequently prescribe penicillin or erythromycin to prevent these complications.

Streptococcus mutans is commonly involved in the formation of dental caries. These gram-positive cocci split the sucrose (cane sugar) in foods into glucose and fructose. The glucose is then polymerized into a polysaccharide called **dextran**. The dextran surrounds the cells and forms a covering called a **glycocalyx** that becomes attached to the teeth. Streptococci and lactobacilli become trapped in this dextran coating. This collection of polysaccharide dextran and bacteria is called **plaque**. The streptococci and lactobacilli produce acids from the glucose and fructose. As the pH drops below 4.8, the lactobacilli multiply and produce sufficient acid to remove the calcium from tooth enamel. These bacilli grow best in an acid environment and enhance the formation of **dental caries**. The Snyder Test measures acid production by oral lactobacilli that produce dental caries.

The student uses melted cooled agar deeps of Snyder Test agar to detect acid produced by lactobacilli present in a 0.2-ml sample of saliva pipetted into this medium, which contains the indicator bromcresol green, dextrose, tryptone, salt and agar. The critical ingredients are the indicator and the sugar. The final pH of the sterilized medium is 4.8, which is ideal for the multiplication of lactobacilli. The lactobacilli ferment the glucose to acids, which further reduces the pH, and the medium changes color from blue green to yellow. After inoculation the tube is rolled in the palms of the hands to distribute the saliva in the medium. The agar deeps are then incubated for 72 hours and examined at 24-hour intervals to determine the time for the color change and the degree of risk of developing dental caries.

Materials

sterile 50-ml beakers covered with aluminum foil

agar deep tubes of Snyder Test agar stored at 50°C in a water bath

sterile 1-ml pipettes

pipette pumps

Procedures

1. Expectorate saliva into a sterile beaker. Collect sufficient saliva to line the bottom of the beaker. (See Figure 52-1)

2. Swirl the beaker to distribute the oral microorganisms evenly in the container.

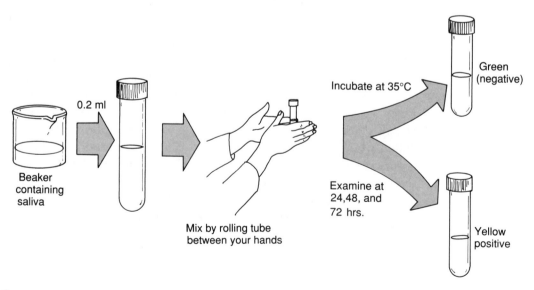

Figure 52-1
Snyder Test for Dental Caries Susceptibility.

3. Pipette 0.2 ml of the saliva into a tube of melted cooled Snyder Test medium. Replace the aluminum foil cover and place the beakers containing saliva into the microbiological discard bin.

4. Rotate the molten agar deep tube between the palms to distribute the saliva sample into the medium.

5. Incubate the agar deeps at 35°C for 72 hours in an upright position. Examine the tubes at 24-hour intervals to determine whether any color change occurred.

Second Period and Later

1. *Evaluation at 24-Hour Intervals for 72 Hours:*
   a. Compare the observed results with the Caries Susceptibility Scale on the following page to determine the degree of risk for developing dental caries.

   b. Record your findings in the Results section.

2. Answer the questions for the exercise.

Caries Susceptibility Scale

| | *Medium Turns Yellow in* | | |
Caries Susceptibility	*24 hours*	*48 hours*	*72 hours*
Marked	+		
Moderate	–	+	
Slight	–	–	+
None	–	–	–

This table is reprinted from Kelley, S. G. and Post, F. J. *Basic Microbiology Techniques* (3rd ed.) 1989 with the permission of Star Publishing Company.

Salmonella Serology Slide Agglutination Test

Warning

This exercise uses a pathogenic organism and purified antigen from this pathogen. Care must be used to avoid spills. All spills must be covered by disinfectant. All accidents must be reported to the instructor. It is strongly recommended that this exercise be completed as a demonstration by the instructor for the students to view in the microscope.

Objectives

1. Describe the agglutination test.
2. Define **antigen**.
3. Define polyvalent antisera.

Background

Agglutination is an example of a serological test available to clinical laboratories that must identify pathogens such as staphylococci, streptococci and enteric gram-negative bacteria. This test can be used to identify microorganisms that cause gastroententis. The **Widal test** for *Salmonella typhi*, which causes typhoid fever, is an example of this kind of test. A sample of sera from a patient is mixed with the organism. If clumping occurs, then positive identification can be made. The exercises on the unknown and on the uses of rapid multimedia test systems demonstrate that enteric pathogens can be identified on the basis of their responses to fermentation of sugars, use of amino adds and responses to specialized tests such as the oxidase, Kligler's iron agar and urease tests. These tests require at least overnight incubation for results.

The serological test offers another approach that is less time-consuming. This exercise examines identification of *Salmonella*. These organisms are gram-negative bacteria that are responsible for a variety of enteric infections. Many of them have a very similar biochemistry. They have a somatic antigen called the **O antigen** and a flagellar antigen called the **H antigen**. The O antigen is part of the polysaccharide endotoxin that is found in this organism. These O antigens are resistant to boiling. The O antigens are separated into groups and identified by capital letters. In the United States the common O antigens are found in groups A, B, C_1, C_2, D and E. **Polyvalent antisera** can be used to rapidly identify the type of *Salmonella* present by the observation of clumping in the presence of the specific type of antisera. Generally serology studies are used together with biochemical unknown type studies for an identification.

Salmonella Serology: Slide Agglutination Test: An Overview

Agglutination of *Salmonella typhimurium* by polyvalent antisera to the O antigens is studied in this exercise. A sample of the bacteria is placed on a slide in a drop of saline. Polyvalent antisera containing antibodies to a variety of O antigens is added to the bacteria. The combination is mixed and then examined for clumping. Since the O antigens are somatic and are located in the cell walls, tight grainy-appearing complexes become visible.

This exercise includes a positive and negative control as well as the test organism *Salmonella typhimurium* culture. The positive control includes a standard *Salmonella* antigen and known specific antisera and will show the typical clumping reaction of agglutination. The negative control includes antibody and saline. This lacks any antigen and does not show any agglutination. The test organism is obtained from a slant culture of *Salmonella typhimurium*.

Materials

test organism: 20-hour trypticase soy agar slant of *Salmonella typhimurium*

sterile serological tubes

sterile bottle containing 20 ml of phenolized saline that contains 0.85% sodium chloride and 0.5% phenol (One ml of phenolized saline should be distributed into separate sterile serological tubes. Before the class meeting the instructor or laboratory technician should prepare separate turbid suspensions of the test organisms by transferring one or more loopfuls of the test organism into the separate tubes of phenolized saline. The phenol serves to attenuate the organisms. The suspensions should be very cloudy. *Under no circumstances should the student make this suspension.* This is for the safety of the student.)

deep well slides or triple depression slides

Salmonella O antigen group B (Difco #2840-56)

Salmonella O polyvalent antisera (Difco #2264-47)

sterile Pasteur pipettes with bulbs

container of sterile toothpicks

container of disinfectant for discarding the Pasteur pipettes and depression slides

Antigens and Antisera

These antigens and antisera are available from Difco Laboratories or BBL.

Difco Laboratories:

Salmonella O antigen Group B (Difco #2840-56)

Salmonella O polyvalent antisera (Difco #2264-47)

BBL:

Salmonella O Group B antigen (somatic 1-4-5-12) 5 ml (catalog #40732)

Salmonella polyvalent antiserurn (Groups A–E) 1 ml (catalog #40707)

BBL product catalog states that each ml of antisera provides a working solution of 3 ml when diluted with sterile saline. Antisera are packed in 1-ml amounts in screw-capped dropper bottles.

Procedures

1. Use triple depression slide or deep well slides. Label three depressions in a deep well slides (1) "saline control," (b) "positive control" (c) "*Salmonella typhimurium.*" (See Figure 53-1)

2. Select three pasteur pipettes. Label them on the bulb end "a," "b" and "c." Transfer a drop of phenolized saline to well a. Transfer a drop of *Salmonella* antigen to well b. Transfer a drop of the *Salmonella typhimurium* phenolized saline suspension to well c.

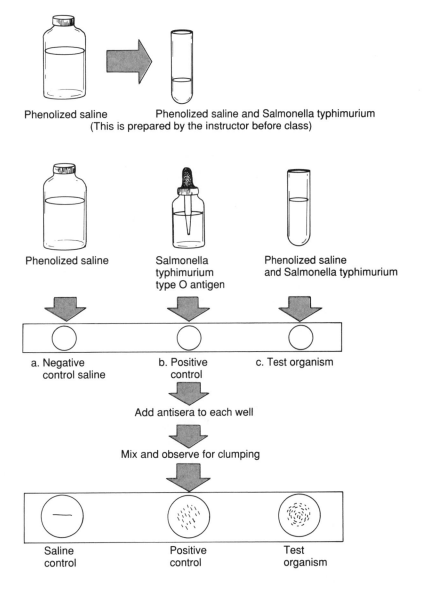

Figure 53-1
Salmonella Serology Slide Agglutination Test.

3. Use a separate sterile pasteur pipette to transfer a drop of *Salmonella* antisera to each of the wells.

4. Mix the contents of each well by gently rocking the slide or by mixing the contents of each well with a separate sterile toothpick. Discard the tooth-pick in the container of disinfectant.

5. Observe each well for the presence of clumping. Record the findings in the Results section.

6. *Be absolutely sure to discard the deep well slides or depression slides, toothpicks and Pasteur pipettes in the container of disinfectant.*

7. Answer the questions for the exercise.

Mutagens and Carcinogens: The Ames Test

Warning

This exercise does not use a positive control because of the dangers and special procedures required in the handling of these compounds. However, care must be used in this exercise since *Salmonella typhimurium* is a pathogen. Any accidents must be reported to the instructor. All spills must be promptly disinfected. All chemicals must be disposed of in a proper and legal fashion.

Objectives

1. Define **mutagen**.
2. Define **carcinogen**.
3. Explain the goal of the Ames Test.
4. Explain the meaning of *reversion* of the histidine gene to prototrophy.

Background

Chemicals that cause cancer are known as **carcinogens**. Many of the known carcinogens also cause changes in the DNA of the chromosomes and are therefore **mutagenic**. In the 1970s Bruce N. Ames developed a procedure to test many potential carcinogens for their mutagenic ability. The Ames Test uses strains of *Salmonella typhimurium* as the test organisms to determine the mutagenic ability of substances. The strain of this organism used in this exercise for mutagenesis requires histidine and biotin. This microorganism has several features that enhance its ability to detect mutations. It has a rfa mutation, which causes a partial loss of the lipopolysaccharide layer in the cell wall. This increases the permeability of the cell wall to large molecules that normally would not penetrate the intact cell wall. It also has a uvr B mutation, which is a deletion in a gene responsible for excision repair of damage in DNA. This mutation increases the sensitivity to many mutagens. The uvr deletion also extends through the biotin gene. Therefore, this organism requires biotin. The test strain also contains an R factor plasmid, which contains genes that enhance error-prone repair of severe DNA damage. This repair results in mutations in the DNA damage. Natural mutagens in the environment produce their damage through this error-prone repair mechanism.

Generally, Ames found that chemicals that are carcinogens show a high mutation rate in the Ames Test. Some carcinogens require processing by liver enzymes to convert them into an active mutagenic state that will react with DNA. In humans these biochemical reactions naturally occur in the liver. For simplicity, this exercise will use test chemical mutagens that do not require any activation by a liver extract. The Ames Test offers a rapid and inexpensive way to screen potentially carcinogenic compounds that humans are exposed to in the environment. The Ames Test does not require the use of laboratory animals. The test has shown that many environmental agents are carcinogenic and mutagenic to DNA.

Mutagens and Carcinogens: The Ames Test: An Overview

The *Salmonella typhimurium* tester strain TA 98 is grown in Oxoid nutrient broth No. 2. 0.1 ml of the overnight culture is transferred to 13 × 100 mm tubes of top agar containing Difco agar and sodium chloride and traces of histidine and biotin. The top agar is held at 45°C in a water bath. The top agar is mixed and poured onto the surface of a glucose salts–minimal agar medium. The plate is gently tilted to distribute the molten agar over the bottom agar surface. The agar is allowed to harden. A variation of the spot test is used to detect mutations. The mutagen is added to sterile filter paper disks. These are placed on the agar surface of the poured plates. The plates are wrapped in foil or brown wrapping paper to exclude light and are incubated at 35°C for 48 hours. During the incubation the traces of histidine allow the bacteria to complete a few divisions. This produces a faint growth on the plate. These divisions are necessary since many mutations only occur in the presence of DNA replication. The mutagen diffuses into the agar and induces histidine revertants to nonhistidine requirement (histidine prototrophy). The revertant colonies grow on the mutagen-treated plate. Control plates lacking the mutagen are also prepared. The number of revertants seen on mutagen-treated plates is compared to the number of spontaneous revertants on the control plates to determine the ability of the tested mutagen to produce mutations.

Materials

20-hour *Salmonella typhimurium* TA 98 tester strain grown in Oxoid nutrient broth No. 2

test mutagens: commercial hair dyes, household liquid cleaning agents or a slurry of finely divided cigarette ash in distilled water dispensed into separate sterile petri dishes in 10-ml amounts

sterile petri dish containing 10 ml of control distilled water

prepoured glucose minimal agar plates containing 30 ml of agar medium (Use number 1029 Falcon petri plates sterilized by gamma radiation. Plates sterilized by ethylene oxide gas show a high spontaneous histidine reversion rate.)

sterile 13 × 100 mm metal capped tubes

sterile 1-ml pipettes

sterile 10-ml pipettes

pipette pumps

water bath set at 45°C

slide forceps

sterile 250 ml solution of 0.5 mM histidine-HCl and 0.5 mM biotin

250-ml screw-capped bottles containing 100 ml of melted top agar, made of 0.6% Difco agar and 0.5% sodium chloride, stored in a water bath at 45°C.

[Before use, 10 ml of a sterile solution of 0.5 mM L-histidine-HCl and 0.5 mM biotin are added to the melted agar. The melted agar is mixed by swirling. 2-ml portions of the prepared top agar are pipetted into 13×100 mm sterile metal-capped tubes stored at 45°C in a water bath.]

sterile petri dish containing sterile filter paper disks

vortex mixer

Procedures

First Period (See Figure 54-1)

1. Obtain three plates of the glucose-minimal salts agar plates and label them "control," "hair dye" and "household liquid cleaning agent" or "cigarette ash slurry."

2. Obtain three tubes containing 2 ml of molten top agar. Pipette 0. 1 ml of the *Salmonella typhimurium* TA98 test strain into a single top agar tube.

3. Mix the contents of a tube with the vortex mixer for 3 seconds or by rolling the tube between the palms of the hands. Pour the top agar on to the surface of a glucose salts–minimal agar plate. Tilt the plate and rotate the plate to distribute the melted top agar evenly over the surface. Repeat this procedure for the remaining two top agar tubes and plates. The pipetting, mixing, pouring and spreading of the top agar must be completed in 20 seconds to avoid stippling of the agar surface. Set the plates aside for several minutes to allow the agar to harden.

4. Flame a slide forceps and pick up a sterile disk and touch it to the surface of the distilled water in the petri dish. Allow the distilled water to just moisten the disk. Place the disk in the center of the control plate and tap it gently to secure it to the agar surface.

5. Flame a slide forceps and pick up a sterile disk and touch it to the surface of the hair dye solution in the petri dish. Allow the hair dye to just moisten the disk. Place the disk in the center of the plate labeled "hair dye" and tap it gently to secure it to the agar surface.

6. Repeat the procedures of Step 5 with the household liquid cleaning agent or the slurry of cigarette ash.

7. Cover all the plates with aluminum foil or brown paper to prevent any changes in chemicals used as mutagenic agents that are sensitive to light.

8. Incubate all plates inverted at 37°C for 48 hours.

Second Period

1. Note the appearance of a light revertant lawn on all the plates because of the small amount of histidine and biotin present in the medium.

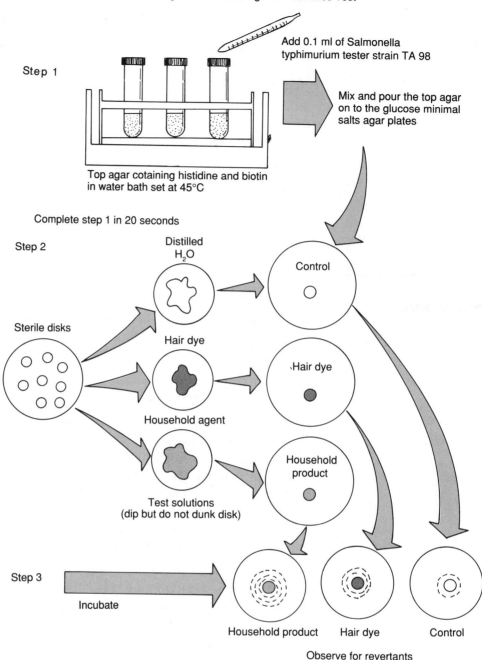

Mutagens and Carcinogens: The Ames Test

Step 1

Add 0.1 ml of Salmonella typhimurium tester strain TA 98

Mix and pour the top agar on to the glucose minimal salts agar plates

Top agar cotaining histidine and biotin in water bath set at 45°C

Complete step 1 in 20 seconds

Step 2

Distilled H₂O

Sterile disks

Hair dye

Household agent

Test solutions (dip but do not dunk disk)

Control

Hair dye

Household product

Step 3

Incubate

Household product   Hair dye   Control

Observe for revertants

Figure 54-1
Mutagens and Carcinogens:
The Ames Test.

2. Note the appearance of revertant colonies on each plate and compare the numbers of revertants seen on the control and chemically treated plates. Count the colonies.

3. Answer the questions for the exercise.

Reference

D. Maron and B. Ames, "Revised methods for the *Salmonella* mutagenicity test," *Mutation Research*, 113 (1983) 173–215. Elsevier Biomedical Press. The author thanks Dr. Bruce N. Ames, Biochemistry Department, University of California, Berkeley, CA 94720 for a copy of this reference.

Case Study 8

An outbreak of severe diarrhea occurs in patients on one floor of a hospital. Stool cultures from patients show the presence of *Salmonella*. Staff members involved with these patients are ordered to supply stool cultures. In the laboratory, enrichment cultures from these are streaked on MacConkey agar and Salmonella-Shigella agar and incubated at 37°C for 48 hours and then analyzed.

The table below lists the summarized results.

Staff Member	MacConkey Agar	Salmonella-Shigella Agar
MD X	pink colonies	no growth
MD Y	pink colonies	no growth
Nurse Z	pink colonies	scattered pink colonies
Food service aide	clear colonies	black centered colonies

Answer the following:

1. Predict the most probable organism for each hospital staff member

_____

_____

2. Name the source of this microbe _____

_____

3. Name some policies that must be instituted to prevent any spread of infection.

_____

_____

4. Name an appropriate therapy to treat the infected person.

_____

_____

RESULTS

Exercise 1 | Microscopy

· ·

Diagrams of Prepared Slides

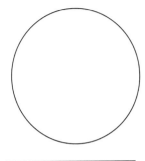

Bacillus species

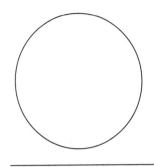

Streptococcus pyogenes

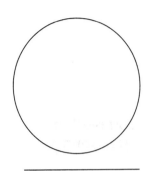

Spirillum species

Questions

1. Define resolving power.

_____

_____

2. Indicate the relationship between numerical aperture and resolving power in the oil immersion lens.

_____

_____

3. Define working distance.

_____

_____

4. Indicate the effect a reduction of illumination has on resolving power.

_____

_____

5. Define parfocal.

_____

_____

6. Distinguish between the shape of *Bacillus anthracis* and *Streptococcus pyogenes*

_____

_____

Completion Questions

1. The amount of light sent to the stage opening is regulated by the

_____

_____

2. The lens that one looks through is called the

_____

_____

3. The magnification of the oil immersion lens is

_____

_____

4. Focusing under high power is done with the

_____

_____

True or False. Correct any false answers with the proper terms.

1. As the magnification increases, resolving power decreases.

_____

_____

2. As magnification increases, working distance decreases.

_____

_____

3. Use of oil with the oil immersion lens decreases the resolving power.

_____

_____

4. The stage or objective is moved the greatest distance by the fine adjustment.

_____

_____

The Fungi: Molds and Yeasts

Diagrams

Rhizopus   Aspergillus   Penicillium   Candida

○   ○   ○   ○

Description of Fungal Cultures

Rhizopus: _____

_____

Aspergillus _____

_____

Penicillium: _____

_____

Saccharomyces: _____

_____

Questions

1. Identify the following terms: mycelium, sporangiophore, conidia, septate, zygospore, dikaryon, and basidia.

_____

_____

2. What is unusual about the *Deuteromycetes*?

_____

_____

3. How does the conidiophore of *Aspergillus* differ from that in *Penicillium*?

_____

_____

4. Explain dimorphism in fungi.

_____

_____

Completion Questions

1. The collection of mold hyphae is called a _____

_____

2. Deuteromycete, molds reproduce _____

_____

3. Naked spores are called _____

_____

4. Two infections produced by *Candida* are _____

_____

True or False. Correct any false answer with the proper terms.

1. Histoplasma can affect structures in the immune system. _____

_____

2. Dikaryons are never found in *Basidiomycetes*. _____

_____

3. Branched conidiophores are typically found in *Aspergillus*. _____

_____

4. Dimorphism in Histoplasma depends on the salinity. _____

_____

Protozoa

Diagrams

Draw diagrams of each of these protozoa in the space provided and identify the disease and its major symptoms.

Organism—Diagrams	Disease	Major Symptoms
Ring stage of malarial plasmodium	_____	_____
		_____
		_____
Trophozoite of *Toxoplasma gondii*	_____	_____
		_____
		_____
Trichomonas vaginalis	_____	_____
		_____
		_____
Giardia lamblia	_____	_____
		_____
		_____
Trypanosoma	_____	_____
		_____
		_____
Balantidium coli	_____	_____
		_____
		_____

1. Identify the characteristics of sporozoans in the phylum *Apicomplexa*.

   _____

   _____

2. Name two ways to contract toxoplasmosis.

   _____

   _____

3. List symptoms of a *Trichomonas* urinary tract infection.

   _____

   _____

4. Describe the anatomy of a trypanosome.

   _____

   _____

5. Distinguish between African Sleeping Sickness and Chagas Disease.

   _____

   _____

6. Indicate the differences in the anatomy of *Balantidium coli* and *Giardia lamblia*.

   _____

   _____

7. Distinguish between erythrocytic schizogony and sporogony.

   _____

   _____

8. Distinguish between (a) merozoite and mature schizont and (b) trophozoite and cyst.

   _____

   _____

**Completion
Questions**

1. The intermediate host in malaria is

   _____

   _____

2. Two medical problems associated with congenital toxoplasmosis

   are _____

   and _____

3. Destruction of nasal septum and hard palate is produced by

   _____

   _____

4. Visceral leishmaniasis, is produced by

   _____

   _____

True or False. Correct any false answers with the proper terms.

1. Ring stages typically are found in trypanosoma infections.

   _____

   _____

2. Dermal sores are associated with cutaneous leishmaniasis.

   _____

   _____

3. *Plasmodium vivax* cells are motile by cilia.

   _____

   _____

4. Liver abscess is found in cases of amebic dysentery.

   _____

   _____

Microbes Are Everywhere

Environmental Survey	Number of Colonies	
doorknob	_____	_____
work counter	_____	_____
student locker/drawer	_____	_____

Human Body Survey	Number of Colonies	
Blood Agar Cough Plate	beta-hemolysis	_____
	alpha-hemolysis	_____
	no-hemolysis	_____
hair		_____
nostrils		_____
hand		_____
other		_____

Air Plate Survey	Number of Colonies	
air plate	_____	_____

Questions

1. Describe a procedure to demonstrate the presence of microbes on the skin.

   _____

   _____

2. Demonstrate how microbes in the air are sampled.

   _____

   _____

3. Define the term **fomite**.

_____

_____

4. Distinguish between beta-hemolysis and alpha-hemolysis.

_____

_____

5. Indicate the major theme of this exercise as demonstrated by your results.

_____

_____

Completion Questions

1. Two living surfaces which contain microorganisms are

_____

and

_____

2. A non-droplet mode of transmission of airborne infections is

_____

_____

3. An example of an airborne infection is

_____

_____

4. Fecal-oral route of infectious organisms is typically found in

_____

_____

True or False. Correct any false answers with the proper terms.

1. Human normal flora are found in the body.

_____

_____

2. Dust usually contains microbes.

_____

_____

3. Environmental surfaces include the human body.

_____

_____

4. Coughing and sneezing favor droplet mode of disease transmission.

_____

_____

Exercise 5 — Aseptic Transfer Techniques

Growth Present/ Not Present In:

Sterile Medium Transfers

Medium Used	*Observation*
nutrient broth A	_____
nutrient broth B	_____
nutrient agar slant B	_____

Staphylococcus aureus Inoculation

Medium Used	*Observation*
nutrient broth	_____
nutrient agar slant	_____
nutrient agar deep	_____

Questions

1. Indicate the purpose of flaming during any transfer.

   _____

   _____

2. Define pure culture.

   _____

   _____

3. Distinguish between an agar slant and an agar deep.

   _____

   _____

4. Name two methods of inoculation completed with an inoculating loop.

_____

_____

Completion Questions

1. Nutrient broth contains distilled water and

_____

_____

2. Sterile means

_____

_____

3. Growth is detected in broth by

_____

_____

True or False. Correct any false answers with the proper terms.

1. Agar deeps contain liquid.

_____

_____

2. *Staphylococcus aureus* forms a yellow colored growth on agar.

_____

_____

3. Agar deeps are stabbed with loops.

_____

_____

Smear Preparation and the Simple Stain

Objectives

Simple Stain Diagrams

Slide _____

Preparation _____

Bacteria color _____

Bacteria shape_____

Slide_____

Preparation _____

Bacteria color _____

Bacteria shape _____

Slide _____

Preparation _____

Bacteria color _____

Bacteria shape _____

Questions

1. Explain the differences in smear preparation when bacteria are taken from cultures in broth or solid agar medium.

   _____

   _____

2. Name two results of heat fixation.

   _____

   _____

3. Define a simple stain.

   _____

   _____

4. Explain the chemistry of staining a bacterial cell.

_____

_____

5. Describe the color and shape of the stained cells. Draw representative cells.

_____

_____

Completion Questions

1. Basic dyes consist of

_____

_____

2. An example of a basic dye is

_____

_____

3. The color of safranin stained cells is

_____

_____

4. Rinsing the slide thoroughly serves to

_____

_____

True or False. Correct any false answers with the proper terms.

1. Stained *Bacillus mycoides* appear as rods in chains when viewed in the microscope.

_____

_____

2. An acidic dye has a non-charged color group.

_____

_____

3. Unstained cells are easily seen.

_____

_____

4. Staphylococci are rodlike in appearance.

_____

_____

The Negative Stain

Bacteria	Negative Stain Diagram
Bacillus subtilis	
Staphylococcus aureus	

Questions

1. Explain how negatively stained bacteria differ in appearance from positively stained bacteria.

   _____

   _____

2. Explain the chemical basis for a negative stain.

   _____

   _____

3. Explain the usefulness of the negative stain in a study of bacterial morphology.

   _____

   _____

Completion Questions

1. In a negative stain bacilli would appear

   _____

   _____

2. The dye used in the negative stain is called

   _____

   _____

3. Chemically, this dye is charged

   _____

   _____

True or False. Correct any false answers with the proper terms.

1. Negatively stained cells are alive.

   _____

   _____

2. The top slide is used to make the smear.

   _____

   _____

3. Unstained cells are easily seen in the microscope after this procedure.

   _____

   _____

The Gram Stain

Bacteria	Gram Reaction	Gram Stain Diagrams Shape and Arrangement
Bacillus mycoides	_____	◯
Bacillius subtilis	_____	◯
Moraxella B. catarrhalis	_____	◯
Escherichia coli	_____	◯
Klebsiella pneumoniae	_____	◯
Myobacterium smegmatis	_____	◯
Proteus vulgaris	_____	◯
Pseudmonas aeruginosa	_____	◯
Staphylococcus aureus	_____	◯
Streptococcus pyogenes	_____	◯

1. Define the terms **primary dye, mordant, decolorizing agent** and **counterstain**.

   _____

   _____

2. Explain a reason for the observed difference in the gram-positive and gram-negative state.

   _____

   _____

3. Name the most important step in the Gram stain procedure and justify your answer.

   _____

   _____

4. Which organisms show endospores?

   _____

   _____

5. What color would be seen if alcohol were left out of the Gram stain procedure? Explain your answer.

   _____

   _____

Completion Questions

1. Gram-positive cells are colored

   _____

   _____

2. Gram-negative cells are colored

   _____

   _____

3. Gram-positive cells are more sensitive to agents such as

_____

_____

4. Most cells stain

_____

_____

True or False. Correct any false answers with the proper terms.

1. Endospores stain in the Gram procedure.

_____

_____

2. Old gram positive cell cultures become gram-variable.

_____

_____

3. *Klebsiella pneumoniae* is gram-positive.

_____

_____

4. *Pseudomonas aeruginosa* appear as round cells in the Gram procedure.

_____

_____

The Acid-Fast Stain

Organism	Acid-Fast Reaction	Acid-Fast Diagrams
		◯
Staphylococcus aureus	_____	
		◯
Mycobacterium smegmatis	_____	

Questions

1. Identify which organisms are acid-fast and which are non-acid-fast.

_____

_____

2. The acid-fast state depends on what property of a cell?

_____

_____

3. Name a disease organism that is acid-fast.

_____

_____

4. Why is heat used in this procedure?

_____

_____

5. Why are acid-fast cells not decolorized despite treatment with acid-alcohol?

_____

_____

**Completion
Questions**

1. The primary dye in the Acid-Fast stain procedure is

   _____

   _____

2. The decolorizing agent in this procedure is

   _____

   _____

3. Acid-fast cells stain the color of

   _____

   _____

4. The counterstain used is

   _____

   _____

True or False. Correct any false answers with the proper terms.

1. Staphylococci contain waxy lipids.

   _____

   _____

2. The tuberculosis bacillus is routinely stained well in the Gram stain.

   _____

   _____

3. Mycolic acid typically binds the counterstain.

   _____

   _____

4. Acid alcohol removes the primary dye from acid-fast cells.

   _____

   _____

The Endospore Stain

Endospore Stain Diagram

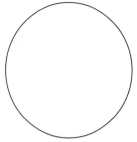

Bacillus subtilis

Questions

1. Define spore and sporangium.

_____

_____

2. Distinguish between germination and sporogenesis.

_____

_____

3. Explain why heat is necessary in the spore stain procedure.

_____

_____

4. What significant medical problems are posed by spores?

_____

_____

5. Indicate any relationship between Gram-reaction and spore formation.

_____

_____

1. The dye used to stain the endospore is

   _____

   _____

2. The counterstain used is

   _____

   _____

3. Endospores are resistant to

   _____

   _____

4. Two chemicals responsible for endospore resistance are

   _____

   _____

True or False. Correct any false answers with the proper terms.

1. Endospores metabolize at a high rate.

   _____

   _____

2. *Escherichia coli* produces endospores.

   _____

   _____

3. Endospore formation is not a method of cell division.

   _____

   _____

4. Endospores survive boiling water.

   _____

   _____

The Capsule Stain

Capsule Stain Diagram

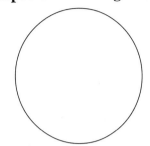

Klebsiella pneumoniae

Questions

1. Define the term **capsule**.

   _____

   _____

2. What is the composition of a capsule?

   _____

   _____

3. List three functions of a capsule.

   _____

   _____

4. Why is the capsule procedure considered a negative stain?

   _____

   _____

5. Explain how the capsule of *Klebsiella pneumoniae* may promote the development of severe necrotizing pneumoniae.

   _____

   _____

6. How would a lab technologist use capsules to identify different encapsulated bacteria?

_____

_____

Completion Questions

1. The negative capsule stain uses the chemical

_____

_____

2. The violet staining of the cell is due to

_____

_____

3. Capsules interfere with a process in neutrophils called

_____

_____

True or False. Correct any false answers with the proper terms.

1. Capsules contain polysaccharide.

_____

_____

2. Care must be used in rinsing a capsule preparation.

_____

_____

3. Complement rapidly destroys encapsulated cells.

_____

_____

Bacterial Motility Studies

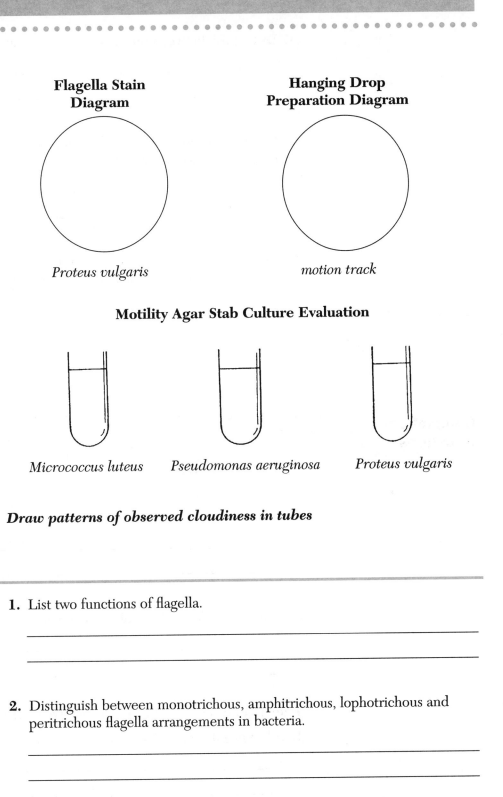

**Flagella Stain
Diagram**

Proteus vulgaris

**Hanging Drop
Preparation Diagram**

motion track

Motility Agar Stab Culture Evaluation

Micrococcus luteus   *Pseudomonas aeruginosa*   *Proteus vulgaris*

Draw patterns of observed cloudiness in tubes

Questions

1. List two functions of flagella.

_____

_____

2. Distinguish between monotrichous, amphitrichous, lophotrichous and peritrichous flagella arrangements in bacteria.

_____

_____

3. List three techniques to demonstrate motility and explain the results seen for each.

_____

_____

4. Distinguish between brownian movement and true motility.

_____

_____

5. Explain the observed differences in results for motile and nonmotile bacteria in motility agar medium.

_____

_____

6. Explain the influence of oxygen on the observed results in motility agar medium and indicate which organism is most influenced by oxygen.

_____

_____

Completion Questions

1. Long protein extensions from the bacterial cell surface are called

_____

_____

2. Positive chemotaxis occurs in the presence of

_____

_____

3. *Micrococcus luteus* is motile or non motile.

_____

_____

True or False. Correct any false answers with the proper terms.

1. A hanging drop preparation observes stained cells.

_____

_____

2. Brownian movement is directed motion.

_____

_____

3. *Proteus vulgaris* is nonmotile.

_____

_____

Morphological Unknown Characterization

Staining Reactions

Gram-stain reaction _____

Shape _____

Arrangements _____

_____

Endospores _____

Acid-Fast stain reaction _____

Capsule stain reaction _____

Culture Studies

Motility _____

Pigment production _____

_____

Summary of Unknown Observations

_____

_____

_____

_____

_____

_____

_____

Questions

1. List information that can be obtained from a Gram-stain.

   _____

   _____

2. Under what circumstances should an Acid-Fast stain be completed?

   _____

   _____

3. Distinguish between diplococci, sarcinae and streptococci.

   _____

   _____

4. List two advantages of capsules to bacteria.

   _____

   _____

5. Describe how motility in bacteria is demonstrated by growth in soft agar medium.

   _____

   _____

Completion Questions

1. Endospores are commonly found in the groupings

   _____

   _____

2. Erythromycin primarily affects cells that are gram-

   _____

   _____

3. Pigments produced by bacteria can color

   _____

   _____

True or False. Correct any false answers with the proper terms.

1. The waxy lipids in mycobacteria cause the cells to dump together.

   _____

   _____

2. Endospores in a Gram stain appear stained pink or purple.

   _____

   _____

3. If a Gram stained preparation shows gram-positive streptococci, a good antibiotic to use is an aminoglycoside.

   _____

   _____

Pure Culture Isolation Skills

Pure Culture Isolation Streak Plates

	Nutrient Agar Colony Appearance	Gram Reaction
Bacillus subtilis	_____ _____	_____
Escherichia coli	_____ _____	_____
Staphylococcus aureus	_____ _____	_____

	MacConkey Agar Colony Appearance	Gram Reaction
Bacillus subtilis	_____ _____	_____
Escherichia coli	_____ _____	_____
Staphylococcus aureus	_____ _____	_____

	PEAB Colony Appearance	Gram Reaction
Bacillus subtilis	_____ _____	_____

Escherichia coli _____   _____

_____

Staphylococcus aureus _____   _____

_____

	Mannitol-Salt Agar Colony Appearance	**Gram Reaction**
Bacillus subtilis	_____	_____
	_____	
Escherichia coli	_____	_____
	_____	
Staphylococcus aureus	_____	_____
	_____	

	Eosin Methylene Blue Agar Colony Appearance	**Gram Reaction**
Bacillus subtilis	_____	_____
	_____	
Escherichia coli	_____	_____
	_____	
Staphylococcus aureus	_____	_____
	_____	

	Salmonella-Shigella Agar Colony Appearance	**Gram Reaction**
Bacillus subtilis	_____	_____
	_____	
Escherichia coli	_____	_____
	_____	

Staphylococcus aureus _____ _____

_____

Salmonella-Shigella Agar
Colony Appearance   **Gram Reaction**

Escherichia coli _____ _____

_____

Salmonella typhimurium _____ _____

_____

Loop Dilution Procedure

Write a statement about the number and appearance of the colonies on each plate.

Plate A: _____

_____

Plate B: _____

_____

Plate C: _____

_____

Questions

1. Explain how streaking a plate can produce pure cultures.

   _____

   _____

2. Identify the key step in the loop dilution procedure that favors isolation of pure cultures.

   _____

   _____

3. Explain why MacConkey agar favors growth of gram-negative bacteria.

   _____

   _____

4. List one advantage of specialized media demonstrated by this exercise.

_____

_____

5. Explain why *Escherichia coli* colonies appear red on MacConkey agar.

_____

_____

Completion Questions

1. A colony that is a pure culture contains

_____

_____

2. Phenylethyl alcohol inhibits

_____

_____

3. Diluting of a bacterial population in a streak plate is accomplished by

_____

_____

4. Differential media is defined as allowing

_____

_____

True or False. Correct any false answers with the proper terms.

1. Selective media allow many bacteria to grow.

_____

_____

2. Lenticulate colonies are found on the surface.

_____

_____

3. *Staphylococcus aureus* forms red colonies on PEAB.

_____

_____

4. *Bacillus subtilis* forms blue colonies on nutrient agar.

_____

_____

Dilution = _____

Number of colonies counted = _____

Dilution factor = _____

Number of bacterial cells per ml equals:

Number of colonies counted × dilution factor or

_____ × _____ = _____ cells per ml

Questions

1. Explain why pipettes should not be left on a counter after use.

   _____

   _____

2. How does a dilution differ from a dilution factor?

   _____

   _____

3. A pour plate made from a 1/1000 dilution shows 40 colonies. Calculate the number of bacteria per ml in the original sample.

   _____

   _____

4. A bottle contains 20,000 bacteria per ml. Calculate the dilution necessary to yield 200 colonies on the plate.

   _____

   _____

5. Distinguish between a total count and a viable count.

_____

_____

1. A viable count measures the ability of bacteria to

_____

_____

2. A total count is carried out with the aid of a

_____

_____

3. A poorly mixed dilution plate may show

_____

_____

True or False. Correct any false answers with the proper terms.

1. It is permissible to lay pipettes on the counter top before use.

_____

_____

2. The final determination of number of cells is based on cells per ml of broth.

_____

_____

3. A 1/100 dilution has more cells per ml than a 1/1000 dilution.

_____

_____

4. The standard for number of colonies on a plate to be counted is between 30 to 300.

_____

_____

Growth Curve Determination

Time	Absorbance Measurement	Cells per ml
Zero time	_____	_____
30 minutes	_____	_____
60 minutes	_____	_____
90 minutes	_____	_____
120 minutes	_____	_____
Calculated generation time	_____	

Questions

1. Define absorbance in a spectrophotometer

   _____

   _____

2. Account for the STATIONARY phase in a growth curve

   _____

   _____

3. Describe binary fission

   _____

   _____

**Completion
Questions**

1. The LAG phase in a growth curve is characterized by

   _____

   _____

2. Absorbance measurements made from a nutrient broth culture containing *Escherichia coli* incubated for 2 hours at 37°C tend to

_____

_____

3. If a single cell in nutrient broth under ideal conditions having a generation time of one hour divides to complete 3 generations, the number of cells present and time spent in division is

_____

_____

True or False. Correct any false answers with the proper terms.

1. Exponential decrease in cell number occurs in the DECLINE phase.

_____

_____

2. Cells in the LOG phase are very dissimilar from one another.

_____

_____

3. A very light culture has a high absorbance in a spectrophotometric measurement.

_____

_____

Growth Curve of *Escherichia coli*

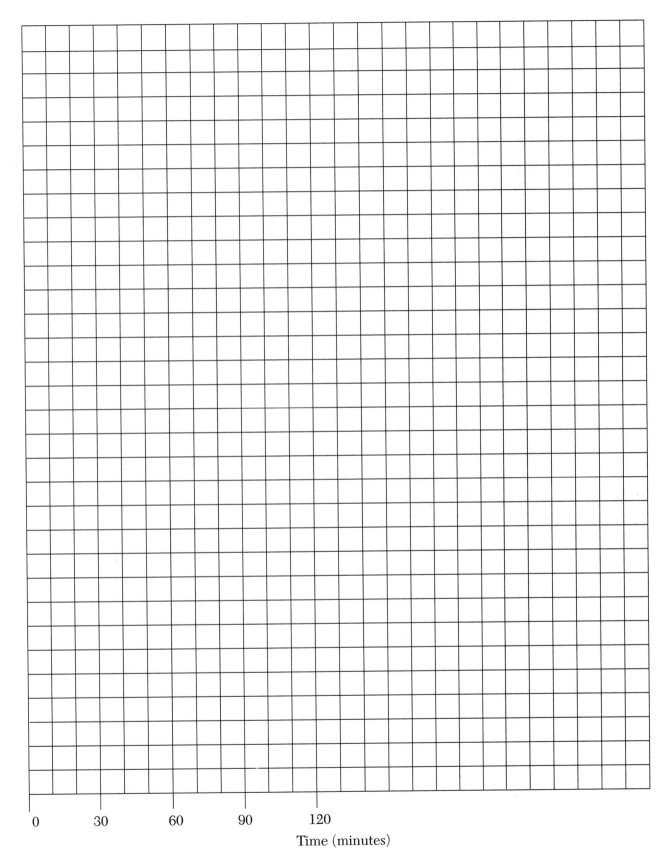

Absorbance Readings

Time (minutes)

0   30   60   90   120

Quantitative T-2 Virus Count

Virus Titer Determination

Dilution	Plaques Counted
1/10	_____
1/100	_____
1/1000	_____
1/10,000	_____
1/100,000	_____
1/1,000,000	_____
1/10,000,000	_____

number of plaques × dilution factor = viruses per ml

_____ × _____ = _____ viruses per ml

Questions

1. Define virus adsorption

   _____

   _____

2. Define virus burst

   _____

   _____

3. Define virus titer

   _____

   _____

4. Indicate the parts of the nucleocapsid

   _____

   _____

Completion Questions

1. During the viral synthesis phase bacterial DNA

   _____

   _____

2. The virus DNA is located in

   _____

   _____

3. The parts of the virus tail are

   _____

   _____

True or False. Correct any false answers with the proper terms.

1. A virus plaque originated from one virus and contains one virus.

   _____

   _____

2. Virus plaques for this T-2 virus are routinely cloudy.

   _____

   _____

3. During penetration the coat protein and DNA are injected into the cell.

   _____

   _____

4. Viruses are obligate parasites because they can only multiply in brain heart infusion broth.

   _____

   _____

Determination of Oxygen Requirements

Thioglycollate Broth

	Growth Location	Oxygen Requirement
E. coli	_____	_____
M. luteus	_____	_____
S. aureus	_____	_____
E. faecalis	_____	_____
C. sporogenes	_____	_____

GasPak Jar System and Aerobic Growth Compared

Bacteria	Aerobic Growth	Anaerobic Growth	Oxygen Requrement
M. luteus	_____	_____	_____
E. coli	_____	_____	_____
E. faecalis	_____	_____	_____
C. sporogenes	_____	_____	_____

Questions

1. Define **aerobe, anaerobe** and **microaerophile**.

   _____

   _____

2. Distinguish between microaerophiles and facultative anaerobes.

   _____

   _____

3. Which organisms can be classified as either an aerotolerant anaerobe or a facultative anaerobe?

_____

_____

4. Which organisms are aerobic or anaerobic?

_____

_____

5. Indicate two damaging effects of toxic oxygen.

_____

_____

6. Describe how toxic oxygen substances are eliminated.

_____

_____

7. Which cells are unable to eliminate toxic oxygen compounds and why?

_____

_____

8. Which method is more sensitive for the determination of oxygen requirements? Support your answer with your results.

_____

_____

Completion Questions

1. In the broth method used, one oxygen scavenging chemical is

_____

_____

2. The purpose of resazaurin is to

_____

_____

3. Bacteria growing in mud in a swamp should be in this category

_____

_____

4. Bacteria on the surface of skin can be

_____

_____

5. Water formed in a GasPak jar is due to

True or False. Correct any false answers with the proper terms.

1. Facultative anaerobes only live in the presence of oxygen.

_____

_____

2. Strict aerobes should grow on plates incubated in air and under anaerobic conditions.

_____

_____

3. *Pseudomonas aeruginosa* is a strict anaerobe.

_____

_____

4. Palladium catalyst promotes production of free oxygen.

_____

_____

5. *Staphylococcus aureus* is an example of a microaerophile.

_____

_____

Cultural Conditions

Cultural Characteristics

Organism	**Nutrient Broth**
Bacillus subtilis	_____
Escherichia coli	_____
Pseudomonas aeruginosa	_____
Staphylococcus aureus	_____
Enterococcus faecalis	_____
Clostridium sporogenes	_____

Nutrient Agar Slant

Bacillus subtilis	_____
Escherichia coli	_____
Pseudomonas aeruginosa	_____
Staphylococcus aureus	_____
Enterococcus faecalis	_____
Clostridium sporogenes	_____

Nutrient Agar Petri Plate

Bacillus subtilis	_____
Escherichia coli	_____
Pseudomonas aeruginosa	_____
Staphylococcus aureus	_____
Enterococcus faecalis	_____
Clostridium sporogenes	_____

Organism	Nutrient Gelatin Stab Tubes	
	Growth	Liquefaction
Bacillus subtilis	_____	_____
Escherichia coli	_____	_____
Pseudomonas aeruginosa	_____	_____
Staphylococcus aureus	_____	_____
Enterococcus faecalis	_____	_____
Clostridium sporogenes	_____	_____

Questions

1. Distinguish between pellicle, flocculent growth and sediment in broth.

   _____

   _____

2. Distinguish between erose and lobate margins.

   _____

   _____

3. Name the organism that produces a golden pigment in its growth on agar.

   _____

   _____

4. Name an organism that produces echinulate growth on a slant and colonies with an erose margin.

   _____

   _____

5. Give an example of an organism that produces lobate growth.

   _____

   _____

6. Distinguish between convex and umbonate elevations.

   _____

   _____

7. Indicate the location of lenticulate colonies.

_____

_____

8. Distinguish between melting and true liquefaction of gelatin.

_____

_____

Completion Questions

1. The term that best describes cloudiness in a broth tube is

_____

_____

2. Growth as a film across the surface of a broth tube is called

_____

_____

3. The edges of echinulate growth in a slant are

_____

_____

4. In beaded growth in a slant, heavier growth is found at

_____

_____

5. An erose margin to a colony is

_____

_____

6. An umbonate elevation is described as

_____

_____

7. Digestion of gelatin is observed for this gram-positive microorganism

_____

_____

True or False. Correct any false answers with the proper terms.

1. Filiform. growth shows smooth edges.

   _____

   _____

2. Sediments settle at the bottom of the broth tube.

   _____

   _____

3. Distinguishing between true gelatin liquefaction and melting requires prior storage at elevated temperature.

   _____

   _____

4. An organism that produces extremely small circular off white colonies is *Escherichia coli*.

   _____

   _____

5. *Bacillus subtilis* typically produces lobate colonies.

   _____

   _____

Temperature and Bacterial Growth

Bacterial Culture	Temperature and Growth				Temperature Category
	5	**25**	**37**	**55 (°C)**	
Pseudomonas fluorescens					_____
Escherichia coli					_____
Staphylococcus aureus					_____
Bacillus stereothermophilus					_____
Serratia marcescens					_____

> 0 = no growth
>
> + = slight growth
>
> + + = moderate growth
>
> + + + = heavy growth

Results: Temperature for Pigment Production in *Serratia marcescens*

_____

Questions

1. Define **psychrophile, mesophile** and **thermophile** and give an example of each.

   _____

   _____

2. Distinguish between psychrophile and psychrotroph.

   _____

   _____

3. Explain why pathogenic bacteria are commonly mesophiles.

_____

_____

4. Describe a hazard psychrotrophs present during refrigeration.

_____

_____

5. Describe a temperature-dependent process in *Serratia marcescens*.

_____

_____

6. Distinguish between facultative and obligate thermophile.

_____

_____

Completion Questions

1. Human pathogens grow optimally at this temperature

_____

_____

2. Food spoilage at somewhat elevated temperatures may be due to

_____

_____

3. The lowest temperature at which growth is possible is called the

_____

_____

4. At the maximum temperature for growth, reproduction is reduced due to

_____

_____

5. Growth in microorganisms means

_____

_____

True or False. Correct any false answers with the proper terms.

1. Thermophiles are typical human pathogens.

   _____

   _____

2. During growth in broth the turbidity should increase.

   _____

   _____

3. Thermophilic spore formers belong in the genus *Bacillus* or *Clostridium*.

   _____

   _____

4. *Staphylococcus aureus* is an example of a psychrophile.

   _____

   _____

5. *Pseudomonas fluorescens* is a mesophile.

   _____

   _____

Lethal Effects of Temperature

80°C Heat Treatment

Time in Minutes	E. coli	S. aureus	B. subtilis	B. stereo-thermophilus
0	_____	_____	_____	_____
5	_____	_____	_____	_____
10	_____	_____	_____	_____
15	_____	_____	_____	_____
20	_____	_____	_____	_____
25	_____	_____	_____	_____
30	_____	_____	_____	_____
35	_____	_____	_____	_____
40	_____	_____	_____	_____

100°C Heat Treatment

Time in Minutes	E. coli	S. aureus	B. subtilis	B. stereo-thermophilus
0	_____	_____	_____	_____
5	_____	_____	_____	_____
10	_____	_____	_____	_____
15	_____	_____	_____	_____
20	_____	_____	_____	_____
25	_____	_____	_____	_____
30	_____	_____	_____	_____
35	_____	_____	_____	_____
40	_____	_____	_____	_____

Legend: Indicate TNC—too numerous to count (too many colonies to count).
All other plates indicate number of colonies counted.

Questions

1. Define **thermal death time**.

_____

_____

2. Define **thermal death point**.

_____

_____

3. Explain why *Bacillus subtilis* and *B. stereothermophilus* show the greatest heat resistance at both temperatures.

_____

_____

4. Explain the purpose of pasteurization.

_____

_____

5. Explain why moist heat is effective in killing microbes.

_____

_____

6. Explain why milk must be refrigerated.

_____

_____

Completion Questions

1. Boiling water kills

_____

_____

2. Endospores are killed by

_____

_____

3. Thermoduric organisms can withstand heat exposure

_____

_____

4. The most heat sensitive organism in this study is

_____

_____

5. Liquid media sensitive to heat are sterilized by

True or False. Correct any false answers with the proper terms.

1. An autoclave is operated at 121°C for 15 minutes for sterilization.

_____

_____

2. Dry heat kills by dehydration.

_____

_____

3. Pasteurization means sterilization.

_____

_____

4. The variable factor in thermal death point is time.

_____

_____

Steam Sterilization: The Autoclave

Culture	Growth Responses Observed
B. stereothermophilus	
control-nonautoclaved	_____
autoclaved	_____

Questions

1. Define sterilization.

_____

_____

2. Explain the observed results.

_____

_____

3. Explain the method of cell death after autoclaving a microbial culture.

_____

_____

Completion Questions

1. Obligate thermophiles grow at a temperature of

_____

_____

2. Sterilization routinely kills

_____

_____

3. Inadequately sterilized cultures of *B. stereothermophilus* when subsequently incubated at 56°C show

_____

_____

4. Obligate thermophiles grown at 37°C show

_____

_____

True or False. Correct any false answers with the proper terms.

1. *B. stereothermophilus* grows at 45°C.

_____

_____

2. Sterilization permits survival of endospores.

_____

_____

3. An increase in steam pressure in an autoclave decreases the temperature.

_____

_____

4. Moist heat refers to heated air.

_____

_____

Osmotic Pressure and Bacterial Growth

Growth Responses Observed

Microorganism	0.5%	5%	10%	25%
Escherichia coli	_____	_____	_____	_____
Staphylococcus aureus	_____	_____	_____	_____
Halobacterium salinarium	_____	_____	_____	_____

Write + for growth and – for no growth in the table. Record the 1-week results first and the results for the *Halobacterium* on the 25% salt agar again after 2 weeks in parentheses to the right of the original results.

Questions

1. List your results in order of increasing salt resistance.

   _____

   _____

2. Account for the results observed.

   _____

   _____

3. Which organism is most sensitive to plasmolysis?

   _____

   _____

4. Explain why the solute proline is valuable to staphylococci.

   _____

   _____

5. Account for the growth of obligate halophiles on *Halobacterium* salt agar.

_____

_____

6. Account for the growth of molds on fruit preserves.

_____

_____

1. Bacterial cells immersed in a hypotonic environment tend to

_____

_____

2. Bacterial cells in a hypertonic environment tend to

_____

_____

3. An osmotolerant microorganism found on human skin is

_____

_____

4. Extreme halophiles are unique since they require

_____

_____

True or False. Correct any false answers with the proper terms.

1. Choline is an example of an osmoprotective solute.

_____

_____

2. In osmosis, water flows from low to high concentration.

_____

_____

3. Spoilage of fruit preserves could be carried out by osmophilic yeasts.

_____

_____

pH and Microbial Growth

Microorganism	pH 3	pH5	pH 7	pH 9
Alcaligenes faecalis	_____	_____	_____	_____
Escherichia coli	_____	_____	_____	_____
Staphylococcus aureus	_____	_____	_____	_____
Saccharomyces cerevisiae	_____	_____	_____	_____

0 = no growth

+ = slight growth

+ + = moderate growth

+ + + = heavy growth

Write a statement showing how your results demonstrate that specific microbes can produce infections in distinct regions of the body that differ in pH.

_____

_____

_____

_____

Questions

1. Indicate the pH range for acidic, alkaline and neutral solutions.

_____

_____

2. Indicate a role of pH in the control of microorganisms.

_____

_____

3. Describe two cases where distinct microorganisms are found in body regions with a particular pH.

   _____

   _____

4. Justify by your results how *Escherichia coli* can cause gastrointestinal and genitourinary tract infections.

   _____

   _____

5. Explain how *Staphylococcus aureus* can cause skin infections.

   _____

   _____

Completion Questions

1. Strong acids kill microbes by

   _____

   _____

2. Enteric pathogens survive the stomach acid because they are

   _____

   _____

3. Dental caries are favored by acid production by the microbes

   _____

   _____

4. An intestinal organism known to produce pyogenic infections in other parts of the body is

   _____

   _____

True or False. Correct any false answers with the proper terms.

1.   Staphylococcus aureus is osmotolerant and tolerant of low pH.

   _____

   _____

2. Uropathogens are suppressed by the normal flora organisms the lactobacilli.

_____

_____

3. Acidophiles prefer to grow at very low pH.

_____

_____

The Importance of Handwashing

Write a statement explaining the results found on the before and after portions of the trypticase soy agar petri plates.

Briefly summarize your conclusions.

Before (water only) _____

_____

_____

After (scrubbing) _____

_____

_____

Conclusions_____

_____

_____

Questions

1. Coliforms are a major microbe found in the large intestine. Explain the problem of fecal-oral transmission of disease in the context of handwashing.

_____

_____

2. Why is it good medical practice for medical personnel to wash hands after examining a patient?

_____

_____

3. Which kind of microbes present on skin will grow on the incubated trypticase soy agar plates?

_____

_____

4. Name some organisms commonly found as resident flora on the skin.

_____

_____

5. Describe two body mechanisms used to eliminate transient flora.

_____

_____

Completion Questions

1. Transient microbes on skin are defined as

_____

_____

2. The incidence of puerperal fever has been dramatically reduced in hospitals by the practice of

_____

_____

3. Anaerobes do not grow under the conditions of this experiment because

_____

_____

True or False. Correct any false answers with the proper terms.

1. Aerobic and facultative organisms grow on the TSA plates for this experiment.

_____

_____

2. Transient, but not resident microflora are found on mucus membranes.

_____

_____

3. Coliforms are an example of transient flora.

_____

_____

4. Low pH on skin surfaces supports the growth of transient flora.

_____

_____

Commensalism

Tube Number	Presence of Turbidity
1. *S. aureus*	_____
2. *C. sporogenes*	_____
3. mixed	_____

Gram-Stain Diagrams

Staphylococcus aureus	*Clostridium sporogenes*	*S. aureus* and *C. sporogenes*

Turbidity Comparisons

Staphylococcus aureus	*Clostridium sporogenes*	*S. aureus* and *C. sporogenes*

Write a brief statement explaining the significance of the differences seen for tubes 1, 2 and 3.

_____

_____

_____

_____

1. Define **commensalism**.

   _____

   _____

2. Which organism benefits by this association and why?

   _____

   _____

3. Name a clinical manifestation of commensalism in humans.

   _____

   _____

4. Why is a separate pipette used to inoculate each organism into the third tube?

   _____

   _____

Completion Questions

1. Commensalism is a relationship involving

   _____

   _____

2. In the intestinal tract, the *Bacteroides fragilis* group of organisms become in commensalism the

   _____

   _____

3. *Bacteroides* produce infections characterized by

   _____

   _____

True or False. Correct any false answers with the proper terms.

1. The oxygen requirement of *Clostridium sporogenes* is strict anaerobe.

   _____

   _____

2. The presence of capsules tends to increase virulence in Bacteroides.

   _____

   _____

3. Anaerobes tend to become less dominant in mixed infections.

   _____

   _____

Synergism

Staphylococcus aureus | Proteus vulgaris | Mixed culture

Reaction Observed After Incubation

_____

_____

_____

Write a brief statement explaining the meaning and significance of the differences in the observed results for tubes 1, 2 and 3.

_____

_____

_____

_____

Questions

1. Define **synergism**.

_____

_____

2. Describe the significance of gas production for this exercise.

_____

_____

3. Indicate a clinical example of a synergistic infection in the human body, and explain why it is so dangerous.

_____

_____

1. *Escherichia coli* by itself cannot produce the compound putrescine from

_____

_____

2. *Enterococcus faecalis* produces ornithine from

_____

_____

3. *Escherichia coli* produces putrescine from

_____

_____

4. Many synergistic infections involve many organisms and are said to be

_____

_____

True or False. Correct any false answers with the proper terms.

1. *Proteus vulgaris* ferments lactose.

_____

_____

2. Synergistic infections reduce the amount of tissue damage produced.

_____

_____

3. *Staphylococcus aureus* normally produces gas from lactose by fermentation.

_____

_____

Antagonism

Test Organisms	Antagonists	
	Streptomyces griseus	*Bacillus subtilis*
S. aureus	_____	_____
S. epidermidis	_____	_____
E. faecalis	_____	_____
S. pyogenes	_____	_____
E. aerogenes	_____	_____
E. coli	_____	_____
K. pneumoniae	_____	_____
P. vulgaris	_____	_____

inhibition = +
no inhibition = –

Questions

1. Define **antagonism**.

   _____

   _____

2. Give an example of a soil organism that produces an antibiotic substance.

   _____

   _____

3. Describe the appearance of a positive and negative result in an antagonism experiment.

   _____

   _____

4. Describe any correlation between antagonism and Gram-reaction for these two antibiotic producers.

_____

_____

5. Distinguish between antagonism and synergism.

_____

_____

Completion Questions

1. In the presence of the mold *Penicillium*, the bacterial culture *Staphylococcus aureus* showed a

_____

_____

2. The gram-positive bacillus, *B. subtilis* produces the antibiotic

_____

_____

3. Incubation of the antagonist for a week at 30°C allows for

_____

_____

True or False. Correct any false answers with the proper terms.

1. Bacteriocins enhance the growth of related organisms.

_____

_____

2. Colicins are lethal to enteric organisms.

_____

_____

3. Streptomycin and bacitracin are bacteriostatic to other microorganisms.

_____

_____

Microbiology of Water

Colilert Test: Colilert MPN Format:

Total Coliforms:

Number of positive tubes with yellow liquid of total number of tubes tested

_____

MPN of total coliforms from table

_____

Fecal Coliforms:

Number of positive tubes with yellow liquid showing fluorescence with UV

_____

MPN of fecal coliforms from table

_____

Colilert Test: Presence/Absence Format:

Yellow Color
Total Coliforms:

      +   = positive
      −   = negative

_____

Fecal Coliforms:
Fluorescence with UV
Fecal Coliforms:

      +   = positive
      −   = negative

_____

Multiple Tube Fermentation Test: Presumptive Test:
Gas Production in Lauryl Tryptose Broth:

Tube:	1	2	3	4	5

Confirmed Test—Total Coliforms:
Gas Production in Brilliant Green Bile Lactose Broth:

Tube:	1	2	3	4	5

Confirmed Test—Fecal Coliforms:
Gas Production in EC Broth:

Tube:	1	2	3	4	5

+ = positive
− = negative

MPN Determination—Total Coliforms and Fecal Coliforms: From Confirmed Test. The number of tubes showing gas production for 100 ml of sample: Complete the table below.

Total Coliforms	Fecal Coliforms
_____	_____
MPN Index	MPN Index
_____	_____

Completed Test:

Colony Growth Patterns on EMB Plate: _____

Gas Production in Lauryl Tryptose, Broth: _____

Gram stain prepared from nutrient agar slant: _____

Questions

1. Describe a purpose of the presumptive test.

   _____

   _____

2. Give a reason to perform the confirmed test.

   _____

   _____

3. Write the rationale for the presence/absence approach adopted by the EPA for analysis of coliforms in drinking water.

_____

_____

4. Define fecal coliform.

_____

_____

5. Describe the reaction in Colilert that is positive for total coliforms.

_____

_____

6. Describe how fecal conforms are detected in the Colilert system.

_____

_____

7. List two advantages of the Colilert system compared to the multiple tube fermentation format.

_____

_____

Completion Questions

1. Total coliforms are defined as

_____

_____

2. Total coliforms include the microorganisms known as

_____

_____

3. Three pathogens that may be found in water together with fecal coliforms are

_____

_____

4. BGBL broth is highly selective for

_____

_____

5. Gas production in a completed test constitutes

_____

_____

True or False. Correct any false answers with the proper terms.

1. An example of a typical fecal coliform is _Klebsiella pneumoniae._

_____

_____

2. The new EPA ruling states that municipal water treatment plants must remove 85% of viruses and Giardia from water.

_____

_____

3. Lauryl tryptose promotes the growth of coliforms.

_____

_____

4. The MPN table lists the most probable number of coliforms per ml of water sample.

_____

_____

Food Microbiology

Bacteria per Gram of Food

Incubation at 35°C

Type of Food	Colonies Counted	×	Dilution Factor	=	Bacteria per Gram
meat or chicken	_____		_____		_____
frozen vegetables	_____		_____		_____
dried fruit	_____		_____		_____

Incubation at 5°C

Type of Food	Colonies Counted	×	Dilution Factor	=	Bacteria per Gram
meat or chicken	_____		_____		_____

MacConkey Agar Streak Plate Results:

_____

_____

_____

_____

Questions

1. Name the type of spoilage commonly found on protein- and carbohydrate-rich foods.

_____

_____

2. Name the kind of spoilage produced by *Pseudomonas*.

_____

_____

3. Define **water activity**.

_____

_____

4. Name a category of food that has a low water activity.

_____

_____

5. Explain the reason why molds and yeasts are spoilage microorganisms in grains.

_____

_____

6. Explain why *Clostridium botulinum* food poisoning is so dangerous.

_____

_____

7. Describe an unusual feature of *Vibrio parahaemolyticus* food poisoning.

_____

_____

8. Based on your results, describe the kinds of organisms that can spoil meats and poultry.

_____

_____

Completion Questions

1. Psychrophiles in foods can be isolated by incubating plates at

_____

_____

2. Two results of blanching of foods during processing are

_____

_____

3. Three organisms killed by pasteurization are

_____

_____

4. Thermoduric microbes are unusual because they can

_____

_____

5. *Clostridium perfringens* food poisoning is unusual because the toxin is produced during

_____

_____

True or False. Correct any false answers with the proper terms.

1. Pasteurization is accomplished by heating the milk to 72°C for one minute.

_____

_____

2. Molds and yeasts tend to spoil dried foods.

_____

_____

3. Salmonellosis is commonly found in eggs and poultry.

_____

_____

4. Foods with a low water content have a high heat resistance.

_____

_____

Microbiology of Milk

Good Quality Milk

Colonies Counted   ×   Dilution Factor   =   Bacteria Per ml

_____   _____   _____

Poor Quality Milk

Colonies Counted   ×   Dilution Factor   =   Bacteria Per ml

_____   _____   _____

Statement of Comparison of Laboratory Results with U.S. Government Milk Standards:

_____

_____

_____

_____

Questions

1. Name two diseases transmitted through milk.

_____

_____

2. Indicate the importance of pasteurization.

_____

_____

3. Define **thermoduric organism**.

_____

_____

4. Indicate the standards for Grade A milk after pasteurization.

_____

_____

1. Nutrients found in milk which make it an excellent nutritional medium for growth of microorganisms are

_____

_____

2. Two reasons for microbial contamination of raw milk are

_____

_____

3. Two examples of thermoduric organisms are

_____

_____

4. Prior to commingling (mixing), raw milk may contain up to

_____

_____

True or False. Correct any false answers with the proper terms.

1. Thermoduric bacteria survive pasteurization.

_____

_____

2. Casein is digested by lipolytic bacteria.

_____

_____

3. Bacteria in the genus _Bacillus_ ferment milk sugar.

_____

_____

Reductase Activity of Milk

Decolorization Time and Milk Quality

Milk Sample	Decolorization Time (min)	Milk Quality
A	_____	_____
B	_____	_____

Questions

1. Describe what happens to the indicator dye in a reductase test of milk.

   _____

   _____

2. What is the significance of a long reduction time?

   _____

   _____

3. In what respect does good quality milk differ from poor quality milk in the reductase test?

   _____

   _____

Completion Questions

1. The dye reduction test is typically used to assay the microbiological quality of

   _____

   _____

2. The dye used for this study is a

_____

_____

True or False. Correct any false answers with the proper terms.

1. Good quality milk has few bacteria.

_____

_____

2. During a dye reduction test for milk, electrons are transferred to bacteria.

_____

_____

3. The greater the microbial population in a milk sample, the faster is the process of decolorization.

_____

_____

Clinical Unknown

Clinical Unknown

Gram Reaction   Shape   Arrangements

_____   _____   _____

Diagram of Clinical Unknown

Questions

1. Define **clinical unknown**.

   _____

   _____

2. List two examples each of respiratory, enteric and urogenital pathogens.

   _____

   _____

3. Define **nosocomial infection**.

   _____

   _____

4. List two reasons for nosocomial infections in patients.

   _____

   _____

5. List a reason why the microbiology laboratory is crucial to the determination of a differential diagnosis of infectious diseases.

_____

_____

1. The organisms causing clinical problems include those that stain gram-

_____

_____

2. The microbial laboratory tests include fermentation, as well as

_____

_____

True or False. Correct any false answers with the proper terms.

1. Infections of burns involve _Proteus_ and _Klebsiella pneumoniae_

_____

_____

2. Necrotizing pneumoniae is caused by _Klebsiella pneumoniae._

_____

_____

Fermentation of Carbohydrates

**Phenol Red Sugar Broth
Durham Tube Fermentation**

Organism	Glucose	Lactose	Mannitol
A. *faecalis*	_____	_____	_____
E. *coli*	_____	_____	_____
P. *aeruginosa*	_____	_____	_____
S. *aureus*	_____	_____	_____
P. *vulgaris*	_____	_____	_____
unknown	_____	_____	_____

Key
0 = no fermentation
A = acid
A/G = acid and gas

Methyl-Red Fermentation

Organism	Glucose Broth (MR Test)
E. *aerogenes*	_____
E. *coli*	_____
unknown	_____

Key
+ = positive
− = negative

Voges-Proskauer Fermentation

Organism	Glucose Broth (VP Test)
E. *aerogenes*	_____
E. *coli*	_____
unknown	_____

Key
+ = positive
− = negative

Statement for presumptive identification of unknown:

_____

_____

_____

Questions

1. Define **fermentation**.

_____

_____

2. Distinguish between the results of mixed acid fermentation and
   2,3 butanediol fermentation.

_____

_____

3. List a reason why the Methyl-Red test and the Voges-Proskauer tests are
   useful in the identification of some enteric bacteria.

_____

_____

4. List the purpose of the Methyl-Red indicator in the Methyl-Red test.

_____

_____

5. Distinguish between oxidative and nonsaccharolytic metabolism of sugars.

_____

_____

**Completion
Questions**

1. Anaerobic breakdown of sugars is called

_____

_____

2. In the preparatory phase of the anaerobic breakdown of sugars, phosphorylation of glucose and fructose to form fructose 1,6 diphosphate is followed by

_____

_____

3. During the conversion of glyceraldehyde-3-phosphate to 1,3 diphospho-glyceric acid, a reduction of the coenzyme

_____

_____

4. After anaerobic breakdown of sugar, the net ATP production is

_____

_____

5. The source of the hydrogens for formation of lactic acid from pyruvic acid in fermentation is

_____

_____

6. The oxidation of the reduced coenzyme by fermentation is necessary for the anaerobic breakdown of sugar because it restores

_____

_____

True or False. Correct any false answers with the proper terms.

1. Homolactic fermentations produce primarily lactic acid.

_____

_____

2. The enzyme formic hydrogenylase converts formic acid to glucose.

_____

_____

3. The final pH of a mixed acid fermentation test is below 5.5.

_____

_____

4. *Pseudomonas aeruginosa* produces strong acids in respiration.

_____

_____

5. The reagents used in the Voges-Proskauer test are hydrogen peroxide and Kovac's reagent.

_____

_____

6. Phenol red changes color to yellow at a pH of 8.

_____

_____

7. *Klebsiella pneumoniae* yields a positive methyl red test and negative Voges-Proskauer test from fermentation of glucose broth.

_____

_____

8. All fermentations produce acidic end products.

_____

_____

The Oxidation-Fermentation (O-F) Test

Organism	Open Tube	Covered Tube	Category
A. *faecalis*	_____	_____	_____
E. *coli*	_____	_____	_____
P. *aeruginosa*	_____	_____	_____
unknown	_____	_____	_____

Record the category as fermentative, oxidative or nonsaccharolytic.

Questions

1. Define **nonsaccharolytic metabolism**.

   _____

   _____

2. Distinguish between fermentative and nonfermentative metabolism.

   _____

   _____

3. Explain the importance of the O-F test in the identification of microorganisms.

   _____

   _____

4. Explain the purpose of the mineral oil in the O-F test.

   _____

   _____

5. Name two gram-negative nonfermentative bacilli and the medical problems they cause.

_____

_____

Completion Questions

1. _Bordetella pertussis_ produces

_____

_____

2. In the O-F test reactions, members of the _Enterobacteriacae_ typically show

_____

_____

3. The higher sugar concentration of O-F medium favors carbohydrate metabolism involving

_____

_____

True or False. Correct any false answers with the proper terms.

1. The ratio of peptone to sugar in O-F medium is 2:1.

_____

_____

2. Brom thymol blue is yellow at a pH of 6.

_____

_____

3. Proteolytic reactions in O-F medium produce a deeper blue color after incubation.

_____

_____

Differences in Respiratory Behavior

Catalase Test

Organism	Observation	Type of Reaction
S. aureus	_____	_____
unknown	_____	_____

Oxidase Test

Organism	Method	Observation	Type of Reaction
P. aeruginosa	_____	_____	_____
E. coli	_____	_____	_____
unknown	_____	_____	_____

Nitrate Reduction Tests

Organism	Observation	Type of Reaction
E. coli	_____	_____
P. aeruginosa	_____	_____
unknown	_____	_____

Reaction Key
+ = positive
− = negative

Questions

1. Describe the reaction carried out by catalase.

_____

_____

2. Explain why *Enterobacteriaceae* fail to produce a positive oxidase test.

_____

_____

3. Describe a diagnostic value for the catalase and oxidase tests.

_____

_____

4. List two advantages of the Oxoid Identification Sticks-Oxidase test method.

_____

_____

5. List two reactions that illustrate different types of nitrate reduction.

_____

_____

6. Explain how the reactions in question 5 differ from each other.

_____

_____

7. Explain why nitrate reduction to nitrite requires anaerobic conditions.

_____

_____

8. Distinguish between the type of nitrate reduction produced by *Escherichia coli* and by *Pseudomonas aeruginosa*.

_____

_____

Completion Questions

1. The positive oxidase test distinguishes between gram-negative enteric bacteria and

_____

_____

2. Two microorganisms that produce a positive oxidase test are

_____

_____

3. Superoxides are made by the process of

_____

_____

4. Three important respiration characteristics of members of the
   Enterobacteriaceae are

_____

_____

True or False. Correct any false answers with the proper terms.

1. Catalase produces superoxides.

_____

_____

2. Dimethyl alpha naphthylamine and sulfanific acid are used for the
   oxidase test.

_____

_____

3. Nitrogen gas is produced in denitrification.

_____

_____

4. *Klebsiella pneumoniae* produces a positive oxidase test.

_____

_____

5. Cytochrome oxidase transfers electrons from the terminal cytochrome to
   oxygen to form water.

_____

_____

Differential Identification I: Amino Acid and Specialty Tests

---

Kligler's Iron Agar

Organism	Observation	Result
S. dysenteriae	_____	_____
E. coli	_____	_____
P. aeruginosa	_____	_____
P. vulgaris	_____	_____
unknown	_____	_____

Tryptophan Hydrolysis (Indole) Test

Organism	Observation	Result
E. coli	_____	_____
E. aerogenes	_____	_____
unknown	_____	_____

Citrate Test

Organism	Observation	Result
E. coli	_____	_____
E. aerogenes	_____	_____
unknown	_____	_____

Urease Test

Organism	Observation	Result
E. coli	_____	_____
P. vulgaris	_____	_____
unknown	_____	_____

Phenylalanine Deaminase Test

Organism	Observation	Result
E. coli	_____	_____
P. vulgaris	_____	_____
unknown	_____	_____

Lysine Decarboxylase Test

Organism	Observation	Result
E. aerogenes	_____	_____
P. vulgaris	_____	_____
unknown	_____	_____

Moltility Test

Organism	Observation	Result
P. vulgaris	_____	_____
K. pneumoniae	_____	_____
unknown	_____	_____

IMViC Test

Organism	I	M	V	C
E. coli	_____	_____	_____	_____
E. aerogenes	_____	_____	_____	_____
unknown	_____	_____	_____	_____

Key for tests
+ = positive test
– = negative test

Questions

1. Explain how the Kligler's iron agar test can be used to distinguish between *Escherichia coli* and *Shigella dysenteriae*.

   _____

   _____

2. Name two groups of bacteria that give a positive hydrogen sulfide test.

   _____

   _____

3. You are given two broth cultures of bacteria. One is *Escherichia coli* and the other is *Enterobacter aerogenes*. Show how one can identify each organism and list the results of the tests used.

   _____

   _____

4. List three distinct metabolic features of *Klebsiella pneumoniae* identified by tests in this exercise.

   _____

   _____

5. Explain what is meant by **deamination** and give an example from this exercise.

   _____

   _____

6. Explain the purpose of the glucose in the Moeller decarboxylase broth.

   _____

   _____

7. Explain why reversion to a purple color is essential in the lysine decarboxylase test.

   _____

   _____

8. Contrast *Klebsiella pneumoniae, Enterobacter aerogenes* and *Proteus vulgaris* for motility.

_____

_____

9. Name two tests that can be used to distinguish between *Klebsiella pneumoniae* and *Enterobacter aerogenes* and list the observed results for each.

_____

_____

10. List three tests that clearly distinguish *Proteus vulgaris* from *Escherichia coli* and give the results observed in each organism.

_____

_____

Completion Questions

1. Reversion observed in an inoculated and incubated Kligler's iron agar slant means that

_____

_____

2. *Klebsiella pneumoniae*, grown on Kligler's iron agar, produces

_____

_____

3. Gram-negative non-fermenting bacilli decarboxylate peptides in Kligler's iron agar to produce

_____

_____

4. Bacteria that produce a positive indole reaction include

_____

_____

5. Three products produced on breakdown of tryptophan are

_____

_____

6. The end products of a positive urease test are

_____

_____

7. Phenylalanine deaminase activity is specific for

_____

_____

8. Lysine decarboxylase enzyme activity results in the formation of

_____

_____

True or False. Correct any false answers with the proper terms.

1. _Klebsiella pneumoniae_ produce a positive urease test.

_____

_____

2. A positive indole test forms a red color throughout the tube.

_____

_____

3. A positive citrate slant is red in color.

_____

_____

4. _Salmonellae_ are motile.

_____

_____

5. An alkaline slant and acid deep means glucose fermentation.

_____

_____

6. The ratio of dextrose to lactose in a Kligler's iron agar slant is 10:1.

_____

_____

7. A positive citrate agar slant is alkaline in pH.

_____

_____

8. Typically, _Escherichia coli_ shows a positive indole and positive methyl red reaction.

_____

_____

Differential Identification II: Macromolecule and Specialty Tests

---

Starch Agar Test

Organism	Observation	Result
Escherichia coli	_____	_____
Bacillus subtilis	_____	_____
unknown	_____	_____

Milk Protein (Casein) Agar Test

Organism	Observation	Result
Escherichia coli	_____	_____
Bacillus subtilis	_____	_____
unknown	_____	_____

Spirit Blue (Lipid) Agar Test

Organism	Observation	Result
Escherichia coli	_____	_____
Bacillus subtilis	_____	_____
unknown	_____	_____

Nutrient Gelatin Agar Test

Organism	Observation	Result
Escherichia coli	_____	_____
Bacillus subtilis	_____	_____
Staphylococcus aureus	_____	_____
unknown	_____	_____

Litmus Milk Broth Test

Organism	Observation	Result
Escherichia coli	_____	_____
Proteus vulgaris	_____	_____
Bacillus subtilis	_____	_____
Enterococcus faecalis	_____	_____
Pseumomonas aeruginosa	_____	_____
unknown	_____	_____

Optional Specialty Tests for _S. aureus_ and _E. faecalis_

Mannitol-Salt Agar Test

Organism	Observation	Result
Staphylococcus aureus	_____	_____
unknown	_____	_____

Bile-Esculin Agar

Organism	Observation	Result
Enterococcus faecalis	_____	_____
unknown	_____	_____

Key for Results
+ = positive
− = negative

Questions

1. Describe the results of a positive starch agar test.

_____

_____

2. Name a single organism that can hydrolyze starch, protein and lipid.

_____

_____

3. Describe the observed reaction that occurs on a positive milk protein test.

_____

_____

4. Indicate how gelatinase activity in bacteria is evaluated after incubation of nutrient gelatin.

_____

_____

5. List three reactions that are observed in litmus milk and explain what happens in each case.

_____

_____

6. Explain why *Staphylococcus aureus* can be identified with the mannitol salt agar test.

_____

_____

7. Explain a use for bile-esculin medium.

_____

_____

Completion Questions

1. The macromolecule enzyme tests employ enzymes that work

_____

_____

2. Hyaluronidase digests

_____

_____

3. Lecithinase destroys the

_____

_____

4. Leukocidin destroys

_____

_____

5. Lipolysis is common in the genera

_____

_____

6. Polysaccharides are hydrolysed to

_____

_____

7. Litmus milk can be used to evaluate hydrolytic reactions on the two organic compounds known as

_____

_____

True or False. Correct any false answers with the proper terms.

1. Fats are hydrolysed to fatty acids and glycerol.

_____

_____

2. Gram's iodine is used to detect the presence of protein digestion.

_____

_____

3. Reduced litmus is colored white.

_____

_____

4. A positive esculin hydrolysis test is diagnostic for *Enterococcus faecalis*.

_____

_____

5. An alkaline reaction is seen for *Proteus vulgaris* on litmus milk.

_____

_____

6. *Bacillus subtilis* produces positive starch, protein, and lipid hydrolysis reactions.

_____

_____

7. A red color at the margin of colonies on mannitol-salt agar indicates *Staphylococcus aureus*.

_____

_____

Clinical Unknown Results and Evaluation

Name of Student _____

Class and Section _____

Unknown Number _____

Tests and Results:

Gram Reaction and Morphology:

_____

Fermentation:

Dextrose _____

Lactose _____

Mannitol _____

Methyl-Red Reaction _____

Voges-Proskauer Reaction _____

O-F Test _____

Respiratory Behavior:

Catalase Test _____

Oxidase Test _____

Nitrate Reduction Tests _____

Amino Acid and Specialty Tests:

Kligler's Iron Agar _____

Indole Test _____

Urease Test _____

Citrate Test _____

Phenylalanine Deaminase Test _____

Lysine Decarboxylase Test _____

Motility Test _____

1MViC Test (where applicable):

I _____

M _____

V _____

C _____

Macromolecule and Specialty Tests:

Starch Test _____

Milk Protein Test _____

Spirit Blue (Lipid) Test _____

Gelatin Test _____

Litmus Milk Test _____

Optional Media Tests (where applicable):

Mannitol-Salt Agar Test _____

Bile-Esculin Agar Test _____

Summary Statement of Reasons for Decision:
Use ruling out (R/O) analysis in report

_____

_____

_____

_____

_____

_____

_____

_____

_____

_____

_____

_____

_____

_____

_____

_____

Name of Clinical Unknown: _____

Rapid Multimedia Test: Enterotube II®

Using Enterotube 110 System to Identify Specific
Members of Enterobacteriaceae

Diagram of Unreacted/Negative Results and
Reacted/Positive Results for Enterotube II®

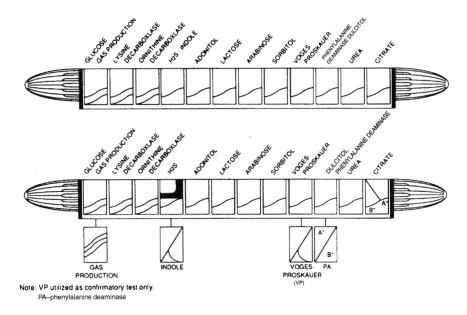

Results: This report sheet is the result for the exercise. The results recorded
depend on the color changes in the Enterotube II® after incubation.

Using Enterotube II® to Identify Specific Members of
Enterobacteriaceae

Enterotube II Coding Sheet

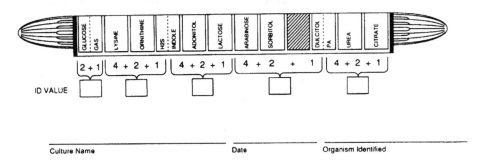

Questions

1. List two culturing advantages of an Enterotube II®.

   _____

   _____

2. Describe what happens when the inoculating wire is pulled through the compartments of the Enterotube II®.

   _____

   _____

Completion Questions

1. The Enterotube II® is a convenient way to rapidly identify members of the family

   _____

   _____

2. The Enterotube II® contains compartments that test for

   _____

   _____

3. The remaining portion of the wire in the tube maintains

   _____

   _____

4. Punching openings in the remaining eight chambers provides for

   _____

   _____

True or False. Correct any false answers with the proper terms.

1. Positive lysine decarboxylase activity is seen as a red color in the compartment.

   _____

   _____

2. Gas is indicated by a separation of the medium from the wax overlay.

_____

_____

3. Arabinose is decarboxylated.

_____

_____

4. The Enterotube II® wire is pulled through the compartments to inoculate the chambers with media.

_____

_____

5. The Enterotube II® eliminates use of many media inoculations and incubations.

_____

_____

Chemical Control
of Microorganisms

	Chemical Agent			
Organism Studied	70% alc.	quat-B	Povidone Iodine	quat-CP
S. aureus	_____	_____	_____	_____
E. coli	_____	_____	_____	_____
E. faecalis	_____	_____	_____	_____
P. aeruginosa	_____	_____	_____	_____
unknown	_____	_____	_____	_____

quat-B = benzalkonium chloride
quat-CP = cetylpyridinium chloride
Record zone of inhibition as +
Record no zone of inhibition as −

Write a brief statement to indicate any correlation between response of an organism to a chemical agent and its Gram stain reaction.

_____

_____

_____

_____

Questions

1. Distinguish between a bactericidal agent and a bacteriostatic agent.

_____

_____

2. Explain the term **zone of inhibition**.

_____

_____

3. Describe the action of a cationic quaternary ammonium compound.

_____

_____

4. Describe the action of iodine-containing compounds.

_____

_____

5. Name an unusual feature of the action of alcohol as an antimicrobial agent.

_____

_____

Completion Questions

1. Disinfectants are used on environmental surfaces such as

_____

_____

2. Disinfectants produce an antimicrobial action that is best characterized as

_____

_____

3. Antiseptics are used on surfaces such as

_____

_____

4. Antiseptics produce an antimicrobial action that is best described as

_____

_____

5. Phenolic compounds damage bacterial cells by

_____

_____

True or False. Correct any false answers with the proper terms.

1. Halogens are oxidizing agents.

   _____

   _____

2. 95% alcohol is more effective than 70% alcohol as an antimicrobial agent.

   _____

   _____

3. Alcohols with a lower molecular weight are more effective as antimicrobial agents than those with a higher molecular weight.

   _____

   _____

4. Cationic quats are more effective against gram-negative than gram-positive bacteria.

   _____

   _____

Antibiotic Sensitivity Testing: A Differential Decision

Gram-Positive Differential Antibiotic Decision				
Response of bacteria—Indicate R, I, or S				
Antibiotic	*E. faecalis*	*S. aureus*	*S. pyogencs*	unknown
amikacin	_____	_____	_____	_____
ampicillin	_____	_____	_____	_____
bacitracin	_____	_____	_____	_____
erythromycin	_____	_____	_____	_____
gentamycin	_____	_____	_____	_____
neomycin	_____	_____	_____	_____
nitrofurantoin	_____	_____	_____	_____
tetracycline	_____	_____	_____	_____
vancomycin	_____	_____	_____	_____

Gram-Negative Differential Antibiotic Decision				
Response of bacteria—Indicate R, I, or S				
Antibiotic	*E. coli*	*K.pneumoniae*	*P. aeruginosa*	unknown
amikacin	_____	_____	_____	_____
ampicillin	_____	_____	_____	_____
bacitracin	_____	_____	_____	_____
erythromycin	_____	_____	_____	_____
gentamycin	_____	_____	_____	_____
neomycin	_____	_____	_____	_____
nitrofurantoin	_____	_____	_____	_____
tetracycline	_____	_____	_____	_____
vancomycin	_____	_____	_____	_____

Statement regarding relationship between Gram reaction and antibiotic sensitivity:

_____

_____

<table>
<tr><td>

Questions

</td><td>

1. Define **broad spectrum antibiotic**.

_____

_____

2. List three modes of action of antibiotics and give an example of each.

_____

_____

3. Define **zone of inhibition**.

_____

_____

4. Explain what is meant by PPNG and MRSA.

_____

_____

5. List three risks associated with aminoglycoside antibiotics.

_____

_____

6. Define **resistant colony**.

_____

_____

7. Explain antibiotic differential decision.

_____

_____

</td></tr>
</table>

Completion Questions

1. Penicillins are lethal to microbes because they

   _____

   _____

2. *Mycoplasmas* are resistant to the antibiotic

   _____

   _____

3. An example of a macrolide antibiotic is

   _____

   _____

4. Quinolones interfere with

   _____

   _____

5. *Chlamydiae* infections are treated by

   _____

   _____

True or. False. Correct any false answers with the proper terms.

1. Non-dividing bacteria are sensitive to penicillin.

   _____

   _____

2. The antibiotic of choice against staphylococcal. and streptococcal infections is penicillin.

   _____

   _____

3. Examples of broad spectrum antibiotics include cephalosporins and tetracyclines.

   _____

   _____

4. Differential decisions for antibiotics favor the use of antibiotics classified as R for the particular microbe.

_____

_____

Effects of Antiseptic Agents on Transmission of Oral Flora or Nasal Flora

Body Cavity

Treatment	Oral Cavity	Nasal Cavity
Cepacol®	_____	_____
Betadine®	_____	_____
Hibiclens®	_____	_____
trypticase soy broth	_____	_____

Questions

1. Define infection.

_____

_____

2. Indicate the key term(s) in direct contact transmission.

_____

_____

3. List two types of indirect contact transmission.

_____

_____

Completion Questions

1. The most rigorous asepsis is called

_____

_____

2. Lack of growth on a trypticase soy agar plate means

_____

_____

3. Fecal-oral transmission is an example of

_____

_____

True or False. Correct any false answers with the proper terms.

1. The presence of organisms is the only requirement for infection.

_____

_____

2. Handwashing is classified as medical asepsis.

_____

_____

3. The term sterile field is commonly found in surgical asepsis.

_____

_____

Beta-Lactamase Activity in Gram-Positive Cocci

Organism	Color of Cefinase Disc	Reaction
Staphylococcus aureus Strain ATCC 29213	_____	_____
Enterococcus faecalis	_____	_____

Questions

1. Name the glycan parts of the cell wall.

   _____

   _____

2. Indicate the kind of linkage in the glycan part of peptidoglycan.

   _____

   _____

3. Describe transpeptidation.

   _____

   _____

Completion Questions

1. Beta-lactam antibiotics kill bacteria by

   _____

   _____

2. Two categories of beta-lactam antibiotics are

   _____

   _____

3. Beta-lactamase alters beta-lactam antibiotics by

   _____

   _____

True or False. Correct any false answers with the proper terms.

1. Peptidoglycan contains only glucose units in its side chain.

_____

_____

2. Penicillin is resistant to beta-lactamase.

_____

_____

3. Osmotic lysis is not bactericidal.

_____

_____

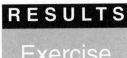

Oligodynamic Action Against Bacteria

Effects of Oligodynamic Action

Organisms Studied	Aluminum	Heavy Metals Copper	Zinc
E. coli	_____	_____	_____
S. aureus	_____	_____	_____

+ means zone of inhibition present
− means no zone of inhibition present

Statement of relationship between oligodynamic action and Gram reaction

_____

_____

_____

Questions

1. Define **oligodynamic action**.

_____

_____

2. Describe a medical use for silver salts.

_____

_____

3. Describe a mechanism that explains the lethal action of mercury.

_____

_____

**Completion
Questions**

1. Three heavy metals that affect microbes are

   _____

   _____

2. A disulfide bridge affects proteins by the process of

   _____

   _____

3. Algae are killed by the heavy metal

   _____

   _____

True or False. Correct any false answers with the proper terms.

1. Merthiolate contains the heavy metal zinc.

   _____

   _____

2. Oligodynarnic action is visualized by zones of inhibition.

   _____

   _____

3. Silver nitrate kills *chlamydiae*.

   _____

   _____

Ultraviolet Light Lethality and Photoreactivation

Effect of Ultraviolet Light

Escherichia coli	UV only	UV + PHR
0 minutes	_____	_____
1 minute	_____	_____
2 minutes	_____	_____
2 minutes + cover	_____	_____

Staphylococcus aureus	UV only	UV + PHR
0 minutes	_____	_____
1 minute	_____	_____
2 minutes	_____	_____
2 minutes + cover	_____	_____

Questions

1. Describe pyrimidine dimer formation during irradiation with ultraviolet light.

   _____

   _____

2. Explain what is accomplished by photoreactivation.

   _____

   _____

3. Describe the results of an experiment that show that ultraviolet light is only effective on surfaces.

_____

_____

Completion Questions

1. Germicidal ultraviolet radiation is in a range near

_____

_____

2. The radiation from a germicidal UV lamp is strongly absorbed by

_____

_____

3. Pyrimidine dimers commonly involve adjacent pyrimidine bases called

_____

_____

True or False. Correct any false answers with the proper terms.

1. Shielding favors increased ultraviolet absorption by the cells.

_____

_____

2. Wrapping irradiated plates with aluminum foil prevents any light induced radiation repair of damage.

_____

_____

3. UV only irradiated plates show a lower survival than UV + photo-reactivation treated plates.

_____

_____

A Model for Soft Tissue Infection

Appearance and odor of apples inoculated with:

Staphylococcus aureus

_____

_____

Escherichia coli

_____

_____

Selective media culture observations.

mannitol-salt agar _____

MacConkey agar _____

Gram Stain reactions from colonies grown on:

mannitol-salt agar _____

MacConkey agar _____

Questions

1. Define infection.

_____

_____

2. Name the layers involved in myonecrosis.

_____

_____

3. Name the three zones observed in progressive bacterial gangrene infections.

_____

_____

Completion Questions

1. Anaerobic cellulitis is characterized by

_____

_____

2. Synergistic myonecrosis is caused by anaerobes and

_____

_____

3. One sign of infection in the apple is

_____

_____

True or False. Correct any false answers with the proper terms.

1. Infection involves only presence of microorganisms at a body site.

_____

_____

2. Synergistic reactions are caused by a single microorganism.

_____

_____

3. Debridement involves removal of infected tissue.

_____

_____

A Lethal Action of Lysozyme on Bacteria

Organism   **Response to Lysozyme Treatment**

Micrococcus luteus _____

Escherichia coli   _____

Questions

1. Define innate immunity.

   _____

   _____

2. Describe the visible effect of lysozyme on a culture of *M. luteus* seen for this experiment.

   _____

   _____

3. Describe the effect of lysozyme on cell wall structure.

   _____

   _____

Completion Questions

1. A zone of inhibition for this experiment means

   _____

   _____

2. The timing for lysozyme production in virus infection is

   _____

   _____

3. Exposure of peptidoglycan to lysozyme causes

_____

_____

True or False. Correct any false answers with the proper terms.

1. Innate immunity is acquired.

_____

_____

2. Osmotic lysis occurs after cell wall formation.

_____

_____

3. 1,4 bonds are commonly found in cell membranes.

_____

_____

Staphylococci on Skin

Medium	Growth Response Observed
staphylococcus medium 110	_____
mannitol-salt agar	_____
tellurite-glycine agar	_____
staphylococcus organism(s) isolated	_____

Questions

1. Explain how low pH is created on skin.

_____

_____

2. Define resident flora.

_____

_____

3. Indicate why *E. coli* is classified as a skin transient flora.

_____

_____

Completion Questions

1. Lipids in sebum are converted to

_____

_____

2. *S. epidermidis* when grown on mannitol-salt agar shows a color in the agar that is

_____

_____

3. Two physiological effects that interfere with growth of transients on skin are

_____

_____

True or False. Correct any false answers with the proper terms.

1. *Propionibacterium* breaks down sugars.

_____

_____

2. Reduction of tellurite produces blue colonies.

_____

_____

3. *S. aureus* when grown on mannitol salt agar forms a green halo due to high pH.

_____

_____

Upper Respiratory Tract Culture

Specialized Test Results

Blood Agar

Organism	Hemolytic Reaction	Gram Reaction	Microscopic Morphology
1	_____	_____	_____
2	_____	_____	_____
3	_____	_____	_____
4	_____	_____	_____
5	_____	_____	_____

Reaction to 0.04 Unit Bacitracin Sensi-Disk _____

_____

Place an X on the proper result line for each test listed below.

Mannitol-Salt Agar

Fermentation _____

No fermentation _____

Tellurite-Glycine Agar

Presence of black colonies _____

Absence of black colonies _____

Presence of small gray colonies _____

DNase Test Agar

Clear halos around colonies mean DNA hydrolysis _____

Cloudiness around colonies means no DNA hydrolysis _____

Coagulase Test

Presence of clotting _____

Absence of clotting _____

ORGANISM IDENTIFIED AS: _____

1. Distinguish between alpha- and beta-hemolysis.

   _____

   _____

2. Explain why *Staphylococcus aureus* produces a yellow-colored halo around the colonies on mannitol-salt agar.

   _____

   _____

3. Name a test that distinguishes between streptococci and staphylococci and list the results found.

   _____

   _____

4. Indicate the importance of the coagulase test.

   _____

   _____

Completion Questions

1. Three viruses that cause upper respiratory infections are

   _____

   _____

2. Three bacterial organisms found in the throat are

   _____

   _____

3. Two features of *Klebsiella pneumoniae* on blood agar are

   _____

   _____

4. Three tests that identify *Staphylococcus aureus* are

   _____

   _____

5. A serious medical problem in children produced by *Hemophilus influenzae* is

_____

_____

6. A purpose of Staphylococcus Medium 110 is to

_____

_____

True or False. Correct any false answers with the proper terms.

1. MRSA refers to streptococci.

_____

_____

2. *Staphylococcus epidermidis* produces a yellow halo around the colonies growing on mannitol-salt agar.

_____

_____

3. Hib vaccine protects against epiglottitis in children.

_____

_____

4. Clearing around colonies on DNA agar plates on addition of 1N hydrochloric acid means no hydrolysis of the DNA.

_____

_____

5. A positive coagulase test is correlated with the presence of pathogenic *Staphylococcus aureus*.

_____

_____

Gastrointestinal Infections

Differentiation in Gastrointestinal Infections

Indicate positive tests by (+) and negative test by (−).

Sample #1

Lactose Fermenter

IMViC Test Results: _____ _____ _____ _____

Name of Organism _____

Lactose Nonfermenter

Confirmation Tests
Urease Activity

_____

Phenylalanine Deaminase Activity

_____

Organism Isolated and Identified as:

_____

Organism Identified in Enterotube® II:

_____

Sample #2

Lactose Fermenter

IMViC Test Results: _____ _____ _____ _____

Name of Organism _____

Lactose Nonfermenter

Confirmation Tests
Urease Activity

_____

Phenylalanine Deaminase Activity

_____

Organism Isolated and Identified as:

_____

Organism Identified in Enterotube® II:

_____

Sample #3

Lactose Fermenter

IMViC Test Results: _____ _____ _____ _____

Name of Organism _____

Lactose Nonfermenter

Confirmation Tests
Urease Activity

_____

Phenylalanine Deaminase Activity

_____

Organism Isolated and Identified as:

_____

Organism Identified in Enterotube® II:

_____

Questions

1. List two features of a gastrointestinal infection.

   _____

   _____

2. Distinguish between *Salmonella* and *Shigella* infections in humans.

   _____

   _____

3. Explain why SS agar is more selective than MacConkey agar.

   _____

   _____

4. List two tests that distinguish between *Salmonella* and *Proteus*.

   _____

   _____

Completion Questions

1. Enteric bacteria, in the oxidase test, routinely show

   _____

   _____

2. Symptomatic features of a *Shigellae* infection include

_____

_____

3. *Shigella* in contrast to *Salmonella* produce damage to

_____

_____

4. *Salmonella* and *Proteus* can be distinguished by the metabolic test known as

_____

_____

5. On Kligler's iron agar, *Salmonella* and *Proteus* can

_____

_____

True or False. Correct any false answer with the proper terms.

1. *Salmonella-Shigella* agar has less bile salts than MacConkey agar.

_____

_____

2. *Salmonella typhimurium* ferments lactose.

_____

_____

3. A mixed culture of *Escherichia coli* and *Salmonella typhimurium* streaked on *Salmonella-Shigella* agar yields some red colonies and some clear to tan colonies.

_____

_____

4. Red colonies on MacConkey agar can indicate the presence *Escherichia coli*.

_____

_____

5. On Kligler's iron agar, *Escherichia coli* produces an acid slant and an acid butt.

_____

_____

Urinary Tract Infections

Urine Sample Chart Number _____

Gram Stain Report _____

Bacterial Count in the Urine Sample _____

Method Used: _____

Colony Morphology on CLED agar _____

Colony Morphology on EMB agar _____

Colony Morphology on Columbia CNA agar with blood_____

Confirmatory Tests: Organism Isolated

SF broth _____

Urea broth _____

Motility agar _____

Kligler's iron agar _____

Simmons citrate agar _____

Nitrate broth _____

Name of organism in urine sample:

_____

Questions

1. Name three organisms that cause urinary tract infections.

   _____

   _____

2. List three symptoms of a urinary tract infection.

   _____

   _____

3. Explain a rationale for the recommended change in bacterial urinary tract standards.

_____

_____

4. Indicate a reason for recurrent urinary tract infections.

_____

_____

5. Name a preferred method for microbiological evaluation of urinary tract infections and list an advantage for it.

_____

_____

Completion Questions

1. Lower urinary tract infections anatomically involve the

_____

_____

2. The current bacterial standard for urinary tract infection is

_____

_____

3. Two indications for a urine culture are

_____

_____

4. Two criteria for selection of an antibiotic for treating a urinary tract infection are

_____

_____

5. Antibiotics that predispose the patient to yeast infections are those that are

_____

_____

True or False. Correct any false answers with the proper terms.

1. Nitrofurantoin is highly concentrated in the urinary bladder.

   _____

   _____

2. Columbia CNA agar promotes the growth of gram-positive bacteria.

   _____

   _____

3. *Enterococcus faecalis* can be selectively isolated using EMB agar.

   _____

   _____

4. Clear colonies on EMB when tested on Kligler's iron agar yield a black color after incubation. These organisms also hydrolyze urea. These are best identified as *Escherichia coli*.

   _____

   _____

5. The presence of several bacteria and white blood cells in a Gram stained smear of a urine sample suggests contamination.

   _____

   _____

Snyder Test for Dental Caries Susceptibility

Observed Dental Caries Susceptibility

Indicate by an X.

Marked _____

Moderate _____

Slight _____

None _____

1. Name the significant ingredients in the Snyder Test medium.

   _____

   _____

2. List the major microbes responsible for dental caries.

   _____

   _____

3. Describe plaque and dental carie formation.

   _____

   _____

1. Procedures which increase the risk of bacteremia and endocarditis are

   _____

   _____

2. Two antibiotics used to prevent these medical problems mentioned above are

_____

_____

3. The dextran covering surrounding bacteria on the teeth is called a

_____

_____

True or False. Correct any false answers with the proper terms.

1. The final pH of Snyder Test agar is 7.

_____

_____

2. Acid in Snyder Test medium incubated with saliva is indicated by a change from blue green to yellow color.

_____

_____

3. Change in color of saliva inoculated and incubated in Snyder Test agar medium after 48 hours indicates a marked risk of dental caries.

_____

_____

Salmonella Serology: Slide Agglutination Test

Evidence of Clumping in Slide Agglutination Test

positive control _____

negative control _____

S. typhimurium _____

Questions

1. List two requirements for a positive agglutination reaction.

   _____

   _____

2. List an advantage of a serological test.

   _____

   _____

3. List a purpose of the phenolized saline.

   _____

   _____

4. Distinguish between O and H antigens in *Salmonella*.

   _____

   _____

Completion Questions

1. Agglutination tests used in clinical laboratories are useful to identify pathogens such as

   _____

   _____

2. The Widal test is specific for the microorganism known as

_____

_____

3. The common O antigens in the United States are

_____

_____

True or False. Correct any false answers with the proper terms.

1. A positive control contains antigen and antibody.

_____

_____

2. A negative control shows no clumping.

_____

_____

3. Polyvalent antisera contains only one antibody.

_____

_____

Mutagens and Carcinogens: The Ames Test

Number of Revertant Colonies

control _____

hair dye _____

household liquid cleaning agent _____

or

slurry of cigarette ash _____

Questions

1. Name a purpose of the Ames Test.

   _____

   _____

2. List three features of the Salmonella tester strain that make it useful for mutagenesis studies.

   _____

   _____

3. Explain why a liver extract is sometimes necessary.

   _____

   _____

4. Name a relationship between carcinogens and mutagens.

   _____

   _____

5. Name the type of mutation studied that is used to indicate a positive Ames Test.

   _____

   _____

**Completion
Questions**

1. rfa mutations cause a loss of this cell wall structure

   _____

   _____

2. Mutations in the uvr gene affect a repair mechanism in DNA called

   _____

   _____

3. Two essential nutrients required for growth of the tester strain are

   _____

   _____

True or False. Correct any false answers with the proper terms.

1. Paper discs used in this exercise contain nutrients.

   _____

   _____

2. Many mutations occur in the absence of DNA replication.

   _____

   _____

3. The Ames Test does not use laboratory animals.

   _____

   _____

Media Directory

Media for use in this manual can be obtained from BBL, Difco Laboratories and from Unipath Co./Oxoid Division. The addresses for these firms and other vendors are listed at the end of this appendix. All media are listed by ingredients per 1000 ml of distilled water. Microbiological media are usually sterilized at 15 pounds steam pressure at 121°C for 15–20 minutes. Exceptions to this rule are noted. The exact directions for preparation of each media are noted on the bottle label. The role of ingredients is in brackets; the pH and purpose of the medium are also provided.

Media

Bile Esculin Agar:

beef extract 3 g

oxgall 40 g [inhibits gram-positive non-enterococcus bacteria]

peptone 5 g

ferric citrate 0.5 g [esculetin + iron forms black complex in the agar]

esculin 1 g [enterococci hydrolyse to esculetin and glucose]

agar 15 g

distilled water 1000 ml

pH 6.6

Purpose: To selectively isolate *Enterococcus faecalis* from cultures. This media is dispensed into slants.

Blood Agar:

trypticase soy agar in 100 ml amounts. Sterilize and cool to 45°C. Add 5 ml of defibrinated sheep red blood cells. Swirl and pour into plates. This media is readily available in poured plates from BBL.

Purpose: To distinguish different hemolytic reactions on blood agar.

Brain Heart Infusion Broth

infusion from calf brains 200 g (source of nutrients)

infusion from beef heart 250 g (source of nutrients)

proteose-peptone 10 g

dextrose 2 g

sodium chloride 5 g

disodium phosphate 2.5 g

distilled water 1000 ml

pH 7.4

Purpose: To cultivate a variety of fastidious microorganisms

Brilliant Green Bile Lactose Broth:

peptone 10 g

lactose 10 g

oxgall or bile 20 g [inhibits gram-positive bacteria]

brilliant green 0.33 g [inhibits gram-positive and negative bacilli]

distilled water 1000 ml

Add a Durham tube to this medium prior to autoclaving.

pH 7.2

Purpose: To use for the selective isolation of total coliforms in the confirmed test.

Brom-Thymol Blue Lactose Broth:

pH-Indicator Solution:

brom-thymol blue 8 g

95% ethyl alcohol 250 ml

distilled water 250 ml

Dissolve the brom-thymol blue pH indicator compound in the alcohol first. Then add the distilled water and mix thoroughly.

Lactose Broth with Brom-Thymol Blue pH Indicator:

lactose 5 g [fermented to acids]

yeast extract 5 g

tryptone 10 g

distilled water 1000 ml

Add 2 ml of the brom-thymol blue pH indicator solution and a Durham tube to the lactose broth and then autoclave.

pH 7.0

Purpose: To use in bacterial interaction studies to detect gas production in mixed culture of *Staphylococcus aureus* and *Proteus vulgaris*.

CLED Agar:

pancreatic digest of gelatin 4 g [nutrients for growth]

pancreatic digest of casein 4 g [nutrients for growth]

beef extract 3 g

lactose 10g [fermentable sugar]

L-cystine 0.128 g [permits growth of small colony coliforms]

bromthymol blue 0.02 g [distinguishes fermented from nonfermenters]

agar 15 g

distilled water 1000 ml

pH 7.3

Purpose: To use for isolation, counting and tentative identification of microorganisms in urine.

Coagulase Plasma Salmonella Serology Test Reagents

Coagulase Testing for *Staphylococcus aureus*, coagulase plasmas.

rabbit-with citrate or EDTA

These are available from Difco, Labs or BBL.

Salmonella Serology

Salmonella 0 antigen Group B (Difco #2840-56-3)

Salmonella polyvalent antisera (Difco #2264-47-2) or

Salmonella 0 Group B antigen (somatic 1-4-5-12) 5 ml

BBL (catalog #40732)

Salmonella polyvalent antiserum (Groups A-E) 1 ml

BBL (catalog # 40707.

Colilert Medium:

U.S. Environment Protective Agency recommends that this medium should be purchased directly from the vendor and not be made up from the individual ingredients. The vendor is Idexx Laboratories.

Columbia CNA Agar with 5% Sheep Blood:

pancreatic digest of casein 12 g [nutrients for growth]

peptic digest of animal tissue 5 g [nutrients for growth]

yeast extract 3 g [supplies B vitamins]

beef extract 3 g

corn starch 1 g

sodium chloride 5 g

agar 13.5 g

colistin 10 mg [inhibits gram-negative bacteria]

nalidixic acid 10 mg [blocks DNA synthesis in gram-negative bacteria]

distilled water 1000 ml

Heat while stirring to dissolve all ingredients. Sterilize at 121°C for 12 minutes. Cool to 45°C and aseptically add 5% sterile defibrinated sheep blood. This medium is available from BBL as prepared plates in a package of 20 plates or a carton of 100 plates.

pH 7.3

Purpose: To isolate and differentiate gram-positive cocci from mixed cultures. This medium is strongly inhibitory to gram-negative bacteria.

DNase Test Agar:

tryptose 20 g

deoxyribonucleic acid 2 g [substrate for DNase activity]

sodium chloride 5 g

agar 15 g

1000 ml distilled water

pH 7.3 at 25°C.

Purpose: To detect DNase activity in staphylococci. Flood plate with 1N HCl after incubation to detect DNA hydrolysis.

EC Broth Medium:

tryptose or trypticase peptone 20 g

lactose 5 g [fermentable sugar]

bile salts No.3 or bile salts mixture 1.5 g [inhibits gram-positive bacilli and enterococci]

dipotassium phosphate 1.5 g [serves as a buffer]

sodium chloride 5 g

distilled water 1000 ml

Add a Durham tube to this medium prior to autoclaving.

pH 6.9

Purpose: To detect fecal coliform bacteria in the confirmed test.

Eosin Methylene Blue Agar (EMB):

peptone 10 g

lactose 10g [fermentable sugar]

dipotassium phosphate 2 g

saccharose 5 g

eosin Y 0.4 g [inhibits gram-positive bacteria]

methylene blue 0.065 g [inhibits gram-positive bacteria]

agar 13.5 g

distilled water 1000 ml

pH 7.1

Purpose: To isolate and detect gram-negative enteric bacteria

Halobacterium Medium (25% NaCl):

sodium chloride 250 g [favors growth of halobacteria]

magnesium sulfate (hydrated) 10 g

potassium chloride 5 g

calcium chloride (hydrated) 0.2 g

yeast extract 10 g

tryptone 2.5 g

agar 20 g

distilled water 1000 ml

Make up one solution of yeast extract, tryptone and agar. Adjust the pH to 7.0. Make up a separate salts solution. Sterilize separately. Mix. Final volume is 1 liter. Pour plates

pH 7.2 – 7.4

Purpose: To grow and isolate Halobacteria cultures and to evaluate the responses of selected bacteria to increasing osmotic pressure.

Kligler's Iron Agar:

beef extract 3 g

yeast extract 3 g

peptone 15 g

proteose peptone 5 g

lactose 10 g [detects lactose fermenters]

dextrose 1 g [detects dextrose fermenters]

ferrous sulfate 0.2 g [used to detect hydrogen sulfide released from thiosulfate]

sodium chloride 0.5g

sodium thiosulfate 0.3 g [source of hydrogen sulfide]

phenol red 0.024 g [pH indicator to detect dextrose fermentation or fermentation of both sugars]

agar 15 g

distilled water 1000 ml

pH 7.4

Purpose: To detect hydrogen sulfide production by bacteria and to differentiate between fermenters and nonfermenters of glucose and lactose.

Lauryl Tryptose Broth:

tryptone or trypticase peptone 20 g

lactose 5 g [fermentable sugar]

dipotassium hydrogen phosphate 2.75 g

potassium dihydrogen phosphate 2.75 g

sodium chloride 5 g

sodium lauryl sulfate 0.1 g [inhibits noncoliform bacteria]

distilled water 1000 ml

Add a Durham tube to this medium prior to autoclaving.

pH 6.8

Purpose: To use for the isolation of the total coliforms in the presumptive test.

Litmus Milk:

skim milk 100 g [substrates for fermentation and proteolysis]

litmus 0.75 g [pH indicator and an oxidation-reduction indicator during growth of bacteria]

distilled water 1000 ml

Autoclave at 12 pounds pressure for 15 minutes.

pH 6.8

Purpose: To detect proteolytic, fermentation and reduction reactions in milk medium.

MacConkey Agar:

peptone 17 g

proteose peplone 3 g

lactose 10 g [fermentable sugar]

sodium chloride 5 g

bile salts 1.5 g [inhibits gram-positive bacteria and favors growth of gram-negative bacteria]

neutral red 0.03 g [pH indicator to detect fermentation]

crystal violet 0.001 g [inhibits gram-positive bacteria]

agar 13.5 g

distilled water 1000 ml

pH 7.1

Purpose: To isolate and differentiate different gram-negative enteric bacteria.

Mannitol-Salt Agar:

proteose-peptone No.3 10 g

beef extract 1 g

D-mannitol 10 g [fermentable sugar]

sodium chloride 75 g [inhibits bacteria other than staphylococci]

phenol red 0.025 g [pH indicator to detect mannitol fermentation]

agar 15 g

distilled water 1000 ml

pH 7.4

Purpose: To isolate staphylococci from mixed cultures

Methyl Red/Voges-Proskauer Medium:

buffered peptone 7 g

dextrose 5 g [fermentable sugar]

dipotassium phosphate 5 g

distilled water 1000 ml

pH 6.9

Purpose: To detect mixed acid fermentation or acetoin fermentation.

Moeller Decarboxylase Base Medium:

peptone 5 g [source of nitrogen compounds]

beef extract 5 g [source of nitrogen compounds]

dextrose 0.5 g [fermentable sugar]

bromcresol purple 0.01 g [pH indicator]

cresol red 0.0005 g [pH indicator]

pyridoxal 0.0005 g [cofactor for decarboxylase enzyme]

distilled water 1000 ml

Prepare equal amounts of the decarboxylase medium base with lysine and without lysine to assay decarboxylase activity For lysine decarboxylase medium, add 10 g/l or 1% of L-lysine. If only DL-lysine is available, add 20 g/l or 2 % of the amino acid. Dispense in tubes and then sterilize-

Prepare tubes of mineral oil. Sterilize by autoclaving.

These are necessary for overlaying of the decarboxylase medium prior to incubation.

Final pH 6.0.

Purpose: To detect lysine decarboxylase activity in bacteria.

Motility Agar Medium:

pancreatic digest of gelatin 10 g

beef extract 3 g

sodium chloride 5 g

agar 4 g [reduced concentration to allow swarming in the agar]

distilled water 1000 ml

Dispense into tubes and autoclave as agar deeps

pH 7.3

Purpose: To detect motility in bacteria.

Mueller-Hinton Agar:

beef infusion 300 g [supports growth of bacteria]

casamino acids 17.5 g [supports growth of bacteria]

starch 1.5 g [interferes with toxic agents in the agar medium]

agar 17 g

distilled water 1000 ml

pH 7.3

Purpose: To test the antibiotic sensitivity of microorganisms by the disk assay method.

Nitrate Broth:

beef extract 3 g

peptone 5 g

potassium nitrate 1 g [source of nitrate for anaerobic reduction to nitrite]

distilled water 1000 ml

pH 7

Purpose: To demonstrate nitrate reduction to nitrites and further.

Nutrient Broth:

beef extract 3 g

peptone 5 g

distilled water 1000 ml

For nutrient agar, add 15 grams of agar to this medium prior to sterilization.

Add proper amounts of sodium chloride to nutrient agar for Exercise 23—Osmotic Pressure and Bacterial Growth.

pH 6.8

Purpose: To grow non-fastidious microorganisms.

Nutrient Gelatin:

beef extract 3 g

peptone 5 g

gelatin 120 g [substrate for gelatin digestion]

distilled water 1000 ml.

pH 6.8

Purpose: To determine the ability of bacteria to digest the protein gelatin by the enzyme gelatinase.

Oxidation/Fermentation (OF) Medium:

pancreatic digest of casein 2 g [low peptone concentration reduces usage of protein]

sodium chloride 5 g

dipotassium phosphate 0.3 g [acts as a buffer]

bromthymol blue 0.03 g

agar 2.5 g

dextrose 10 g [differentiates oxidative from fermentative from nonsaccharolytic behavior in bacteria]

distilled water 1000 ml.

Prepare separately a 10% dextrose solution and sterilize. Mix and sterilize all other ingredients. Cool and add 10 ml of the 10% carbohydrate solution. Pour medium into sterile tubes as agar deeps.

Prepare tubes of mineral oil. Sterilize by autoclaving. These are necessary for overlaying of one of the pair of OF medium agar deeps after inoculation.

pH 7.1

Purpose: To determine whether bacteria use sugars by fermentation, or by oxidation or are nonsaccharolytic.

Phenol Red Broth:

trypticase 10 g

sodium chloride 5 g

phenol red 0.018 g

carbohydrate 5 g [fermentable sugar]

Add a single sugar and Durham tube before autoclaving.

distilled water 1000 ml

Carbohydrates used are dextrose, lactose and mannitol.

pH 7.3

Purpose: To describe the fermentation behavior of microorganisms.

Phenylalanine Agar:

yeast extract 3 g

DL-phenylalanine 2 g [deaminated by deaminase enzyme to phenylpyruvic acid]

sodium chloride 5 g

dipotassium phosphate 1 g

agar 12 g

distilled water 1000 ml

pH 7.3

Dispense into tube. Sterilize and allow to solidify as slants.

Purpose: To use phenylalanine deaminase reaction to differentiate *Proteus* from other bacteria.

Phenylethanol Agar with Blood:

pancreatic digest of casein 15 g

papaic digest of soy meal 5 g

sodium chloride 5 g

phenylethanol 2.5 g [inhibits gram-negative bacteria]

agar 15 g

distilled water 1000 ml

Sterilize the base medium. Add 50 ml of sterile blood after autoclaving. This media is commercially available in plates.

pH 7.3

Purpose: To differentiate gram-positive cocci from other bacteria in mixed cultures.

Plate Count Agar:

yeast extract 2.5 g [source of nutrients]

tryptone 5 g [source of nutrients]

dextrose I g

agar 15 g

distilled water 1000 ml

pH 7

Purpose: To measure colony forming units present in dilutions from water, food and dairy products.

Sabourauds Dextrose Agar:

polypeptone or neopeptone 10 g [supports growth]

dextrose 40 g

agar 15 g

distilled water 1000 ml

Adjust pH to 5.6 before sterilizing [favors growth of fungi instead of bacteria]

Purpose: To grow yeasts and molds

Salmonella-Shigella Agar (SS Agar):

peptone or polypeptone 5 g

beef extract 5 g

lactose 10g [fermentable sugar]

bile salts mixture 8.5 g [inhibits gram-positive bacteria and coliforms]

sodium citrate 8.5 g [inhibits gram-positive bacteria]

sodium thiosulfate 8.5 g [source of hydrogen sulfide]

ferric citrate 1 g [source of indicator of hydrogen sulfide]

brilliant green 0.00033 g [inhibits gram-positive bacteria]

neutral red 0.025 g

agar 13.5 g

distilled water 1000 ml

Heat to boiling with stirring to dissolve all ingredients.

Do not autoclave. Cool to 45°C and pour plates.

Refrigerate plates until use.

pH 7

Purpose: To isolate *Salmonella* and *Shigella* from mixed cultures.

Simmons Citrate Agar:

sodium citrate 2 g [sole source of carbon]

sodium chloride 5 g

dipotassium phosphate I g

monoammonium phosphate 1 g [sole nitrogen source]

magnesium sulfate 0.2 g

bromthymol blue 0.08 g [pH indicator]

agar 15 g

distilled water 1000 ml

Dispense into tubes and sterilize. Allow to solidify as slants.

pH 6.8

Purpose: To distinguish between gram-negative bacteria that utilize citrate and those that do not.

Skim Milk Agar:

Prepare an infusion agar medium such as nutrient agar, plate count agar or trypticase soy agar. Sterilize this medium.

Prepare skim milk medium as follows:

skim milk powder 20 g [source of protein]

distilled water 100 ml

Stir until dissolved. Sterilize for 12 minutes at 121°C. Do not oversterilize otherwise the sugar in the milk will caramelize.

Mix 20 ml of sterile skim milk with 100 ml sterile cooled base infusion medium held at 50°C. Dispense into petri dishes. Allow to harden and refrigerate plates until they are used. This medium should be prepared shortly before its use.

Do not adjust the pH of this medium.

Purpose: To detect hydrolysis of casein by bacteria.

Snyder Test Agar:

tryptone 20 g

dextrose 20 g [fermentable carbohydrate]

sodium chloride 5 g

bromcresol green 0.02 g [pH indicator]

agar 20 g

distilled water 1000 ml

Sterilize as agar deeps and keep at 50°C in a water bath prior to use.

pH 4.8 [favors growth of lactobacilli]

Purpose: To detect lactobacilli in saliva.

Spirit Blue Agar:

tryptone 10 g

yeast extract 5 g

spirit blue 0.15 g [pH indicator]

lipase reagent 30 ml or suitable lipid [source of lipid for hydrolysis]

agar 20 g

distilled water 1000 ml

pH 6.8

Purpose: To detect lipolytic activity in bacteria.

Staphylococcus Medium 110

tryptone 10 g

yeast extract 2.5 g (source of nutrient)

gelatin 30 g (substrate for gelatinase activity)

lactose 2 g (sugar for energy)

D-mannitol 10 g (fermentable sugar)

sodium chloride 75 g (inhibits nonstaphylococcal bacteria)

dipotassium phosphate 5 g

agar 15 g

distilled water 1000 ml

pH 7.0

Purpose: To isolate pathogenic and toxin producing *staphylococci*

Starch Agar:

beef extract 3 g

peptone 5 g

soluble starch 10 g [substrate to study polysaccharide hydrolysis]

agar 12 g

distilled water 1000 ml

pH 7.5

Purpose: To detect organisms capable of starch hydrolysis.

Streptococcus faecalis Broth (SF Broth):

tryptone 20 g [provides nutrients for growth]

dextrose 5 g

sodium azide 0.5 g [inhibits gram-negative bacteria]

monopotassium phosphate 1.5 g

dipotassium phosphate 4 g

sodium chloride 5 g

bromcresol purple 0.032 g [pH indicator]

distilled water 1000 ml

Azide inhibits the transfer of electrons from cytochromes to oxygen. This media inhibits gram-negative organisms and permits the growth of the enterococcus. This organism lacks cytochromes and ferments the sugar to acids causing the indicator to change to yellow.

pH 6.9

Purpose: To isolate enterococci from cultures derived from urine, water, feces or food.

Tellurite-Glycine Agar:

yeast extract 6.5 g

tryptone 10 g

soytone 3.5 g

D-mannitol 5 g [fermentable sugar]

glycine 10 g [agent selective for staphylococci]

dipotassium phosphate 5 g

lithium chloride 5 g [inhibits nonstaphylococcal bacteria]

agar 17.5 g

distilled water 1000 ml

Sterilize in the autoclave. Cool to 55°C and aseptically add 1 ml of sterile 1% Bacto Chapman potassium tellurite solution for each 100 ml of sterile tellurite glycine agar. Tellurite is a selective agent for coagulase-positive staphylococci.

pH 7.2

Purpose: To isolate coagulase positive staphylococci. They form black colonies after 24 hours incubation at 37°C.

Thioglycollate Broth:

pancreatic digest of casein - 15 g

yeast extract 5 g

dextrose 5.5 g

L-cystine 0.75 g [source of growth factors]

Sodium thioglycollate -0.5 g oxygen scavenging compound

sodium chloride 2.5 g

agar 0.75 g

resazaurin 0.001 g [oxidation-reduction indicator]

distilled water 1000 ml

pH 7. 1

Purpose: To detect oxygen requirements of microorganisms and to grow anaerobes.

Trypticase Soy Broth Without Dextrose:

trypticase peptone (pancreatic digest of casein) 17 g

phytone (papaic digest of soybean meal) 3 g [nutrients]

sodium chloride 5 g

dipotassium phosphate 2.5 g

distilled water 1000 ml

For trypticase soy broth with dextrose, add dextrose 2.5 g to the medium prior to sterilization.

pH 7.3

Purpose: To use as a general medium for the growth of non-fastidious and fastidious microorganisms.

Trypticase Soy Agar:

pancreatic digest of casein 15 g

papaic digest of soybean meal 5 g [nutrients]

sodium chloride 5 g

agar 15 g

distilled water 1000 ml

pH 7.3

Purpose: To use as a general medium for the growth of non-fastidious and fastidious microorganisms.

Tryptone Broth (indole test):

tryptone (pancreatic digest of casein) 10 g [source of tryptophane for hydrolysis to indole]

distilled water 1000 ml

pH 7

Purpose: To detect indole production from tryptophane after hydrolysis of the amino acid

Tryptone Broth for Virus Dilutions:

tryptone 10 g

sodium chloride 5 g (required electrolyte)

distilled water 1000 ml

pH 7.0

Purpose: To provide a dilution medium for the T-2 virus.

Tryptone Bottom Agar for Virus Platings:

tryptone 10 g

sodium chloride 5 g (source of required electrolyte)

magnesium sulfate-hydrated $MgSO_4–7H_2O$ 1 g

agar 15 g

distilled water 1000 ml

pH 7.0

Purpose: To supply a base bottom agar medium for plating of T-2 virus and the host *Escherichia coli* b cells.

Tryptone Soft Top Agar Overlay for Virus Platings:

Use the same formula noted in Tryptone Bottom Agar, but substitute 7 g of agar for the 15 g of agar.

Urea Broth:

urea 20 g [substrate for hydrolysis to ammonia and carbon dioxide]

yeast extract 0.1 g

monopotassium phosphate 9.1 g

disodium phosphate 9.5 g

phenol red 0.01 g [pH indicator]

distilled water 1000 ml

Do not autoclave this media. Urea decomposes on heating. Sterilize this media by filtration only

pH 6.8

Purpose: To differentiate those bacteria that hydrolyze urea to ammonia and carbon dioxide.

Specialized Media for Mutagenic Studies
Media for the Ames Test

The pH is not indicated for any of The Ames Media. The pH must not be adjusted for any of these media.

Ames Minimal Agar:

Vogel Bonner Medium E (50X)

warm distilled water at 45°C 670 ml

magnesium sulfate (MgSO4-7H20 10 g

citric acid monohydrate 100 g

potassium phosphate, dibasic(anhydrous) 500 g

sodium ammonium phosphate ($NaHNH_4PO_4-4H_2O$) 175 g

Add salts in the order given to the warm water in a two liter beaker. Dissolve each salt completely before adding the next salt. Adjust the volume to one liter. Distribute into two one-liter glass bottles and sterilize at 121°C for 20 minutes with the caps loosened. Tighten the caps after sterilization when the solutions have cooled.

Purpose: Use for minimal agar

Ames Minimal Glucose Plate Medium:

Minimal Glucose Plates:

agar 15g

distilled water 930 ml.

50X Vogel Bonner salts 20 ml

40% glucose 50 ml

Prepare a 40% glucose solution. Sterilize this solution. Add 15 g of agar to 930 ml of distilled water in a 2 liter flask. Autoclave for 20 minutes and use a slow exhaust. Cool the solution slightly and add 20 ml of the sterile 50X Vogel Bonner (VB) salts solution and 50 ml of the sterile 40% glucose solution. Mix the contents thoroughly after adding all the ingredients. Pour 30 ml of the finished medium into each petri dish.

Reminder: The 50X VB salts solution and 40% glucose solution must be sterilized separately.

Purpose: To use for a bottom agar in the petri dishes in the mutagenicity assay.

Ames Mutagenicity Assay Medium

0.5 mM histidine/biotin solution:

D-biotin (F.W. 247.3) 30.9 mg

L-histidine-HCl (F.W. 191.7) 24.0 mg

distilled water 250 ml

Dissolve the biotin by boiling the water. Sterilize by autoclaving at 121°C for 20 minutes. Store in a glass bottle in a refrigerator.

Purpose: To assay mutations (Add 10 ml to the top agar)

Ames Top Agar:

Top Agar:

agar 6 g

sodium chloride 5 g

distilled water 1000 ml.

Dissolve the agar by heating. Mix thoroughly and transfer 100 ml portions to 250 ml glass bottles with screw caps. Autoclave for 20 minutes with the caps loosened. Exhaust slowly. Cool the agar and tighten the caps.

Purpose: To use in the mutation assay

Oxoid Nutrient Broth No. 2:

"Lab-Lemco" Powder 10 g

peptone 10 g

sodium chloride 5 g

distilled water 1000 ml

pH 7.5

Purpose: To grow the *Salmonella typhimurium* tester strain TA 98.

Stains, Chemicals and Equipment Directory

Stains and Chemicals

Acid-Fast Stain Reagents:

Ziehl-Neelson Carbol Fuchsin: [primary dye in acid-fast stain]

Solution A

basic fuchsin 0.3 g (90% dye content)

95% ethyl alcohol 10 ml

Solution B

phenol 5 g

distilled water 95 ml

Mix solution A and B and let stand for several days before use. Filter through paper into stock bottle.

Kinyoun Carhol Fuchsin:

basic fuchsin 4 g

phenol crystals 8 g

95% ethyl alcohol 20 ml

distilled water 100 ml

Tergitol No. 7

Dissolve the basic fuchsin in the alcohol. Add the distilled water to the dye solution while mixing. Melt the phenol crystals in a water bath. Add the melted phenol to the dye solution. Add 4 drops of Tergitol No. 7 detergent to the carbol fuchsin stain.

Acid Alcohol: [decolorizing agent in acid-fast stain]

95% alcohol 100 ml.

3% (v/v) concentrated hydrochloric acid

Dissolve the HCl in the alcohol

Loeffler's Methylene Blue [counterstain for acid-fast stain]

Solution A:

methylene blue 0.3 g (90% dye content)

95% ethyl alcohol 30 ml

Dissolve dye in alcohol

Solution B:

potassium hydroxide 0.01 g

distilled water 100 ml

Dissolve base in water.

Mix solutions A and B and filter through paper into stock bottle.

Barritts Reagent A: [reagent for Voges-Proskauer test]

alpha naphthol 5 g

95% ethyl alcohol 100 ml

Barritts Reagent B: [reagent for Voges-Proskauer test]

potassium hydroxide 40 g

creatine 0.3 g

distilled water 100 ml

alpha napthol is a possible carcinogen wash hands immediately if spilled.

Capsule Stain Reagents:

India Ink (purchased locally) [reagent for capsule stain.]

Gram's Crystal Violet-See Gram Stain Reagents

Gram Stain Reagents:

Gram's Crystal Violet:-primary dye in Gram stain

Solution A:

crystal violet (85% dye content) 2 g

95% ethyl alcohol 20 ml

Dissolve dye in alcohol

Solution B:

ammonium oxalate 0.8 g

distilled water 80 ml.

Dissolve the salt in distilled water.

Mix solutions A and B and store 24 hours. Filter through paper into stock bottle.

Gram's Iodine: [mordant in Gram stain]

iodide 1 g

potassium iodide 2 g

distilled water 300 ml

Dissolve the salt in distilled water and then add 1 gram of iodine crystals

95% Ethyl Alcohol: [decolorizing agent in Gram stain]

ethyl alcohol (100%) 95 ml

distilled water 5 ml

Safranin: [counterstain in Gram stain]

safranin O (2.5% solution in 95% ethyl alcohol) 10 ml

distilled water 100 ml

Ferric Chloride: [test reagent for detection of phenylpyruvic acid from deamination of phenylalanine]

ferric chloride 10 g

distilled water 100 ml

Hydrochloric Acid 1N [detects DNA hydrolysis by bacteria for DNase activity testing]

Hydrogen Peroxide 3% [reagent for catalase activity detection - stored in darkened bottle]

Kovac's Indole Reagent: [reagent for indole production from tryptophan]

para-dimethyl-aminobenzaldehyde 5 g

amyl alcohol 75 ml

concentrated hydrochloric acid 25 ml

Dissolve the first chemical in the amyl alcohol. Warm gently to 37°C in a water bath until completely dissolved. Add the hydrochloric acid while stirring. Caution—This reagent has an unpleasant odor. Use in a hood with an exhaust.(Caution—possible carcinogen)

Lysozyme:

Purpose: To study the differential lethal action of the enzyme lysozyme on gram-positive and gram-negative bacteria.

Sigma Lysozyme from chicken egg white, catalog number 2879 containing 57,000 units per mg solid and 65,000 units per mg protein. Lysozyme powder must be stored in a freezer at –20°C.

Preparation and storage of lysozyme solution:

Add 1.0 g of lysozyme in a final volume of 100 ml of distilled water to make a 1% solution. Filter sterilize with a Nalgene disposable filter (cellulose nitrate filter pad with a 0.45 nm pore size) can be used. Information regarding this filter available from Technical Services, Nalge Nunc International, 1-800-625-4327, Fax 1-716-264-3985.

Decant filtrate to a sterile Ehrlenmeyer flask and then dispense in 0.5 ml samples in sterile small tubes for use by the students. Lysozyme solution remains stable in the refrigerator for 4 weeks and frozen in the freezer for 8 weeks.

Methyl Red [reagent to detect fermentation of glucose to mixed acids]

methyl red 0.2 g

95% ethyl alcohol 500 ml

distilled water 500 ml

Mix the reagents and filter if necessary.

Nigrosin: [reagent for negative stain]

nigrosin (water soluble) 10 g

distilled water 100 ml

Dissolve dye in distilled water and boil container for 30 minutes. Add 0.5 ml of formalin as a preservative. Filter twice through double filter paper and store in closed container.

Nitrite Reagent A: [reagent to detect nitrites after nitrate reduction]

sulfanilic acid 0.8 g

acetic acid 5N (1 part glacial acetic acid to 2.5 parts water) 100 ml

Nitrite Reagent B: [reagent to detect nitrites after nitrate reduction]

N,N dimethyl-alpha-naphthylamine 0.5 g

acetic acid 5N 100 ml

Dissolve the reagent in the acid. Do not mix these solutions.

Caution: Nitrite Reagent B is carcinogenic. Keep this off the skin.

Oxidase Reagent: [used to detect presence of cytochrome c]

dimethyl-p-phenylenediamine hydrochloride 1.0 g

distilled water 100 ml

Dissolve the reagent in the distilled water. This reagent should preferably be made fresh daily. It can be stored under refrigeration for no longer than one week.

Spore Stain Reagents

Malachite Green: [reagent used in endospore stain]

malachite green 5 g

distilled water 100 ml

Dissolve the dye in distilled water

Filter if necessary

Safranin (aq): [counterstain for spore stain]

safranin 0.5 g

distilled water 100 ml

Dissolve the dye in distilled water

Equipment

Cefinase® Disks

Purpose: Used for the detection of beta-lactamase activity in isolated colonies of *Staphylococcus aureus*.

Product Information: Disks are ¼ inch disks of high quality absorbent paper containing Nitrocephin. Cefinase®. Disks available as cartridges containing 50 disks.

For information contact:

Becton Dickinson Microbiology Systems
P.O. Box 243
250 Schilling Circle
Cockeysville, MD 21030
Tel. 1-800-638-8663

Nalgene Sterile Disposable Filter

Information regarding this filter may be obtained from:

Technical Services
Nalge Nunc International
P.O. Box 20365
75 Panorama Creek Drive
Rochester, NY 14602-0365
Tel: 1-800-625-4327
Fax: 1-716-264-3985

Filter may be purchased from Carolina Biological Supply Co.

Spectronic 20-Spectrophotometer

Spectronic Instruments
820 Linden Avenue
Rochester, NY 14625
1-800-645-9955

Call above number for information and technical assistance.

Taxo® A Disks

Purpose: Used for the presumptive identification of group A beta-hemolytic streptococci.

Product information: Disks are $\frac{1}{4}$ inch discs of absorbent paper containing 0.04 unit of bacitracin. They are available in vials and cartridges of 50 disks.

For information contact:

Becton Dickinson Microbiology Systems
P.O. Box 243
250 Schilling Circle
Cockeysville, MD 21030
Tel: 1-800-638-8663

Vendor Index

This partial list of vendors is for the convenience of those adopting this manual. It does not imply endorsement of nor discrimination against any vendor. Toll-free (800) numbers are supplied where available.

Culture Media

Baltimore Biological Laboratory
BBL Division of Becton Dickinson and Company
Cockeysville, Maryland 21030
1-800-638-8663

Difco Laboratories
P.O. Box 1058A
Detroit, Michigan 48232
1-800-521-0851

Unipath Co./Oxoid Division
P.O. Box 691
Ogdensburg, New York 13669
1-800-567-8378
Call above number for ordering media, Oxoid oxidase stick tests and technical assistance.

Idexx Laboratories
1 Idexx Drive
Westbrook, ME 04092
1-800 321-0207
Call the above number for technical information and ordering information for Colilert coliform tests.

Enterotube II®
Becton Dickinson Microbiology Systems
Becton Dickinson and Company
250 Schilling Circle
Cockeysville, MD 21030
1-800 638-8663

This firm has information on Cefinase® discs and Taxo® A disks

Call above number for information and technical assistance.

URICULT® Culture–Paddles

CLED/EMB medium in plastic screw cap container and URICULT® reference chart (an easy to follow flow chart for the identification of common urinary tract pathogens).

Information and chart available from:

LifeSign
P.O. Box 218
Somerset, NJ 08875-0218
Tel: 1-800-526-2125; in New Jersey, 1-908-246-3326
Fax: 1-908-246-0570

Sources of Cultures

American Type Culture Collection
12301 Parklawn Drive
Rockville, Maryland 20852
1-800-638-6597

Presque Isle Cultures
P.O. Box 8191
Presque Isle, Pennsylvania 16505
1-814-833-6262

Midwest Culture Collection
1924 North Seventh Street
Terra Haute, Indiana 47804

Prepared Slides

Carolina Biological Supply Co.
2700 York Road
Burlington, North Carolina 27215
1-800-334-5551—outside of North Carolina
1-800-632-1231—in North Carolina

Ward's Natural Science Est.
P.O. Box 92921
Rochester, New York 14692

Chemicals and Equipment

Bel-Art Products
Pequannock, New Jersey 07440
Tel. 201-694-0500 Telex 13-8303

This firm supplies the pipette pump, a device used to avoid mouth pipetting of cultures. These devices are available in 2 ml and 10 ml sizes. Pipette pumps and other pipette safety devices are also available from Fisher Scientific and Carolina Biological Supply Company (listed below) and other companies.

Carolina Biological Supply Co.
2700 York Road
Burlington, North Carolina 27215
1-800-334-5551—outside of North Carolina
1-800-632-1231—in North Carolina

Evergreen Scientific
2300 East 49th Street
P.O. Box 58248
Los Angeles, California 90058-0248
1-800 421-6261 -outside of California
1-800 372-7300-in California

This firm supplies the Inoculoop, a calibrated loop, for the determination of numbers of bacteria in a urine sample.

Cat. no. 333-5001-BIO 20 trays of 25 loops each (500) 1 uL
Cat. no. 333-5010-YlO 20 trays of 25 loops each (500) 10 uL

Fisher Scientific
711 Forbes Avenue
Pittsburgh, Pennsylvania. 15219

Sigma Chemical Company
P.O. Box 14508
Saint Louis, Missouri 63178
1-800-325-3010

Spectronic 20—Spectrophotometer
Spectronic Instruments
820 Linden Avenue
Rochester, NY 14625
1-800-645-9955

Call above number for information and technical assistance.

VWR Scientific, Inc.
P.O. Box 3200
San Francisco, California 94119

Wards Natural Science Est.
P.O. Box 92921
Rochester, NY 14692

Descriptive Directory of Commonly Used Microorganisms

Gram-Positive Bacteria

Bacillus mycoides This is a gram-positive bacillus that is 3 µm to 5 µm long and 1 µm wide. It occurs in long filaments. It shows spreading growth on agar and may have highly branched edges (rhizoid growth). It is widely found in nature in soil and dust.

Bacillus subtilis This is a gram-positive aerobic bacillus that is 2 µm to 8 µm long and 0.7 µm to 0.8 µm wide. It can occur as a single bacillus, short chains, or palisade layers. It makes an endospore and lacks a capsule. The agar colonies appear off-white and show spreading. This is a common contaminant. It has been reported to cause respiratory infections in immunocompromised persons.

Clostridium sporogenes This is a gram-positive anaerobic bacillus that is 3 µm to 7 µm long and 0.6 µm to 0.8 µm wide. It can occur in pairs or long chains. It forms an endospore. The agar colonies are fine and show spreading with highly irregular edges. It produces a foul odor on growth in thioglycollate broth. It may be responsible for the foul odor of wounds in which there is tissue damage.

Enterococcus faecalis This is a gram-positive coccus that is 0.5 µm to 1 µm in diameter. It can occur as a diplococcus, short chains of cocci and clusters of cocci. This organism ferments common sugars to acids. *E. faecalis* is able to grow in 6.5% salt broth. This organism is an aerotolerant anaerobe. It lacks cytochromes and respires by fermentation. Colonies of this organism whether grown aerobically or anaerobically are extremely small and appear off white to gray. *E. faecalis* is found in the human intestine and can cause gram-positive urinary infections, peritonitis and abdominal wound infections. Many strains are extremely resistant to a variety of antibiotics and have beta-lactamase activity. This activity can be transferred from *S. aureus* to *E. faecalis*. Some strains of *E. faecalis* are resistant to vancomycin (VREF). Combination therapy is frequently used to treat this type of infection.

Micrococcus luteus This is a gram-positive coccus that is 1 µm to 1.2 µm in diameter. It is a strict aerobe. It occurs as a diplococcus and as groups of 4 cocci (tetrads). It is nonmotile. The agar colonies are raised and yellow in color. It is nonpathogenic and is found in dairy products before pasteurization, air, water, dust and soil.

Mycobacterium smegmatis This is a weakly gram-positive bacillus that frequently shows beaded staining in the Gram stain. It may be 3 µm to 5 µm long and frequently occurs in clumps of fine bacilli in a staining procedure. The clumping is due to the presence of a waxy lipid called mycolic acid present in the cell walls. These bacilli are acid-fast. It is widely found in the environment and may be found in smegma.

Staphylococcus aureus This is a gram-positive facultative anaerobic coccus that is 0.8 µm to 1 µm in diameter. It can occur singly or as diplococci or commonly as irregular grape like clusters of staphylococci. Agar colonies are circular and show a yellow to orange pigment. It is osmotolerant and ferments glucose and mannitol. It is also found on skin. It is responsible for skin infections such as boils, impetigo and carbuncles. It is also involved in wound infections particularly burn wound infections, food poisoning, toxic shock syndrome, osteomyelitis and pneumonia. Many strains produce a beta-lactamase and are resistant to penicillins and cephalosporins. Some strains are methicillin resistant and are called MRSA. These are a serious problem in hospitals and nursing homes.

Staphylococcus epidermidis This is a gram-positive facultative anaerobic coccus that is 0.5 µm to 0.6 µm in diameter. It can occur singly, as diplococci or commonly as irregular grape like clusters of cocci. It is a common resident flora organism on skin. Agar colonies are round and white in color. It can cause urinary infections, wound infections and infections of surgically implanted devices. Some strains are also resistant to methicillin and are called MRSE. Antibiotic resistance is becoming a serious problem with this organism.

Streptococcus pyogenes This is a gram-positive coccus that is 0.5 µm to 1 µm in diameter. These bacteria grow aerobically and anaerobically. This organism is classified as a Group A streptococcus by the Lancefield classification. This classification is based on the presence of a specific form of carbohydrate antigen called C-substance. This organism forms small colonies on blood agar that are surrounded by a clear halo known as beta-hemolysis. This organism is pathogenic and is responsible for cellulitis, sinusitis, tonsillitis, scarlet fever, streptococcal sore throat, pneumonia, toxic shock syndrome and the tissue destruction found in myositis and fasciitis. This organism produces a variety of toxins and tissue destructive enzymes. Rheumatic fever or glomerulonephritis can be complications of inadequately treated streptococcal infections.

Streptomyces griseus This is a gram-positive actinomycete bacteria. These bacteria form a mycelium during growth that contains aerial hyphae. These aerial hyphae fragment into a chain of spores called conidia. This organism produces the antibiotic streptomycin.

Gram-Negative Bacteria

Alcaligenes faecalis This is a gram-negative bacillus that is 1 µm to 2 µm long by 0.5 µm wide. It may appear as cocco-bacillus to bacillus in shape. It is aerobic. Colonies are opaque and white and show a slightly irregular (erose) edge. *A. faecalis* has peritrichous flagella. *A. faecalis* does not ferment common sugars to acids or acids and gas. This organism gives a positive oxidase test. It can be found in the respiratory tract or intestinal tract. It may cause wound infections, blood and urinary tract infections.

Enterobacter aerogenes This is a gram-negative bacillus that is 1 µm to 2 µm long by 0.5 µm to 0.8 µm wide. It is a facultative anaerobe. Colonies are white in color. It ferments most sugars to acid and gas. It gives negative methyl red and indole tests. They are responsible for urinary tract infections and gram-negative nosocomial infections especially those in the intensive care unit. Many are antibiotic resistant.

Escherichia coli This is a gram-negative bacillus that is 1 µm to 3 µm long by 0.3 µm wide. It may appear as cocco-bacillus to bacillus in shape. It is a facultative anaerobe. Colonies are off-white in color and may show slightly irregular (erose) edges. Colonies on Levine's eosin methylene blue agar appear black and produce a green metallic sheen by reflected light. *E. coli* ferments most sugars to produce acid and gas, produces a positive methyl red test and produces indole from tryptophan. This organism is responsible commonly for most urinary tract infections in women. It also produces food poisoning, infant meningitis and gram-negative pneumonias. It is responsible for gram-negative nosocomial infections. *E. coli 0157:H7* is responsible for a serious form of food poisoning which is accompanied by kidney disease and hemolysis of erythrocytes. This strain can be found in poorly cooked meat products.

Halobacterium salinarium   This is a gram-negative microorganism that may appear as a bacillus or a coccus. The coccus is 0.8 μm to 1.4 μm in diameter and the bacillus is 1 μm to 6 μm long by 0.6 μm to 1.5 μm wide. This is an obligate halophile and requires a high concentration of salts in the environment for growth. 25% salt is commonly present in the media in which this organism grows. A red pigment develops in the colonies seen on agar after growth at 37°C for two weeks.

Klebsiella pneumoniae   This is a gram-negative bacillus that is 5 μm long and 0.3 μm to 0.5 μm wide. The ends of this organism tend to be rounded. It produces a capsule. It is a facultative anaerobe. Colonies on agar are shiny and mucoid-like. They may appear runny on the agar. This microorganism is non-motile. It is responsible for severe necrotizing pneumonia, urinary infections and upper respiratory infections. Many are antibiotic resistant and cause nosocomial infections.

Moraxella (Branhamella) catarrhalis   This is a gram-negative diplococcus that is 0.6 μm to 1 μm in diameter. It does not ferment any carbohydrate. It forms small colonies on agar and is a facultative anaerobe. It is commonly found in the nasopharynx and can cause sinusitis, middle ear infections and pneumonia. Many strains produce beta-lactamase, cause nosocomial infections and are resistant to penicillin.

Proteus vulgaris   This is a gram-negative bacillus that is 1 μm to 3 μm long by 0.5 μm to 1 μm wide. It may appear as a single bacillus, diplobacilli or long filaments. It is a facultative anaerobe. It is actively motile with peritrichous flagella. It produces a strong odor during growth. It produces hydrogen sulfide, hydrolyzes urea to ammonia and carbon dioxide and deaminates phenylalanine to phenylpyruvic acid. It is responsible for cystitis, wound infections, urinary infections and diarrhea. Many cause nosocomial infections.

Pseudomonas aeruginosa   This is a gram-negative bacillus that is 1.5 μm long and 0.5 μm to 0.6 μm wide. It is aerobic but can grow anaerobically by reducing nitrates to nitrogen gas. This latter process is called denitrification. It produces a positive oxidase test and is a gram-negative bacteria that does not ferment sugars. It metabolizes sugars in an oxidative fashion. Many species produce a blue green pigment on growth on agar. This color of the growth is partly due to the production of the pigment pyocyanin. Colonies may show a slightly irregular edge during growth. A musty grape like odor is frequently noticed. It is widely found in nature. It is responsible for burn wound infections, puncture wounds, gram-negative pneumonia, infections of heart valves and other systemic infections. It is one of the major bacteria that causes gram-negative infections in the intensive care unit of hospitals and is therefore a cause of nosocomial infections. It produces a wide variety of toxins and enzymes that aid in the process of infection. *P. aeruginosa* is extremely antibiotic resistant. *Pseudomonas* infections are treated by aminoglycoside antibiotics which are nephrotoxic, ototoxic or neurotoxic. Other less toxic antibiotics used are cefipime or timentin.

Pseudomonas fluorescens This is a gram-negative bacillus that is 1 μm to 1.8 μm long by 0.3 μm to 0.5 μm wide. Some varieties are motile and have a polar flagellum. The colonies develop a reddish color during growth. The surrounding agar may develop a green to brown color. This organism does not produce pyocanin, but produces other pigments. It grows well at psychrophilic temperatures. It is an opportunistic microorganism.

Salmonella typhimurium This is a gram-negative bacillus that is 1 μm to 3.5 μm long and 0.5 μm to 0.8 μm wide. It may occur singly or in pairs. It is a facultative anaerobe. Colonies are gray to translucent on agar. It produces hydrogen sulfide and does not hydrolyze urea. All are pathogenic. It is responsible for a severe food poisoning called salmonellosis. Complications can lead to osteomyelitis and meningitis.

Serratia marcescens This is a gram-negative coccus-like organism that is 0.5 μm long by 0.5 μm to 1 μm wide. It is a facultative anaerobe and produces a reddish pigment on growth at 25°C. Colonies are large and smooth. It is responsible for serious nosocomial infections. It is associated with infections during intravenous therapy, urinary tract catheterization and respiratory therapy and is found frequently in chronically ill weakened patients or those on steroid therapy or on extended antibiotic treatments.

Shigella dysenteriae This is a gram-negative bacillus that is 1 μm to 3 μm long and 0.4 μm to 0.5 μm wide. It is non-motile and ferments glucose to acids. Hydrogen sulfide and indole are not produced. It causes severe dysentery in humans. This is characterized by inflammatory colitis and severe bloody diarrhea. This microbe is a pathogen. Plasmid mediated antibiotic resistance can be transferred from *Escherichia coli* to *Shigella* in the intestinal tract. Quinolones and third generation cephalosporins are used as treatments because of the problems associated with antibiotic resistance.

Fungi

Aspergillus nidulans This mold is a common laboratory contaminant. It produces conidiophores and long chains of naked spores of conidia. Hyphae and mycelia are common. Aspergillosis infections can infect the sinuses, skin, bronchii, lungs, meninges and bone. These infections can appear as secondary infections to a primary bacterial infection. Aspergillosis can be a secondary complication to a primary mycobacterial tuberculosis infection. This mold also can produce aflatoxins which can cause liver damage and liver cancer.

Rhizopus nigricans This mold is commonly found. It produces stalk-like sporangiophores which bear sac-like sporangia on their ends. These sporangia contain sporangiospores. Hyphae and mycelia are common. This mold can produce mucormycosis which can develop into a fatal infection. This infection frequently infects weakened patients given antibiotics, steroid drugs or antimetabolites for treatment of cancers. It frequently invades the sinuses, eyes, brain and blood vessels and produces serious inflammations with much tissue damage.

Penicillium notatum   This mold is also a culture contaminant. It shows branched conidiophores which bear chains of conidiospores. Hyphae and mycelia are common. It also produces lung and middle ear infections. This mold produces the antibiotic penicillin.

Saccharomyces cerevisiae   This is a yeast. It may be found as a laboratory contaminant. The cells appear as ovals that are 3 μm to 7 μm in diameter. It reproduces asexually by budding and sexually by forming 4 ascospores contained in a sac called an ascus. These ascospores are produced by meiosis. This yeast does not produce hyphae or mycelia which are commonly found in the molds.

Index

A

Abdominal infections
  anaerobes and, 87
  Bacteroides and, 87
  commensalism and, 125
  Escherichia coli and, 87
  Peptostreptococcus and, 65
  pH and, 113
Acetoin production, testing for, 175
Acid-fast stain, 43–46
  in morphological characterization, 59–61
Acid and gas reaction, 174
  in Enterotube II™ test, 218–219
Acidic fermentation indicator, 174
Acidophiles, obligate, 113
Acids, bactericidal, 113
Acremonium, 133
Actinomyces, in mouth, 299
Adonitol reaction, in Enterotube II™, 216, 218, 221
Adsorption (in infection cycle), 81
Aerobes, defined, 87
Aerobic respiration, 185
Aerotolerant anaerobes, 87
Aflatoxins, 11
Agar, smear preparation from, 31. *See also specific kinds.*
Agglutination test, 303–306
Airborne infections, mechanisms of spread, 19
Alcaligenes faecilis, 175
  differential identification tests, 196–197
  fermentation and, 174–179, 181–184
  nosocomial infections, 169
  Oxidation-Fermentation test, 182–184
  pH range for, 114
  problems caused by, 169, 170, 181
  respiratory reactions, 185, 188
Alcohols, disinfection by, 227
Alkali, bactericidal, 113
Alkaline solutions, 113
Alkali reversion, Kligler's iron slants and, 288
Alkalophiles, 113
Alkyldimethylbenzylammonium chloride (benzalkonium chloride), 228
Alpha-hemolytic reaction, 271
Aluminum, oligodynamic action by, 245–247
Amanita, poisoning caused by, 11
Ames Test, 307–310
Amino acid and specialty tests, 195–204
  citrate test, 196–197, 198, 200–201, 202
  IMVIC test, 198, 203
  indications for, 212–214
  indole test, 196, 198, 200, 203
  Kligler's iron agar, 195–196, 199, 201, 203
  lysine decarboxylase activity, 197, 201, 202, 203
  motility test, 198, 201, 202, 203
  phenylalanine deaminase activity, 197, 201, 202
  urease test, 197, 202, 203
Aminoglycoside antibiotics, 59
Amphitrichous bacteria, 53
Ampicillin
  sensitivity chart, 236
  for typhoid fever, 282
Anaerobes, 87–89
  commensalism and, 125–127

culturing and, 87–92
in oropharynx, 271
problems caused by, 88, 129, 257
synergism and 88, 129
toxic oxygen compounds and, 87–88
types of, 87
Anaerobic respiration, 186, 187
Anionic vs. cationic compounds, 227–228
Anopheles mosquito, 15, 178
Antagonism, 133–136. *See also Antibiotics; Antimicrobial agents; Chemical control.*
Anthrax, 43
Antibiotics, 231
  antagonism and, 133–134
  broad spectrum, 232
  decision-making case history, 232–233
  defined, 231
  Gram stain and, 59
  modes of action, 231
  resistance to, 190, 231
  sensitivity testing, 233–236
  side effects of, 231
  types of, 190, 231–232. *See also specific types*
Antigens, 303
Antimicrobial agents, 227–230. *See also Antibiotics, see also antiseptic agents.*
  antagonism and, 133–136
  oligodynamic action against, 245
  testing, 227–240
Antiseptic agents, 237–240
Apicomplexa, 15–17
Arabinose reaction, in Enterotube II™, 219, 221–222
Arborescent growth, in slant media, 94
Ascomycetes, 9–10
Asepsis, defined, 25
Aseptic transfer techniques, 25–29
Aspergillosis, 10
Aspergillus, 9–13
  disease caused by, 10–11
  microscopic identification, 12–13
ATP, glycolysis and, 173
Atrichous bacteria, 53
Autoclave, sterilization in, 103, 107

B

Bacillary dysentery (shigellosis), 282
Bacilli
  aerobic spore-forming, handwashing and, 117
  antimicrobial-substance-producing, 133
  heat resistance of, 152
  nonfermentative, 175, 176–178
  pasteurization and, 103
  thermal death point of, 103
Bacillus
  anthracis
    disease caused by, 6, 48
    microscopic identification, 3–7
  cereus
    differential identification tests, 198
    food poisoning by, 153
    in milk, 159
  mycoides
    Gram staining, 40–42

staining, 33–36
polymyxa, 133
stereothermophilus, temperature and growth, 100–101
subtilis
    antagonism and, 133–134
    differential identification tests, 198, 206–213
    disease caused by, 6
    Gram staining, 40–42
    microscopic identification, 6–7
    negative staining, 37–38
    problems caused by, 169, 170
    pure culture isolation, 65–69
    Schaeffer-Fulton staining, 48–49
    thermal death and, 104–106
    unknown characterization, 60–61
Bacitracin
    Bacillus subtilis and, 133
    sensitivity chart, 236
Bacteremia, dental surgery and, 299
Bacteria. *See also specific bacteria.*
    aerobic vs. anaerobic, 87
    amphitrichous, 53
    antagonism and, 133–136
    antibiotic sensitivity and, 231–236
    atrichous, 53
    chemical control of, 227–230
    commensalism and, 125
    culturing
        conditions for, 93–98
        determining oxygen requirements, 87–92
        handwashing and, 117–120
        osmotic pressure and, 109–112
        pH and, 113–115
        pure culture isolation skills, 65–70
        quantitative plate count, 71–80
        temperature and, 99–106
    differential identification of
        amino acid and specialty tests, 195–203
        macromolecule and specialty tests, 205–214
    enzyme action by, 205–206
    fermentation end products, 173–174
    in food, 151–159
    halotolerant (osmotolerant), 110
    lophotrichous, 53
    in milk, 65, 159
    monotrichous (polar), 53
    morphological characterization of, 59–61
    motility studies, 53, 54–58
      morphological characterization and, 60, 61
    nonfermenters, 174, 181–183
    nonhalophilic, 110
    nonsaccharolytic, 181, 182
    oligodynamic action against, 245–247
    omnipresence of, 21–23
    osmotic pressure and growth of, 109–112
    oxygen requirements for, 87–92
    peritrichous, 53
    pH and growth of, 113–115
    pigment production by
      morphological characterization and, 60, 61
      streak plate patterns and, 95–96
    respiratory reactions of, 185–193
    salt concentration and, 109–112
    smear preparation, 33–36
    staining, 33–36
      acid-fast stain, 43–46
      capsule stain, 51–52
      endospore stain (Schaeffer-Fulton procedure), 47–49
      Gram stain, 39–42
      negative stain, 37–38
      simple method, 36
      smear preparation for, 33–36
    synergism and, 129–131

unknown morphological characterization, 59–61
UV light and, 249–252
in water, 65, 141–142
Bactericidal vs. bacteriostatic agents, 227, 238–239
Bacteriocins, 133
Bacteroides, 65, 87
    fragilis, commensalism and, 125
    pH and, 113–114
    synergism and, 129–131
Balantidiumi coli, 19
    disease caused by, 19
    microscopic identification, 20
Basidia, 11
Basidiomycetes, 9–11
Beaded growth, in slant media, 94
Benzalkonium chloride, as disinfecting agent, 228
Benzoic acid, as bacteriocidal, 113
Beta-hemolysis, 272
Beta-lactamases, antibiotic resistance and, 272
BGBL broth. *See Brilliant green bile lactose broth.*
Bile-esculin agar test, 206, 209, 210
    indications for, 206, 209
Blanching, food preservation by, 152
Blastomyces, 9–10
Bordetella
    fermentation and, 181
    pertussis, 181
      fermentation and, 175
      problems caused by, 181
      respiratory reactions and, 188
Borrelia
    recurrentis
      disease caused by, 6
      microscopic identification, 6–7
      synergism and, 129
Botulism, 48, 153
Branhamella. See Moraxella.
Brilliant green bile lactose (BGBL) broth, for water test, 142
Broad spectrum antibiotics, 232
Bromthymol blue, in oxidation-fermentation test, 181–182
Broth culture
    bacterial growth in, 93–94, 97
    in clinical unknown testing, 170, 171
    in nitrate reduction test, 188–189
    in oxidation-fermentation (O–F) test, 182–184
    smear preparation from, 34, 35
Brownian movement, 54
Brucella, in milk, 159
    pasteurization and, 103, 152
Burn infections
    nonfermentative bacteria and, 181
    organisms causing, 169
Burn ointment, silver in, 245
Buttlauxella, Enterotube II™ test, 221

C

Cadaverine, 197
Campylobacter, 65
    in gastrointestinal infections, 281–283
    jejuni, 283
Candida
    albicans, 12–13, 273
      vaginal pH and, 113–114
    diseases caused by, 12, 273
    microscopic identification, 12–13
Canning, heat killing in, 103
Capsule, 51, 273
Capsule stain, 51
Carbenicillin, sensitivity chart, 236
Carbohydrate fermentation, 173
    end products, 173–179
Carbon dioxide, as fermentation end product, 173

Carcinogens
  Ames test and, 307–310
  defined, 307
Cardinal temperatures, 99
Casein, bacterial enzymes and, 207–208
Casein agar test, 207, 210
Catalase, 186
  toxic oxygen compounds and, 87, 186
Catalase test, 186–187, 189–190
  indications for, 186
  staphylococci and, 273
  streptococci and, 273
Cationic compounds, as antibacterials, 227–228
Cedecea, Enterotube II™ test, 221
Cells, arrangements of, 7
Cephalexin, 232
Cephaloglycin, sensitivity chart, 236
Cephaloridine, sensitivity chart, 236
Cephalosporins, 232
Cephalothin, 133
  sensitivity chart, 236
Cetyl pyridinium chloride, as disinfecting agent, 228
Chagas Disease, 18
Chemical control, 227–230
  sensitivity testing, 231–236
Chemoreceptors, 54
Chemical control, 227–230
Chemotaxis, 54
"Childbed fever," handwashing and, 117
Chlamydiae, tetracyclines for, 223
Chloramphenicol
  sensitivity chart, 236
  for Shigella infection, 282
  Streptomyces venezuelae and, 133
Chlorine, as halogen, 227
Cholera, 141
  cidal agents, defined, 227
Ciliophora, 15–19
Ciprofloxacin, 232
Circular growth, on streak plate, 95
Citrate test, 196–197, 200–201
  in Enterotube II™, 217, 219, 221–222
  in IMViC test, 160, 202, 203
Citrobacter
  in Enterotube II™ test, 221
  in water, 141
Claviceps, 10
CLED agar, in urine culture, 291–295
Clindamycin, sensitivity chart, 236
Clinical unknown, 169–172
  amino acid and specialty tests, 195–203
  culturing, 170–171
  defined, 169
  fermentation reaction tests, 173–179
  macromolecule and specialty tests, 205–214
  oxidation-fermentation (O–F) test, 181–184
  rapid multimedia test (Enterotube II™, 215–222
  respiratory behavior tests, 185–193
Clostridia, 206
Clostridium, 47, 48, 59, 87, 213
  bacteriocins and, 133
  botulinum, food poisoning by, 153
  differential identification tests, 208
  handwashing and, 117
  hyaluronidase (spreading factor) in, 205
  perfringens
    differential identification tests, 205
    food poisoning by, 151, 153
    tissue destroying enzymes in, 206
  sporogenes
    commensalism and, 125–127
    culturing, media conditions and, 96–98
    oxygen requirements, 87–92

tetani, 47
  disease caused by, 48
  thermophiles, 99
Cocci
  heat resistance of, 152
  thermal death point, 103
Coccidioides, disease caused by, 12
Coccidiomycosis, 12
Colicins, 133
Coliform bacteria, 141–144
  handwashing and, 117
  IMViC test for, 198, 203
  in milk, 159, 162
  as nonhalophilic, 87
  pH and, 110
  testing water for, 141–150
Colilert test, 143–144, 146–147
Colitis, hemorrhagic, 282
Collagenase, 206
Colony growth, plate patterns of, 94–95
Columbia CNA agar, in urine culture, 291–295
Commensalism, 125–127
Confirmed test, of water, 142
Conidia, 10
Convex growth, on streak plate, 95
Copper, oligodynamic action by, 133–135
Corynebacterium, handwashing and, 117
Coxiella burnetii, pasteurization and, 152
Cresols, as phenols, 227
Culture sensitivity, standards for reporting, 233–234, 236
Culturing, 65–120
  conditions for, 93–98
  osmotic pressure and bacterial growth, 109–111
  oxygen requirements, 88–92
  pure culture isolation skills, 65–69
  temperature effects
    on growth, 99–101
    thermal death, 103–105
  urine, 290
Cysts, 15
Cytochrome c, testing for, 186

D

Decarboxylase reaction, 197, 201, 202
Decision making empiric vs. differential, 232–233
Dehydration
  cell death and, 109
  food preservation by, 152
Denitrification, 188, 189, 192
Dental caries
  pH and, 113
  Streptococcus mutans and, 271
  Synder Test and, 299–301
Dental plaque, 299
Deuteromycetes, 9
Dextran, 299
Dextrins, starch hydrolysis and, 206
Diabetes, opportunistic infections in, 10
Diarrhea. See Gastrointestinal infections; specific types of infections.
Differential decisions, empiric decisions vs., 233
Differential identification
  amino acid and specialty tests, 195–214
    citrate test, 196–197, 200–202, 203–204
    IMViC test, 198, 203
    indole test, 196, 198, 203
    Kligler's iron agar, 195–196, 199–200, 201, 203
    lysine decarboxylase activity, 197, 201, 202, 203
    motility test, 198, 201, 202, 203
    phenylalanine deaminase activity, 197, 202–203
    urease test, 197, 201, 202, 203
  charts for, 213, 214
  macromolecule and specialty tests, 205–214

bile-esculin agar slants, 207–208, 209–211
litmus milk broth test, 206–207, 208–209, 211
mannitol-salt-agar test, 207–208, 209–211
milk protein agar test, 206–207, 208, 210, 211
nutrient gelatin agar test, 206–207, 208, 210, 211
spirit blue agar test, 206–207, 208, 210, 211
starch agar test, 206–207, 208, 210, 211
Differential media, 66
Dikaryon, 11
Dimers, damage by, 249
Dimorphism, in fungi, 12
Diphtheroids, in upper respiratory tract, 271
Diplococci, 59
Disinfectants, 227–228
DNase Test agar, in throat culture, 274–279
Doxycycline, 232
for traveler's diarrhea, 282
Dry heat, sterilization by, 103
Drying food preservation by, 152
Dulcitol reaction, in Enterotube II™, 219, 221, 222
Durham tube fermentations, 174–179, 212
Dye reduction test, for milk quality, 163–164
Dysentery
bacillary (shigellosis), 282
water contamination and, 143

E

Ear infections, otitis media, oxidase test for, 186
Echinulate growth, in slant media, 94
Edwardsiella, Enterotube II™ test, 221
Effuse growth, in slant media, 94
Elevation patterns, on streak plate, 95
EMB agar
in urine culture, 291–296
in water test, 142, 149–150
Empiric vs. differential decisions, 232–233
Encapsulated bacteria, capsule stain of, 51–52
Endocarditis
dental surgery and, 299
Endospores, 47, 59
heat resistance of, 152
morphological characterization and, 59
thermal death point, 103
Endospore stain (Schaeffer-Fulton procedure), 47–49
Entamoeba, 18
histolytica, 18, 141–142
Enteric bacteria
bacteriocins and, 133
in mouth, 299
serology testing for, 303–306
Enteric infections, organisms causing 169, 282–283. *See also*
Gastrointestinal infections.
Enterobacteriaceae
aerogenes, 59, 214
antagonism and, 134–136
differential identification tests, 195–204, 207, 214
Enterotube II™ test, 215–222
fermentation and, 173–179
in gastrointestinal infections, 283–284
problems caused by, 169, 170
respiratory activity test for, 150–152
respiratory reactions, 185
in water, 150
Enterotube II™ test, 215, 285
in water, 88
Enterococcus
detecting in food, 151
faecalis, 39
antagonism and, 134–136
antibiotic sensitivity, 234–236
chemical control tests, 228–229
culturing, media conditions and, 96–98, 290–291

differential identification tests, 195–204, 207, 214
fermentation and, 174
oxygen requirements, 87–89
problems caused by, 170
respiratory reactions, 185
synergism and, 129
in urinary tract infections, 290–291
Enterotube II™ test, 215–222
in gastrointestinal infection, 285, 287–288
Entire margin, on streak plate, 95
Enzymes
antibiotic resistance and, 232
bacterial growth and, 205–206
Eosin methylene blue agar. *See EMB agar.*
Ergot poisoning, 10
Erose margin, on streak plate, 95
Erythromycin, 232
for *Campylobacter* infection, 232, 283
in dental surgery, 299
gram-positive bacteria and, 59
sensitivity chart, 236
Streptomyces erythraeus and, 133
Escherichia coli, 35, 53, 282
antagonism and, 130–136
antibiotic sensitivity, 234–336
chemical control tests, 228–229
Commensalism and, 125
differential identification tests, 196
Enterotube II™ test, 216–222
fermentation and, 174–179
food poisoning by, 153
in gastrointestinal infections, 281, 282, 283
Gram staining, 40–42
lactose fermentation and, 154
media conditions and, 96–98
mesophiles, 99
nosocomial infections, 169
oligodynamic action against, 245–247
osmotic pressure and, 110–112
oxidation-fermentation test, 182–184
oxygen requirements, 87–91
pH range for, 113, 114
problems caused by, 170, 281–282
pure culture isolation, 66–69
quantitative plate count, 71–74
staining, 33–36
synergism and, 129
temperature and growth, 99–101
thermal death and, 104–105
unknown characterization, 60–61
urinary tract infections and, 289–296
UV light and photoreactivation, 250–252
vaginal pH and, 113–114
in water, 141–150
fermentation and, 173–179
gastrointestinal infections and, 281, 282
respiratory reactions, 185–193
Espundia (mucocutaneous leishmaniasis), 18
Ewingella, Enterotube II™ test, 221
Extreme halophiles, 110

F

Facultative anaerobes, 87
commensalism and, 125
Facultative thermophiles, 99
Fecal colifoms, 141
Fermentation, 173, 176–177
acidic, indicator of, 174
Camylobacter and, 282
in diffential identification, 173, 174, 175, 206–207
end products of, 173–175

enteric bacilli and, 281–284
in Enterotube II™, 218–219
food spoilage by, 151
homolactic vs. heterolactic, 173
methyl-red test, 174–179
oxidation-fermentation (O–F) test, 181–193
oxidation vs., 173–174, 181
Voges-Proskauer test, 174–179
Filamentous margin, on streak plate, 95
Filiform growth, in slant media, 94
Filter paper method
in antimicrobial agent test, 286
in oxidase test, 188, 189, 191
Filtration, sterilization by, 103
Flagella, 53–54
motility studies, 54–58
staining, 53
Flagellin, 53
Flat growth, on streak plate, 95
Flavobacterium
fermentation and, 181
respiratory reactions, 188
Flocculent growth, 74
Fomites, 21, 237, 272
strep throats and, 272
Food, 151–157
detecting microorganisms in, 151, 154–157
IMViC test and, 198
infections caused by, 153–154, 281, 282
handwashing and, 118
mechanisms of spread, 21, 281
preservation methods, 151–152
osmotic pressure and, 110, 152
spoilage processes, 151
Food infections, 153–154
Food intoxications, 153
Food poisoning, 153
Freezing, food preservation by, 152
Fungi, 9–13
dimorphism in, 12

G

Gaffkya (tetrads), 59
Gas gangrene, 48, 205
GasPak jar system, thioglycollate broth vs., 87–91
Gastroenteritis. See also Gastrointestinal infections.
food contamination and, 153, 281–282
Giardia and, 18
Norwalk agent and, 281
Salmonella and, 282–283
water contamination and, 141, 281–283
Gastrointestinal infections, 281
modes of transmission, 281–282
organisms causing, 169
pH and, 113
Gelatinase enzyme, testing for, 96, 98
Gelatin media. See Nutrient gelatin.
Gentamycin, 232
sensitivity chart, 236
Giardia lamblia, 18
microscopic identification, 19–20
in water, 141
Giardiasis, 18
Glucose
dental caries and, 299
fermentation of, 173
in Enterotube II™ test, 216, 221, 222
Glycocalyx, dental caries and, 299
Glycolysis, 299
end products of, 173–175
Gonorrhea, oxidase test for, 186
Gram stain, 39–42

in clinical unknown testing, 170, 171
in differential identification, 212–214
in morphological characterization, 59, 60
in urine testing, 290

H

Haemophilus
in upper respiratory tract, 273
Hafnia, Enterotube II™ test, 221
Halobacterium salinarium
as extreme halophile, 110
osmotic pressure and, 110–113
Halogens, 227
Halophiles, extreme, 110
Halotolerant (osmotolerant) bacteria, 110
food poisoning and, 154
Handwashing importance of, 117–120
Haploid, 11
H antigens, 303
Heart valve infections, Staphylococcus epidermidis and, 299
Heat fixation, 35–36
Heat resistance of microbial cells, 152
Heat sensitivity of bacteria, 103–106
Heavy metals, oligodynamic action by, 245–247
Hektoen agar, food tests on, 151
Hemolytic–uremic syndrome, 282
Hepatitis A virus, in gastrointestinal infections, 281
Herpes, synergism and, 129
Heterolactic fermentation, 173
Hexachlorophene, as phenol, 227
Histoplasma capsulatum, 12
HIV, 273
Homolactic fermentation, 173
Hot water treatment, food preservation by, 152
Hugh and Leifson O-F medium, 181, 182
Hyaluronidase, bacterial growth and, 205
Hydrogen peroxide
anaerobes and, 87–88, 186
catalase and, 186
Hydrogen sulfide reaction test, in Enterotube II™, 218, 221, 222.
See also Kligler's iron agar.
Hypertonic vs. hypotonic environment, 109
Hyphae, 9, 10

I

Immunocompromised patients, opportunistic infections in
Zygomycetes and, 9–10
IMViC test, 198, 203
indications for, 198, 213
Indole test, 196
in Enterotube II™, 218, 221, 222
in IMViC test, 198, 203
Infection defined, 257
Influenza viruses, 271
Inoculating loop, aseptic techniques, 25–26
Intermediate antibiotic sensitivity, 234
Iodine, as halogen, 227
Irregular growth, on streak plate, 95

K

Kanamycin, sensitivity chart, 236
KF agar, food tests on, 151
Kirby-Bauer agar disk diffusion, 233–234
Klebsiella, 23, 291
fermentation and, 174
pneumoniae, 59, 214, 273, 291
antagonism and, 134–136
antibiotic sensitivity, 234–236
differential identification tests, 196–199, 221
Enterotube II™ test for, 216–222

Gram staining 40–42
  negative capsule staining, 51–52
  nosocomial infections, 169
  problems caused by, 273
  pure culture isolation, 66
  respiratory reactions, 185
  unknown-characterization, 60–61
  in urinary tract infections, 289
  vaginal pH and, 113–114
  in water, 141
Kligler's iron agar test, 195–196, 199–202
  for gastrointestinal infection, 285–288
  indications for, 212
  for urinary tract infection, 291
Kluyvera, Enterotube II™ test, 221

L

Laboratory safety. *See Safety guidelines.*
Lactic acid, as fermentation end product, 173
Lactobacilli
  dental caries and, 299
  fermentation of, lactic acid and, 173
  in milk, 159
  in mouth, 299
  as thermoduric, 152
  vaginal pH and, 113–114
Lactobacillus arabinosus, synergism and, 129
Lactose production, in Enterotube II™, 216, 217, 219, 221–222
Lag phase, 75
Lauryl tryptose broth, in water tests, 142, 143
Lecithinase, 208
Leeuwenhoek, Anton von, 3
Legionella pneumophila, in water, 142
Legionnaires disease, erythromycin for, 232
Leishmania, 18
Leishmaniasis, 18
Leminorella, Enterotube II™ test, 221
Lenticulate (lens-shaped) colonies, 96
Leprosy, *Mycobacterium* and, 43
Leukocidin, 206
Levine's eosin methylene blue agar. *See EMB agar.*
Lincomycin, sensitivity chart, 236
Lipid, bacterial enzymes and, 205–206
Lipid tests, 205–210
Litmus milk broth test, 206, 207, 208, 210, 211
Liver abscess
  synergism and, 129
  water contamination and, 141
Lobate margin, on streak plate, 95
Log phase, 75–76
Loop dilution procedure, 66, 69
Lophotrichous bacteria, 53
Lower urinary tract infections, 289–290
Lung infections, 9, 10. *See also Pneumonia.*
Lysine decarboxylase activity test, 197, 201, 202–203
  in Enterotube II™ test, 217, 218, 221, 222
  indications for, 216
Lysol™ as phenol, 227
Lysozyme, 263–270

M

MacConkey agar, 66
  food tests on, 151
  in gastrointestinal organism test, 283–285
Macrolide antibiotics, 232
Macromolecule and specialty tests, 205–214
  bile–esculin agar slants, 207–208, 209–210
  indications for, 210, 211
  litmus milk broth test, 207, 208, 209, 210–211
  mannitol-salt-agar test 207–208, 209–210

milk protein agar test, 207, 208, 209, 210
  nutrient gelatin agar test, 207, 208, 209, 210
  spirit blue agar test, 207, 208, 209, 210
  starch agar test, 206, 207, 208, 210
Magnification, 4
Malaria, 15–17
Mannitol-salt-agar test, 207–208, 209, 211
  for bacterial enzymes, 206
  for food microorganisms, 151
  indications for, 210, 213
Margin growth patterns, on streak plate, 95
Mastigophora, 18
Maximum temperature, 99
Media
  See also specific types.
  bacterial growth and, 93–98
  in clinical unknown testing, 170, 171
  differential, 66
  for food testing, 151
  selective, 66
  sterilization of, 103
Medical microbiology, 255–310
  dental caries susceptibility test (Snyder Test), 229–301
  gastrointestinal infections, 281–285
  mutagen and carcinogen test (Ames Test), 307–310
  Salmonella serology, 303–306
  urinary tract infections, 289–291
Membrane filter technique, for water testing, 143
Meningitis
  fungal, 12
  infant
    coliform bacteria and, 198
    nonfermentative bacteria and, 181
  oxiclase test for, 151
Mercury, oligodynamic action by, 245
Merozoites, 15
Merthiolate (thimerosal), 245
Mesophiles, 99
  detecting in food, 156
  heat sensitivity of, 152
Metabolic tests, in differential identification, 212. *See also specific tests.*
Metabolism
  nonsaccharolytic, 181, 182
  oxidative vs. fermentative, 173–175
Methicillin, sensitivity chart, 236
Methicillin-resistant *Staphylococcus aureus* (MRSA), 232, 274
Methylene blue dye reduction test, of milk, 163–165
Methyl–red test, 173–179
  in IMViC test, 198
Microaerophiles, 87
Microbes, omnipresence of, 21–23
Micrococcus lutea
  motility, 56–57
  oxygen requirements, 87–92
  unknown characterization, 60–61
Microorganisms, omnipresence of, 21–23
Microscope; Microscopy, 3–7
  cell arrangement examples, 7
  magnification, 4
  numerical aperture, 4
  as parfocal, 7
  parts of, 3–4, 6
  resolving power, 4
  rules for use of, 5, 6
  working distance, 4–5
Milk, 159–165
  microorganisms in, 65, 159
  standards for, 159–160
  pasteurization of, 103
  testing
    dye reduction test, 163–165
    IMViC test, 198

standard plate count, 159, 160–162
Milk protein, bacterial enzymes and, 205–206, 207
Milk protein agar test, 206, 207, 208, 211
Miller-Hinton agar, in sensitivity testing, 233–236
Minimum temperature, 99
Mixed culture, commensalism in, 125–127
Moeller decarboxylase broth, in lysine decarboxylase test, 197, 201
Moellerella, Enterotube II™ test, 221
Moist heat, sterilization by, 103
Molds, 9–13
    ascomycetes, 10–11
    food spoilage by, 151
Monotrichous (polar) bacteria, 53
Moraxella (Branhamella) catarrhalis, 214, 273
    differential identification tests
    Gram staining, 36–38
    Nosocomiali-infections and, 137
    problems caused by, 138, 207
    respiratory reactions, 151,153
    unknown characterization, 54–55
    in upper respiratory tract, 205
Morganella, Enterotube II™ test, 181
Most probable number (MPN) analysis, of water, 142, 145–147
Motility, 47
    morphological characterization and, 54,55
    testing for, 48–52
        for differential identification, 198–199, 201, 202–203
        indications for, 198, 199
        in urinary tract infection, 291
Motility agar stab inoculation, 56–57
Mouth, microorganisms in, 299
MPN analysis. *See Most probable number analysis.*
MRSA (methicillin-resistant *Staphylococcus aureus)*, 232, 274
MTF (multiple tube fermentation) technique, 142–143, 144
Mucor, 109
MUG compound, in Colilert test, 143
Multiple tube fermentation (MTF) technique, 142–143, 144
Mushrooms, 11
Mutagens
    Ames Test and, 307–310
    defined, 307
Mutations, pyrimidine dimers and, 249
Mycelium, 9
Mycobacterium, 43
    morphological characterization and staining, 59
    smegmatis
        acid-fast staining, 43–46
        Gram staining, 43
        unknown characterization, 60–61
    tuberculosis
        antagonists used for, 133
        mesophiles, 99
        presence in milk, 159
Mycolic acid, 43
Mycology, defined, 9
Mycoplasma infections, 232

N

Nafcillin, sensitivity chart, 236
Nalidixic acid, sensitivity chart, 236
Nature, microorganisms in, 21
Negative stain, 37–38
    capsule stain procedure, 51–52
Neisseriae, 59
    gonorrhoeae, penicillinase producing (PPNG), 232
    mesophiles, 99
    respiratory reactions, 186–188
Neomycin, sensitivity chart, 236
Netilimycin, 232
Neutral pH, 113
Neutral solutions, 113
Neutrophiles, 113

Nitrate, in anaerobic respiration, 187
Nitrate reduction test, 186, 188–193
    enteric bacilli and, 281
Nitrofurantoin, sensitivity chart, 236
Nonfermenters. *See bacteria, nonfermenters.*
Nonhalophic bacteria, 110
Nonsaccharolytic bacteria, 181, 182
Nonseptate vs. septate hyphae, 9, 10
Norwalk agent, in gastrointestinal infections, 217, 281
Nosocomial infections
    aminoglycosides for, 232
    causes of, 169
    handwashing and, 118
    nonfermentative bacteria and, 181
Novobiocin, sensitivity chart, 236
Numerical aperture, 4
Nutrient agar slant. *See Slant media.*
Nutrient broth. *See Broth culture.*
Nutrient gelatin agar test, 207, 208, 209, 210
    for bacterial enzymes, 206
Nutrient gelatin stab tube
    bacterial growth in, 96
    culture techniques, 96, 98
Nystatin, *Streptomyces noursei* and, 12, 133

O

O antigens, 303
Obesumbacterium, Enterotube II™ test, 221
Obligate acidophiles, 113
Obligate anaerobes, toxic oxygen compounds and, 87–88, 186
Obligate thermophiles, 99
Ocular, 4
O–F test. *See Oxidation-fermentation test.*
Oil immersion lens, 4, 5–7
Oleandomycin, sensitivity chart, 236
Oligodynamic action, 245
ONPG compound, in Colilert test, 143
Optimal temperature, 99
Oral mucocandidiasis (thrush), 12, 273
Ornithine reaction, in Enterotube II™ test, 217, 221, 222
Oropharynx, bacteria in, 271–275
Orophenylphenol, as phenol, 227
Osmosis, defined, 109
Osmotic pressure
    bacteria growth and, 109–112
    defined, 109
Osmotolerant (halotolerant) bacteria, 110
Otitis media
    Haemophilus influenzae and, 273
    Moraxella cattarrhalis and, 187, 273
Oxacillin, sensitivity chart, 236
Oxidase test, 187, 188, 190–191
    Campylobacter and, 282
    enteric bacilli and, 281
    indications for, 212–213
Oxidation-fermentation (O–F) test, 181–184
Oxidative vs. fermentative metabolism, 173–174, 181–182
Oxidizing agents, 227
Oxoid Identification Sticks-Oxidase method, 188
Oxygen requirements, determining, 87–92
Oxytetracycline, 232

P

PAD. *See Phenylalanine deaminase activity test.*
Parfocal, defined, 7
Pasteurization, 103, 122
Pathogenic bacteria, optimal temperature and, 99
PEAB. *See Phenylethyl alcohol agar with blood.*
Pellicle, in broth culture, 94
Pelvic infections
    organisms causing, 65, 88

pH and, 113
Penicillinase producing *Neisseria gonorrhoeae* (PPNG), 232
Penicillins, 11, 231–232
    bacteria resistant to, 232
    in dental surgery, 299
    gram-positive bacteria and, 59
    mode of action, 231–232
    resistance to, 232
    sensitivity chart, 236
Penicillium, 9, 11, 231
    antagonism and, 133, 231
    disease caused by, 9–10
    microscopic identification, 12–13
Peptostreptococcus, 65
Peritrichous bacteria, 53
Petri plates, bacterial growth on, 94–96
pH
    defined, 113
    fermentation and, 173–175
    microbial growth and, 113–115
Phenols, 227
Phenylalanine deaminase activity test, 197, 198
    in Enterotube II™, 219, 221, 222
    in gastrointestinal infection, 284
Phenylananine agar, 197, 198, 201
Phenylethyl alcohol agar with blood (PEAB), 66
    in urine culture, 291–292
Photoreactivation, 249–251
Photoreactivation photolyase enzyme, 249–250
Pigment production
    morphological characterization and, 60, 61
    streak plate patterns and, 96
Pipette pump, 72
Pipettes, handling, 72
Plaque, 299
Plasmodium, 15
Plasmodium falciparumo, 19
Plasmolysis, 109
Plate counts, 71–74
Pneumonia
    bacteria causing, 273–274
    oxidase test for, 186
    streptococcal, 273
Polar (monotrichous) bacteria, 53
Polymyxins, 232
    Bacillus polymyxa and, 133
    sensitivity chart, 236
Polysaccharide starch tests, 205–207
Polyvalent antisera, in *Salmonella* identification, 303
Postsurgical infections, aminoglycosides for, 232
Povidone iodine, as halogen, 227
PPNG (penicillinase producing *Neisseria gonorrhoeae*), 232
Presence/absence approach, to water contamination, 142–144
Preservatives, bacteriocidal, 113
Presumptive test, of water, 142
Propionibacterium, handwashing and, 117
Proteins, bacterial enzymes and, 205–206
Proteolytic activity, 96
    food spoilage by, 151
Proteus
    differential identification tests, 197, 207
    Enterotube II™ test, 221
    fermentation and, 173–175
    lactose fermentation and, 154, 157
    urinary tract infections, 289
    vaginal pH and, 114
    vulgaris, 214
        antagonism and, 134–136
        differential identification tests, 196–199
        Enterotube II™ test, 216–222
        in gastrointestinal infections, 283
        Gram staining, 40–42
        motility, 55–57

nosocomial infections, 169
    problems caused by, 170
    pure culture isolation, 66
    synergism and, 130–131
    in urinary tract infections, 291
Protozoa, 15–20
Providencia
    differential identification tests, 197
    Enterotube II™ test, 221
Pseudomonads, as nonhalophilic, 110
Pseudomonas, 291
    aeruginosa, 214
        antibiotic sensitivity, 232, 234–235
        chemical control tests, 228–229
        differential identification tests, 196–203
        fermentation and, 174–175
        Gram staining, 40–42
        media conditions and, 96–98
        motility, 54, 55–57
        nosocomial infections, 169
        oligodynamic action against, 245
        oxidation-fermentation test, 182–184
        problems caused by, 170, 181, 272
        respiratory reactions, 187–193
        unknown-characterization, 60–61
        urinary tract infections, 290
    fermentation and, 174, 176–179
    fluorescens, temperature and growth, 100–101
    food spoilage by, 151
    lactose fermentation and, 154
    respiratory reactions, 188
    in urinary tract infections, 290–291
Psychrophiles, 99
    detecting in food, 151, 154, 157
    food preservation and,
    heat sensitivity of, 152
Psychrotrophes, 99
    detecting in food, 151
    food preservative and, 151, 152
Puerperal sepsis, handwashing and, 117
Puncture infections, aminoglycosides for, 232
Pure culture isolation skills, 65–67
Pyrimidine dimer, 249
Pyruvic acid, glycolysis and, 173

Q

Q fever rickettsiae, pasteurization and, 103
Quantitative counts, use of, 71
Quantitative plate count, 71–76
Quaternary ammonium compounds (quats), 227–228
Quellung Test, 51
Quinolones, 232, 290

R

Raised growth, on streak plate, 95
Rapid multimedia test (Enterotube II™), 214–222
Reductase activity in milk, 163–165
Reduviid bug, 18
Refraction, 4
Refractive index, 4
Refrigeration, nutrient gelatin stab tube and, 96
Resident flora of skin, 117
Resistant, defined, 234
Resolving power, 4
Respiration, anaerobic, 186
Respiratory behavior tests, 185–193
Respiratory infections
    erythromycin for, 232
    food poisoning and, 153
    macrolide antibiotics for, 232

nonfermentative bacteria and, 181
  organisms causing, 169, 238
Reticuloendothelial problems, Ascomycetes and, 10
Rhanella, Enterotube II™ test, 221
Rheumatic fever in, 272
Rhinoviruses, respiratory infections and, 272
Rhizoids, 10
  in slant media, 94
  on streak plate, 95
Rhizopus, 10
  microscopic identification, 10, 13
  reproduction of, 10
Rickttsias, tetracyclines for, 232
Rifampin, sensitivity chart, 236
Ring, in broth culture, 94
Rotavirus, in gastrointestinal infections, 281
Rusts, 11

S

Saccharomyces cerevisiae, 10
  microscopic identification, 10–13
  pH range for, 113–114
Safety guidelines, xiv–xv, xvii–xviii
  Ames Test, 307–310
  antibiotic sensitivity testing, 231
  bacterial viruses, 81
  health care alert, 280
  oral and nasal flora, 237
  respiratory tract culture, 271
  Salmonella culture, 281
  Snyder Test, 299
  soft tissue infections, 257
  urine culture, 289
  UV light handling, 249
Salmonella, 214, 303
  detecting in food, 153, 154, 159
  differential identification tests, 196–197
  Enterotube II™ test, 221
  fermentation and, 173–175
  food poisoning by, 153–154, 282–283
  in gastrointestinal infections, 281–282
  nosocomial infections, 169
  pasteurization and, 103, 152
  sexology testing for, 303
  slide agglutination test, 303–306
  typhi, 282
    presence in milk, 159
    in water, 141
  typhimurium
    in Ames test, 307–310
    in gastrointestinal infections, 283
    problems caused by, 170
    serology test, 304–306
    in water, 141
Salmonella-Shigella agar (SS agar), 285–286
  food tests on, 151
  in gastrointestinal organism test, 284–288
Salt concentration, bacterial response to, 109–110
Sandflies, 18
Sarcinae, 59
Sarcodina, 18
Sarcomastigophora, 15–18
Schaeffer-Fulton procedure (endospore stain), 47–49
Schizogony cycle in malaria life cycle, 15–17
Sediment, in broth culture, 94
Selective media, 66
Sensitive, defined, 234
Sensitivity chart, 236
Sensitivity testing, 231–236
Sepsis, aminoglycosides for, 232
Septate vs. nonseptate hyphae, 9–10
Serology testing for *Salmonella*, 303–306

Serratia
  Enterotube II™ test, 221
  fermentation and, 174
  marcescens
    differential identification tests, 196–197
    pigmentation of, 95–96
    temperature and growth, 99–101
SF broth test, in urinary tract infection, 291–293
Sheep blood agar, for throat culture, 272
Shellfish poisoning, 154
Shigella, 214
  detecting in food, 152
  differential identification tests, 196–198
  dysenteriae
    differential identification tests, 199–203
    problems caused by, 282
    pure culture isolation, 66
  Enterotube II™ test, 221
  fermentation and, 173–175
  flexneri, problems caused by, 282
  in gastrointestinal infections, 281–284
  modes of transmission, 282
  nosocomial infections and, 169
  sonnei, problems caused by, 282
  in water, 141
Shigellosis, 282
Silver, oligodynamic action by, 245
Sinusitis, Moraxella catarrhalis and, 273
Skin, bacteria on, 117
  food intoxications and, 153
  handwashing and, 117–120
Skin infections
  food poisoning and, 153
  organisms causing, 169
  staphylococci and, 110
Slant media
  bacterial growth in, 94
  in clinical unknown testing, 170–171
    bile-esculin agar test, 206
    catalase test, 188, 190
Sleeping sickness, 18
Slide agglutination test, for *Salmonella*, 303
Smear preparation, 33–36
Smuts, 11
Snyder Test, 299
Snyder Test agar, 300
Soft tissue infection, 257–261
Sorbic acid, as bacteriocidal, 90
Sorbitol reaction, in Enterotube II™,
Spectrophotometer, use of, 77
Spirit blue agar test, 206, 207, 208, 209, 210
Sporangiophores, 9–10
Sporangiospores, 9
Spores, 9, 10, 47
  conidia, 10, 12
  endospore staining of, 47–49
Sporogenesis, endospores and, 47
Sporogony, in malaria life cycle, 16–17
Sporozoites, in malaria life cycle, 16–17
Spreading factor, 205
SS agar. *See Salmonella–Shigella agar.*
Staining, 33–58
  acid-fast, 43–46
  capsule stain, 51–52
  endospore (Schaeffer-Fulton procedure), 47–52
  of flagella, 54
  Gram stain, 39–42
  negative, 37
  simple stain, 33
  smear preparation for, 34–36
Standard plate count (SPC), 151
  in milk testing, 159, 160–161
Staphylococci, 267–270 See also *Staphylococcus.*

enzymes in, 205–206
as halotolerant, 110
hyaluronidase (spreading factor) in, 205
identifying in, 273–274
in mouth, 299
penicillins and, 232
upper respiratory tract, 271–279
Staphylococcus
  aureus, 48,75
    acid-fast staining, 44–45
    antagonism and, 134–138
    antibiotic resistance, 232
    antibiotic sensitivity, 133, 231, 234–236
    aseptic culture techniques, 26–29
    chemical control tests, 228
    commensalism and, 125–127
    detecting in food, 151
    differential identification tests, 196
    fermentation and, 173–179
    food poisoning by, 153
    Gram staining, 40–42
    as halotolerant, 110
    handwashing and, 117
    media conditions and, 96–98, 291
    methicillin-resistant (MESA), 232, 274
    negative staining, 37–38
    nosocomial infections and, 169
    oligodynamic action against, 245–247
    osmotic pressure and, 110–112
    oxygen requirements, 89–92
    pH range for, 113–115
    pigmentation and, 95
    problems caused by, 170, 257, 291
    pure culture isolation, 66–69
    respiratory reactions, 185–191
    on skin, 267–270
    staining, 33–36
    synergism and, 130–131
    temperature and growth, 100–101
    thermal death and, 104–105
    in upper respiratory tract, 271, 273–274
    UV light and photoreactivation, 250–252
  epidermis, 213
    antagonism and, 134–136
    handwashing and, 117
    in upper respiratory tract, 271
  saphrophyticus, urinary tract infections, 289
Starch, bacterial enzymes and, 205–207
Starch agar test, 206, 207, 208, 209, 210
Static agents, defined, 227
Stationery phase, 75
Stationery phase microbial cells, heat resistance of, 152
Sterilization, 26, 107
  pasteurization vs., 103
  steam, 107
Stool cultures,
Streak plate
  growth patterns, 94–95
  technique, 65, 67–69
Streptococci
  as thermoduric, 152
  fermentation of, lactic acid and, 173
  in upper respiratory tract, 271–279
  microaerophiles, 87
  in milk, 159
  in mouth, 299
  pasteurization and, 103, 152
  penicillins and, 232
  pH and, 113
  Streptococcus
    lactis, in milk, 159
    mitis, 271
    mutans, 271, 273

pneumoniae, 39
  in respiratory tract, 271–273
pyogenes, 55
  antagonism and, 134–136
  antibiotic sensitivity, 234–236
  diseases caused by, 6, 272
  Gram staining, 40–42
  microscopic identification, 6–7
  nosocomial infections, 169
  respiratory reactions, 185
salivarius, 299
Streptomyces, 231
  antagonism and, 133
  bacteriocins and, 133
  erythraeus, 133
  griseus
    antagonism and, 133–136
    discovery of, 231
  noursei, 133
  venezuelae, 133
Streptomycin, 232
  sensitivity chart, 236
  Streptomyces griseus and, 133, 231
Strict anaerobes, 87. *See also Obligate anaerobes.*
Sugar fermentation tests, 173–179
Sugar oxidation test, 181–184
Sulfate, in anaerobic respiration, 186
Sulfa, triple, sensitivity chart, 236
Superoxide, 186
Superoxide dismutase, toxic oxygen compounds and, 68
Synergism 129–131, 258

T

Tatumella, Enterotube II™ test, 221
Tellurite agar, in throat culture, 274–278
Temperature
  bacterial growth and, 99–101
  lethal effects of, 103–105
Tetanus, 48
Tetracyclines, 232
  sensitivity chart, 236
Tetrads (gaffkya), 59
Thermal death exercises, 104–106
Thermal death point, 103
Thermal death time, 103
  food spoilage and, 152
Thermoduric organisms, 103, 152, 159
  pasteurization and, 152, 159
Thermophiles, 99
  detecting in food, 151
  as heat resistant, 152
Thimerosal (Merthiolate), 245
Thioglycollate broth, GasPak jar system vs., 88–91
Throat, organisms found in, 272–273
Throat culture, 272–273
Thrush, 12–13, 273
Thymine dimer, 249
Toadstools, 11
Tobramycin, 232
Total (plate) count, defined, 71
Toxic oxygen compounds
  anaerobes and, 87–88
  catalase and, 87, 186
Toxoplasma gondii, 19–20
  disease caused by, 16
  microscopic identification, 19–20
Toxoplasmosis, 18
Transient flora of skin, 117
Traveler's diarrhea
  coliform bacteria and, 198
  Escherichia coli and, 282
  food poisoning and, 282

Trichomonas vaginalis, 18
  disease caused by, 18
  microscopic identification, 19–20
Trimethoprim-sulfamethoxsazole
  for *Shigella* infection, 282
  for traveler's diarrhea, 282
Triple sulfa, sensitivity chart, 236
Trophozoites, 15, 16, 17, 19, 20
  in malaria life cycle, 15–17
Trypanosoma, 16, 18
  brucei gambiense, disease caused by, 18
  brucei rhodesiense, disease caused by, 18
  cruzi, disease caused by, 18
  microscopic identification, 19–20
Trypanosomiasis, 18
Trypticase soy agar
  in chemical control test, 228, 229
  in Enterotube II™ test, 216
  in oxidase test, 188, 190
  in UV light exercise, 250
Trypticase soy broth, in clinical unknown testing, 170, 171, 208
Tryptophan broth, in indole test, 196
Tsetse fly, 18
Tuberculosis
  antagonists used for, 133
  Mycobacterium and, 43
  pasteurization and, 103, 157
Turbidity, 94
Typhoid fever, 141, 282

U

Ultraviolet (UV) light effects, 249–252
Umbonate growth, on streak plate, 95
Undulate margin, on streak plate, 95
Unknown organism, morphological characterization, 59–61
  See also Clinical Unknown (Exercise 33).
Upper respiratory tract, organisms found in, 271–274
Urea broth, in urease test, 197
Urease test, 197, 201, 203
  in Enterotube II™, 217, 219
  in gastrointestinal infection, 284
  in urinary tract infection, 222, 224, 227
Uricult, 297
Urinary tract infections, 71, 289–296, 297–301
  See also Urogenital infections.
  antibiotics for, 232, 290
  modes of transmission, 289–290
Urine
  bacteria in
    quantitative count and, 71
    vaginal pH and, 113–114
  culturing, 290–296
    indications for, 289
  Gram stain of, 39
Urogenital infections. *See also Urinary tract infections.*
  coliform bacteria and, 198
  nonfermentative bacteria and, 181
  organisms causing, 169, 289, 290
Uterine contractions, Claviceps and, 10
UV light effects, 249–252

V

Vaginal pH, infections and, 113–114
Vancomycin
  for MRSA, 232, 274
  sensitivity chart, 236
Verotoxin-producing *E. coli,* 282
Viable count, defined, 71
Vibrio
  cholerae, in water, 141
  parahaemolyticus, food poisoning by, 153–154
Virulence factor, proteolytic activity as, 96
Viruses, 81
  gastrointestinal infections and, 281
  infection cycle, 81
  respiratory infections and, 271
Voges-Proskauer test, 174–179
  in Enterotube II™, 217, 219
  in IMViC test, 198
von Leeuwenhoek, 3
Vulvovaginitis
  Candida and, 12
  Trichomonas and, 18

W

Warnings. *See Safety guidelines,* xiv–xviii
Water
  bacteria in, 65, 141
    quantitative count and, 71
  microbiology of, 141–150
    coliform standards, 141–142
    test descriptions, 141–144
    test procedures, 144–150, 160, 164–165
Water activity, food spoilage and, 152
Water-borne infections, mechanisms of spread, 21, 281–283
Whooping cough
  erythromycin for, 232
  macrolide antibiotics for, 232
  nonfermentative bacteria and, 181
Widal test, 303
Working distance, 4
Wound infections, 257–261
  nonfermentative bacteria and, 181

Y

Yeasts, 8–12, 257
  food spoilage by, 151
  reproduction of, 9–12
Yersinia
  Enterotube II™ test, 221
  fermentation and, 173

Z

Zinc, oligodynamic action by, 245–247
Zones of inhibition, 228, 229, 233–234
  interpretive chart, 236
Zygomycetes, 9